A-Level Mathematics for AQA Core 2

The Complete Course for AQA C2

Contents

Introduction

About this book i

Chapter 1

Algebra and Functions

1. Laws of Indices

Laws of indices 1

2. Transformations

Translations 5

Stretches and reflections 9

Review Exercise — Chapter 1 14

Exam-Style Questions — Chapter 1 15

Chapter 2

Trigonometry

1. Arcs and Sectors

Radians 16

Arc length and sector area 18

2. The Sine and Cosine Rules

Trig values from triangles 21

The sine and cosine rules 22

3. Trig Identities

Trig identities 28

4. Trig Functions

Graphs of trig functions 30

5. Solving Trig Equations

Sketching a graph 35

Using a CAST diagram 37

Changing the interval 39

Using trig identities to solve equations 43

Review Exercise — Chapter 2 46

Exam-Style Questions — Chapter 2 48

Chapter 3

Logarithms and Exponentials

1. Logs

Logs 50

Laws of logs 52

2. Exponentials

Exponentials 55

Exponentials and logs 56

Review Exercise — Chapter 3 60

Exam-Style Questions — Chapter 3 61

Chapter 4

Sequences and Series

1. Sequences
- n^{th} term 63
- Recurrence relations 64
- Convergent sequences 69

2. Arithmetic Sequences & Series
- Arithmetic sequences 71
- Arithmetic series 74
- Sum of the first n natural numbers 78

3. Geometric Sequences & Series
- Geometric sequences 80
- Geometric series 83
- Convergent geometric series 85

4. Sequences & Series Problems
- Sequences & series problems 89

5. Binomial Expansions
- Pascal's triangle 92
- Binomial expansions — $(1 + x)^n$ 93
- Binomial expansions — $(1 + ax)^n$ 96
- Binomial expansions — $(a + b)^n$ 97

Review Exercise — Chapter 4 102
Exam-Style Questions — Chapter 4 104

Chapter 5

Differentiation

1. Differentiating x^n
- When n is a positive integer 106
- When n is negative or a fraction 107
- Differentiating functions 108

2. Using Differentiation
- Finding tangents and normals 111
- Finding second order derivatives 113
- Stationary points 115
- Maximum and minimum points 116
- Increasing and decreasing functions 118

Review Exercise — Chapter 5 120
Exam-Style Questions — Chapter 5 122

Chapter 6

Integration

1. Integration
- Integrating x^n 124
- Integrating functions 126
- Integrating to find equations of curves 128
- Definite integrals 129
- Finding the area between a curve and a line 132

2. The Trapezium Rule
- The trapezium rule 134

Review Exercise — Chapter 6 139
Exam-Style Questions — Chapter 6 141

Reference

Answers 143
Glossary 201
Index 203
Formula Sheet 204

About this book

In this book you'll find...

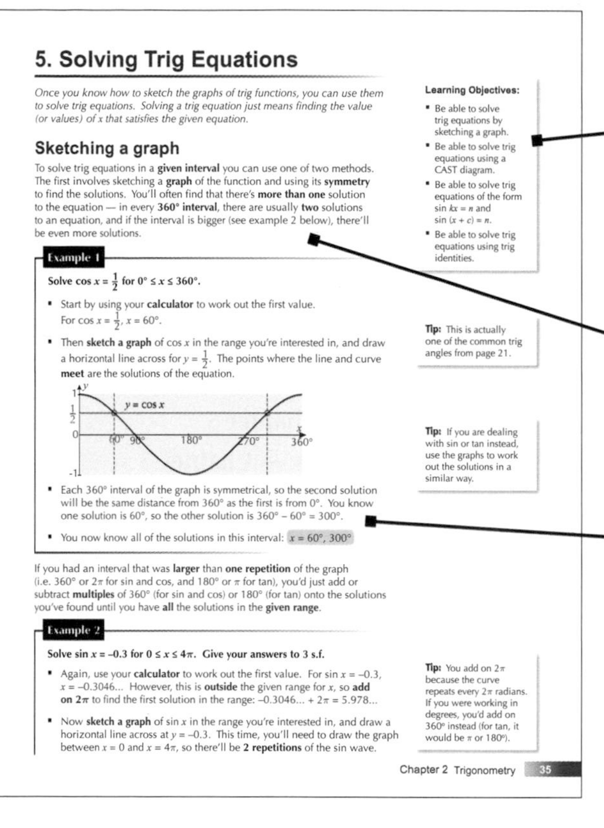

5. Solving Trig Equations

Once you know how to sketch the graphs of trig functions, you can use them to solve trig equations. Solving a trig equation just means finding the value (or values) of x that satisfies the given equation.

Sketching a graph

To solve trig equations in a **given interval** you can use one of two methods. The first involves sketching a **graph** of the function and using its **symmetry** to find the solutions. You'll often find that there's **more than one** solution to the equation — in every **360° interval**, there are usually **two** solutions to an equation, and if the interval is bigger (see example 2 below), there'll be even more solutions.

Example 1

Solve $\cos x = \frac{1}{2}$ for $0° \leq x \leq 360°$.

- Start by using your **calculator** to work out the first value. For $\cos x = \frac{1}{2}$, $x = 60°$.
- Then **sketch a graph** of $\cos x$ in the range you're interested in, and draw a horizontal line across for $y = \frac{1}{2}$. The points where the line and curve **meet** are the solutions of the equation.
- Each 360° interval of the graph is symmetrical, so the second solution will be the same distance from 360° as the first is from 0°. You know one solution is 60°, so the other solution is $360° - 60° = 300°$.
- You now know all of the solutions in this interval: $x = 60°, 300°$

If you had an interval that was **larger** than **one repetition** of the graph (i.e. 360° or 2π for sin and cos, and 180° or π for tan), you'd just add or subtract **multiples** of 360° (for sin and cos) or 180° (for tan) onto the solutions you've found until you have **all** the solutions in the **given range**.

Example 2

Solve $\sin x = -0.3$ for $0 \leq x \leq 4\pi$. Give your answers to 3 s.f.

- Again, use your **calculator** to work out the first value. For $\sin x = -0.3$, $x = -0.3046...$ However, this is **outside** the given range for x, so **add on** 2π to find the first solution in the range: $-0.3046... + 2\pi = 5.978...$
- Now **sketch a graph** of $\sin x$ in the range you're interested in, and draw a horizontal line across at $y = -0.3$. This time, you'll need to draw the graph between $x = 0$ and $x = 4\pi$, so there'll be **2 repetitions** of the sin wave.

Learning Objectives:
- Be able to solve trig equations by sketching a graph.
- Be able to solve trig equations using a CAST diagram.
- Be able to solve trig equations of the form $\sin kx = n$ and $\sin (x + c) = n$.
- Be able to solve trig equations using trig identities.

Tip: This is actually one of the common trig angles from page 21.

Tip: If you are dealing with sin or tan instead, use the graphs to work out the solutions in a similar way.

Tip: You add on 2π because the curve repeats every 2π radians. If you were working in degrees, you'd add on 360° instead (for tan, it would be π or 180°).

Chapter 2 Trigonometry 35

Learning Objectives
Showing which bits of the AQA specification are covered in each section.

Explanations
Clear explanations for every topic, with lots of helpful tips.

Examples
Plenty of step-by-step worked examples.

Exercises (with worked answers)
Lots of practice for every topic, with fully worked answers at the back of the book.

Question Hints
Occasional hints to point you in the right direction.

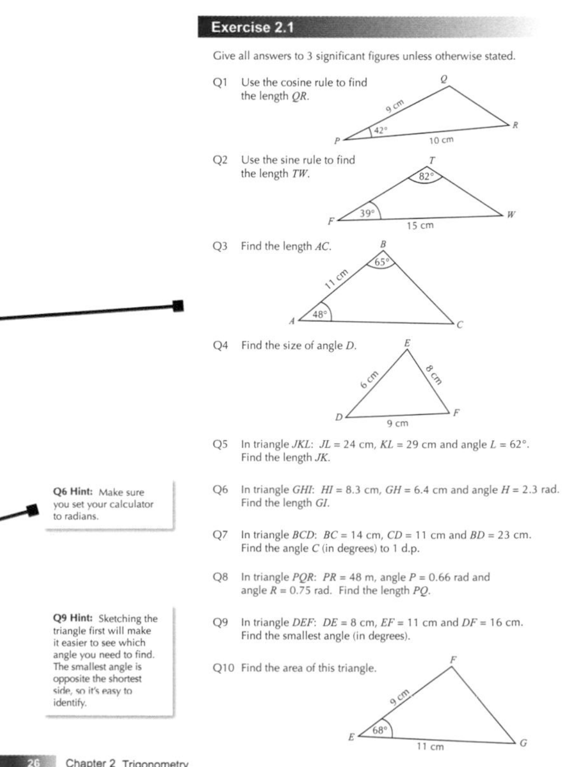

Exercise 2.1

Give all answers to 3 significant figures unless otherwise stated.

Q1 Use the cosine rule to find the length QR.

Q2 Use the sine rule to find the length TW.

Q3 Find the length AC.

Q4 Find the size of angle D.

Q5 In triangle JKL: $JL = 24$ cm, $KL = 29$ cm and angle $L = 62°$. Find the length JK.

Q6 In triangle GHI: $HI = 8.3$ cm, $GH = 6.4$ cm and angle $H = 2.3$ rad. Find the length GI.

Q7 In triangle BCD: $BC = 14$ cm, $CD = 11$ cm and $BD = 23$ cm. Find the angle C (in degrees) to 1 d.p.

Q8 In triangle PQR: $PR = 48$ m, angle $P = 0.66$ rad and angle $R = 0.75$ rad. Find the length PQ.

Q9 In triangle DEF: $DE = 8$ cm, $EF = 11$ cm and $DF = 16$ cm. Find the smallest angle (in degrees).

Q10 Find the area of this triangle.

Q6 Hint: Make sure you set your calculator to radians.

Q9 Hint: Sketching the triangle first will make it easier to see which angle you need to find. The smallest angle is opposite the shortest side, so it's easy to identify.

26 Chapter 2 Trigonometry

Review Exercise — Chapter 2

Q1 The diagram on the right shows a sector ABC of a circle, with centre A and a radius of 10 cm. The angle BAC is 0.7 radians.

Find the arc length BC and area of this sector.

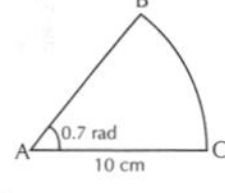

Q2 The sector ABC shown on the right is part of a circle, where the angle BAC is 50°. Given that the area of the sector is 20π cm², find the arc length BC. Give your answer in terms of π.

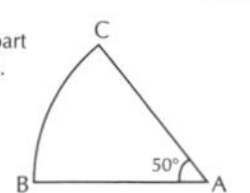

Q3 Write down the exact values of cos 30°, sin 30°, tan 30°, cos 45°, sin 45°, tan 45°, cos 60°, sin 60° and tan 60°.

Q4 For triangle ΔABC, in which $A = 30°$, $C = 25°$ and $b = 6$ m:

a) Find all the sides and angles of the triangle.

b) Find the area of the triangle.

Q5 For triangle ΔPQR, in which $p = 13$ km, $q = 23$ km and $R = 20°$:

a) Find all the sides and angles of the triangle.

b) Find the area of the triangle.

Q6 Find all the angles in the triangle on the right, in degrees to 1 d.p.

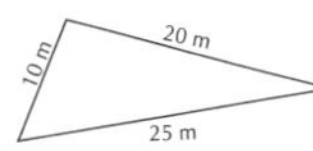

Q7 Find the missing sides and angles for the 2 possible triangles ΔABC which satisfy $b = 5$, $a = 3$, $A = 35°$.

Q7 Hint: This is tricky — sketch it first and try to think how you could make 2 triangles from the numbers given.

Q8 Show that $\tan x - \sin x \cos x \equiv \sin^2 x \tan x$.

Q9 Show that $\tan^2 x - \cos^2 x + 1 \equiv \tan^2 x(1 + \cos^2 x)$.

Q10 Simplify: $(\sin y + \cos y)^2 + (\cos y - \sin y)^2$.

Q11 Show that $\frac{\sin^4 x + \sin^2 x \cos^2 x}{\cos^2 x - 1} \equiv -1$.

46 Chapter 2 Trigonometry

Review Exercises

Mixed questions covering the whole chapter, with fully worked answers.

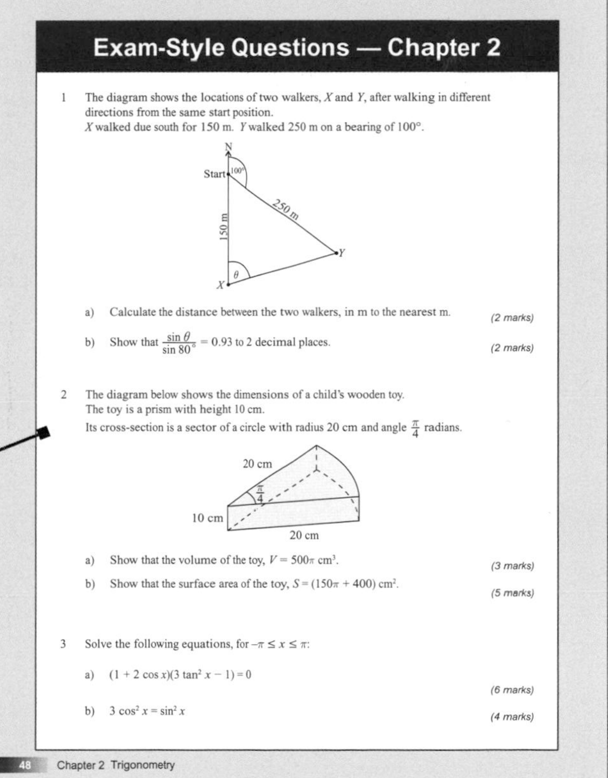

Exam-Style Questions — Chapter 2

1 The diagram shows the locations of two walkers, X and Y, after walking in different directions from the same start position.
X walked due south for 150 m. Y walked 250 m on a bearing of 100°.

a) Calculate the distance between the two walkers, in m to the nearest m. *(2 marks)*

b) Show that $\frac{\sin\theta}{\sin 80°} = 0.93$ to 2 decimal places. *(2 marks)*

2 The diagram below shows the dimensions of a child's wooden toy.
The toy is a prism with height 10 cm.
Its cross-section is a sector of a circle with radius 20 cm and angle $\frac{\pi}{4}$ radians.

a) Show that the volume of the toy, $V = 500\pi$ cm³. *(3 marks)*

b) Show that the surface area of the toy, $S = (150\pi + 400)$ cm². *(5 marks)*

3 Solve the following equations, for $-\pi \leq x \leq \pi$:

a) $(1 + 2\cos x)(3\tan^2 x - 1) = 0$ *(6 marks)*

b) $3\cos^2 x = \sin^2 x$ *(4 marks)*

48 Chapter 2 Trigonometry

Exam-Style Questions

Questions in the same style as the ones you'll get in the exam, with worked solutions and mark schemes.

Formula Sheet

Contains all the formulas you'll be given in the C2 exam.

Glossary

All the definitions you need to know for the exam, plus other useful words.

Practice Exam Papers (on CD-ROM)

Two printable exam papers, with fully worked answers and mark schemes.

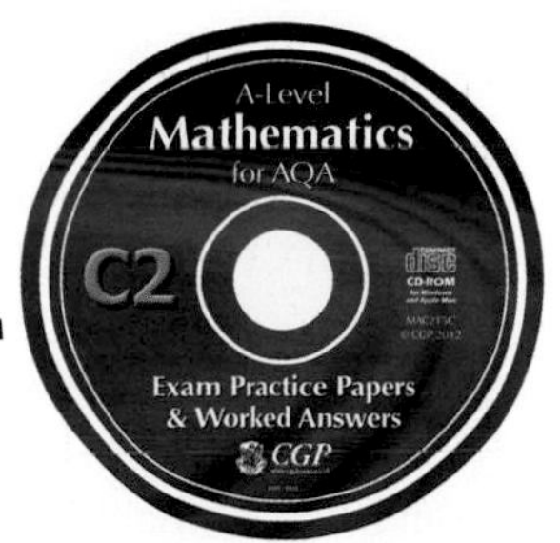

Published by CGP

Editors:
Helena Hayes, Paul Jordin, Simon Little, Kirstie McHale, Matteo Orsini Jones,
David Ryan, Caley Simpson, Charlotte Whiteley, Dawn Wright.

Contributors:
Jean Blencowe, Katharine Brown, Michael Coe, Bill Dolling, Josephine Gibbons,
Stephen Green, Andy Pierson, Mike Smith, Caroline Starkey, Janet West.

ISBN: 978 1 84762 803 9

With thanks to Alastair Duncombe and Jonathan Wray for the proofreading.

Groovy website: www.cgpbooks.co.uk

Printed by Elanders Ltd, Newcastle upon Tyne.
Jolly bits of clipart from CorelDRAW®

Chapter 1 Algebra and Functions

1. Laws of Indices

The laws of indices are just a set of simple rules for manipulating expressions involving indices (powers). They'll be used regularly in this module and others for simplifying expressions, equations and formulas.

Learning Objective:

- Be able to use the laws of indices to simplify expressions.

Laws of indices

You should already know that the expression x^n just means ***n* lots** of x multiplied together. The n is called the **index** or power of x. So when you square a number, the index or power is 2.

OK, now you're ready to see the laws. Here are the first **three** you need to know:

If you multiply two numbers — you **add** their powers.

$$a^m \times a^n = a^{m+n}$$

If you divide two numbers — you **subtract** their powers.

$$\frac{a^m}{a^n} = a^{m-n}$$

Tip: Don't forget — index and power mean the same thing. We'll use power for the rest of the section.

If you have a power to the power of something else — you **multiply** the powers together.

$$(a^m)^n = a^{mn}$$

There are also laws for manipulating **fractional** and **negative** powers...

$$a^{\frac{1}{m}} = \sqrt[m]{a}$$

$$a^{-m} = \frac{1}{a^m}$$

Tip: $\sqrt[m]{a}$ is the mth root of a.

$$a^{\frac{m}{n}} = \sqrt[n]{a^m} = (\sqrt[n]{a})^m$$

...and one simple law for **zero** powers, which works for any non-zero number or letter.

$$a^0 = 1$$

Now, let's see the laws in action in some worked examples.

Examples

Simplify the following:

a) (i) a^2a (ii) $x^{-2} \cdot x^5$ (iii) $(a+b)^2(a+b)^5$ (iv) $ab^3 \cdot a^2b$

Tip: Note that $x = x^1$.

(i) $a^2a = a^{2+1} = a^3$

$a^m \times a^n = a^{m+n}$

(ii) $x^{-2} \cdot x^5 = x^{-2+5} = x^3$

(iii) $(a+b)^2(a+b)^5 = (a+b)^{2+5} = (a+b)^7$

(iv) $ab^3 \cdot a^2b = a^{1+2}b^{3+1} = a^3b^4$

Add the powers of a and b separately.

b) (i) $(x^2)^3$ (ii) $\{(a+b)^3\}^4$ (iii) $(ab^2)^4$

Tip: To understand part b) (iii), remember that:

$(ab^2)^4 = (ab^2)(ab^2)(ab^2)(ab^2)$

$= a \cdot a \cdot a \cdot a \cdot b^2 \cdot b^2 \cdot b^2 \cdot b^2$

$= a^4 \cdot (b^2)^4 = a^4b^8$.

(i) $(x^2)^3 = x^6$

$(a^m)^n = a^{mn}$

(ii) $\{(a+b)^3\}^4 = (a+b)^{12}$

(iii) $(ab^2)^4 = a^4(b^2)^4 = a^4b^8$

This power of 4 applies to both bits inside the brackets.

c) (i) $\frac{x^{\frac{3}{4}}}{x}$ (ii) $\frac{x^3y^2}{xy^3}$

(i) $\frac{x^{\frac{3}{4}}}{x} = x^{\frac{3}{4}-1} = x^{-\frac{1}{4}}$

$\frac{a^m}{a^n} = a^{m-n}$

(ii) $\frac{x^3y^2}{xy^3} = x^{3-1}y^{2-3} = x^2y^{-1}$

Subtract the powers of x and y separately.

d) (i) $4^{\frac{1}{2}}$ (ii) $125^{\frac{1}{3}}$

(i) $4^{\frac{1}{2}} = \sqrt{4} = 2$

$a^{\frac{1}{m}} = \sqrt[m]{a}$

(ii) $125^{\frac{1}{3}} = \sqrt[3]{125} = 5$

e) (i) $9^{\frac{3}{2}}$ (ii) $16^{\frac{3}{4}}$

$a^{\frac{m}{n}} = \sqrt[n]{a^m} = (\sqrt[n]{a})^m$

(i) $9^{\frac{3}{2}} = \left(9^{\frac{1}{2}}\right)^3 = (\sqrt{9})^3 = 3^3 = 27$

(ii) $16^{\frac{3}{4}} = \left(16^{\frac{1}{4}}\right)^3 = (\sqrt[4]{16})^3 = 2^3 = 8$

It's often easier to work out the root first, then raise it to the power.

f) (i) 2^{-3} (ii) $(x + 1)^{-1}$

$a^{-m} = \frac{1}{a^m}$

(i) $2^{-3} = \frac{1}{2^3} = \frac{1}{8}$

(ii) $(x + 1)^{-1} = \frac{1}{x + 1}$

g) (i) 2^0 (ii) $(a + b)^0$

$a^0 = 1$

(i) $2^0 = 1$

(ii) $(a + b)^0 = 1$

Example

Express $\frac{\left(7^{\frac{1}{3}}\right)^6 \times (7^{-1})^4}{(7^{-4})^{-2}}$ **as** 7^k**, where** k **is an integer.**

This one looks really complicated but it's just a series of easy steps. Just make sure to work through it slowly and don't jump ahead.

$$\frac{\left(7^{\frac{1}{3}}\right)^6 \times (7^{-1})^4}{(7^{-4})^{-2}} = \frac{7^{\frac{6}{3}} \times 7^{-1 \times 4}}{7^{-4 \times -2}}$$

$(a^m)^n = a^{mn}$

$$= \frac{7^2 \times 7^{-4}}{7^8}$$

$$= \frac{7^{2-4}}{7^8}$$

$a^m \times a^n = a^{m+n}$

$$= \frac{7^{-2}}{7^8}$$

$$= 7^{-2-8}$$

$\frac{a^m}{a^n} = a^{m-n}$

$$= 7^{-10}$$

Exercise 1.1

Q1 Simplify the following, leaving your answer as a power:

a) $2^3 \times 2^4$ b) 10×10^4 c) $7^2 \times 7^5 \times 7^3$

d) $p^6 \times p^{-4} \times p^5$ e) $y^{-1} \times y^{-2} \times y^7$ f) $5^{\frac{1}{2}} \times 5^3 \times 5^{-\frac{3}{2}}$

g) $6^5 \div 6^2$ h) $x^{10} \div x^9$ i) $3^4 \div 3^{-1}$

j) $\frac{7^{15}}{7^5}$ k) $\frac{6^{11}}{6}$ l) $\frac{r^2}{r^6}$

m) $(3^2)^3$ n) $(10^6)^{-1}$ o) $(k^{-2})^5$

p) $(t^8)^{\frac{1}{2}}$ q) $(z^4)^{-\frac{1}{8}}$ r) $(8^{-6})^{-\frac{1}{2}}$

s) $cd^2 \times c^3d^4$ t) $\frac{p^5q^4}{p^4q}$ u) $\frac{c^{-1}d^{-2}}{c^2d^4}$

v) $(ab^2)^2$ w) $(x^2y^3z^4)^5$ x) $\frac{12yz^{-\frac{1}{2}}}{4yz^{\frac{1}{2}}}$

Q2 Find the value of q in each of the following:

a) $4^{\frac{1}{2}} \times 4^{\frac{3}{2}} = 2^q$ b) $1^0 = q$

c) $\left(\frac{4}{5}\right)^q = 1$ d) $\frac{7^5 \times 7^3}{7^q} = 49$

e) $\frac{2^q \times 2}{2^5} = \frac{1}{2}$ f) $(3^2)^5 \div (3^q)^3 = 3$

g) $(4^q)^2 \times (4^{-3})^{-\frac{1}{3}} = 1$ h) $\frac{(2^{\frac{1}{2}})^6 \times (2^{-2})^{-2}}{(2^{-1})^q} = 64$

Q2 d) Hint: Start by writing 49 as a power of 7, then work out what q needs to be.

Q3 Express the following as negative or fractional powers or both:

a) $\frac{1}{p}$ b) $\sqrt{q}$ c) $\sqrt{r^3}$

d) $\sqrt[4]{s^5}$ e) $\frac{1}{\sqrt[3]{t}}$

Q4 Find the value of r in each of the following:

a) $r^{\frac{1}{2}} = 3$ b) $8^{\frac{1}{3}} = r$ c) $4^r = 8$

d) $27^{-\frac{1}{3}} = \frac{1}{r}$ e) $r^{-\frac{3}{4}} = \frac{1}{8}$

Q4 Hint: Some of these are quite tricky — the key here is to think about the ways you could rewrite the numbers using indices.

2. Transformations

If you have a function f(x), you can transform its graph in three different ways — by translating it, stretching it or reflecting it.

Learning Objectives:

- Know the effect of the transformations $y = f(x) + a$, $y = f(x + a)$, $y = af(x)$, $y = f(ax)$.
- Apply any of these transformations to quadratic and cubic functions.
- Given the graph of a function f(x), sketch the graph resulting from any of the above transformations.

Translations

Translating the graph of a function means moving it either horizontally or vertically. The shape of the graph itself doesn't change, it just moves. There are two types of translation:

$y = f(x) + a$

Adding a number, a, to the **whole function** translates the graph **vertically** (i.e. in the **y-direction**).

- If $a > 0$, the graph moves **a units upwards**.
- If $a < 0$, the graph moves **a units downwards**.
- In **vector notation**, this is a translation by $\begin{pmatrix} 0 \\ a \end{pmatrix}$.

$y = f(x + a)$

Writing '$x + a$' instead of 'x' means the graph is translated **horizontally** (i.e. in the **x-direction**).

- If $a > 0$, the graph moves **a units** to the **left**.
- If $a < 0$, the graph moves **a units** to the **right**.
- In **vector notation**, this is a translation by $\begin{pmatrix} -a \\ 0 \end{pmatrix}$.

Get used to saying 'translation in the positive (or negative) x-direction (or y-direction)' — this is what you'll need to write in the exam to get full marks.

Tip: Function notation is used a lot in this section — don't get confused, it's quite simple.

E.g. if $f(x) = 3x^2$ then...

$f(5)$ means $3(5)^2 = 75$

$f(x - 2)$ means $3(x - 2)^2$

$af(x)$ means $a \times 3x^2$

Example 1

Shown below is the graph of $y = f(x)$, where $f(x) = x(x + 2)(x - 2)$.

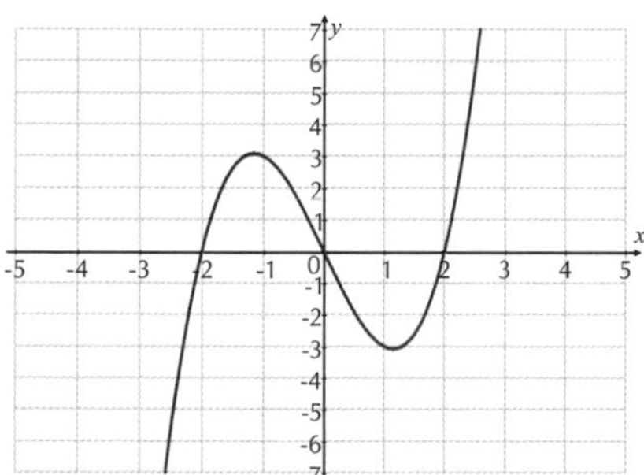

a) Sketch the graph $y = f(x) + 2$.

- Here 2 has been added to the **whole function**, i.e. $a = 2$.
- So the graph will be translated 2 units in the positive y-direction, i.e. shifted upwards by 2.

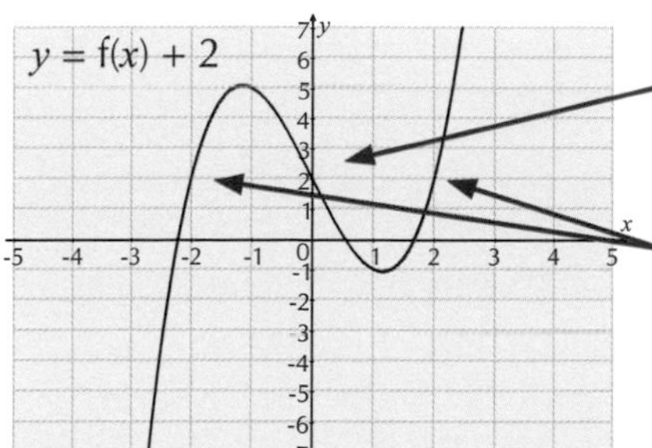

The point (0, 0) on f(x) has become the point (0, 2).

The other roots of f(x), (–2, 0) and (2, 0), have become (–2, 2) and (2, 2).

This is a translation of $\begin{pmatrix} 0 \\ 2 \end{pmatrix}$.

Tip: The equation of the transformed function is:

$y = x(x + 2)(x - 2) + 2,$
$= x^3 - 4x + 2.$

But you don't need to know this to sketch the transformed function.

Tip: When sketching a transformed graph, you need to show what happens to its **key points**, e.g. where it crosses the axes, max / min points, etc.

Exactly how much info to give will depend on the question.

b) Sketch the graph $y = f(x) - 4$.

- Here –4 has been added to the whole function, so $a = -4$
- The graph will move 4 units in the **negative** y-direction, i.e. down 4.

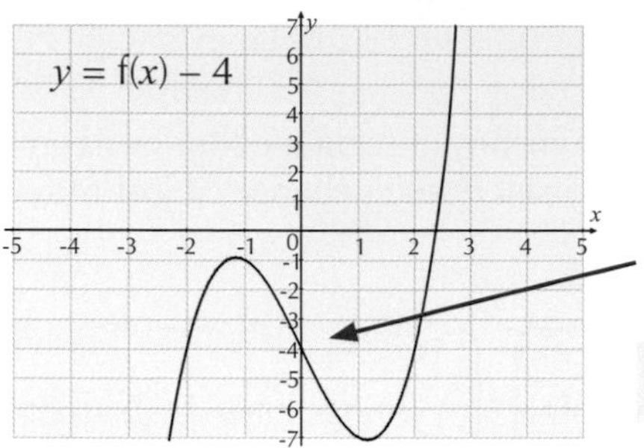

The point (0, 0) on $f(x)$ has become the point (0, –4).

This is a translation of $\begin{pmatrix} 0 \\ -4 \end{pmatrix}$.

c) Sketch the graph $y = f(x + 2)$.

- It's of the form $y = f(x + a)$ so it's a translation in the x-direction.
- $a = 2$ — so as a is positive, it's a translation 2 units in the **negative** x-direction — that's 2 units to the left.

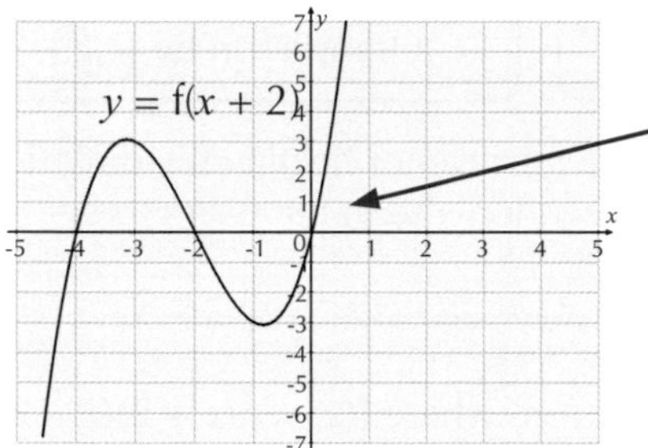

The x-coordinate of every point becomes 2 less.

E.g. the three roots of $f(x)$, (–2, 0), (0, 0) and (2, 0) are now (–4, 0), (–2, 0) and (0, 0).

This is a translation of $\begin{pmatrix} -2 \\ 0 \end{pmatrix}$.

Tip: If you wanted to know the equation of the new curve, replace the x's in the original equation with $x + 2$:

Original equation is:
$f(x) = x(x - 2)(x + 2)$

So...
$f(x + 2) = (x + 2)(x)(x + 4)$
$= x(x + 2)(x + 4)$

d) Sketch the graph $y = f(x - 1)$.

- Again, it's of the form $y = f(x + a)$ so it's a translation in the x-direction.
- $a = -1$, so it's a translation 1 unit in the **positive** x-direction (1 unit right).

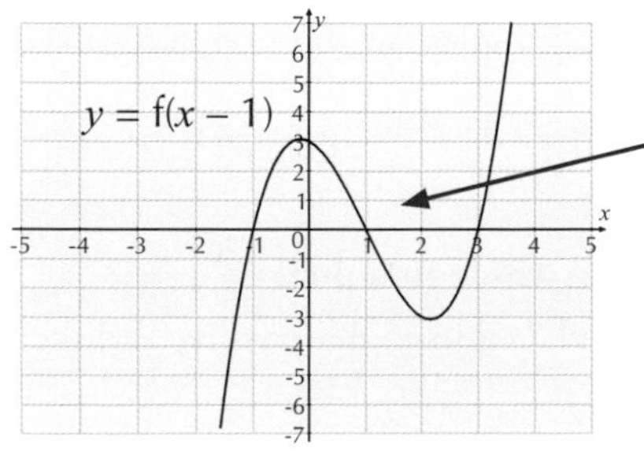

1 is added to the x-coordinate of every point.

E.g. (–2, 0) becomes (–1, 0).

This is a translation of $\begin{pmatrix} 1 \\ 0 \end{pmatrix}$.

Example 2

The sketch on the right is of the graph of $f(x) = \frac{1}{x}$.

The lines $x = 0$ and $y = 0$ are asymptotes of the graph.

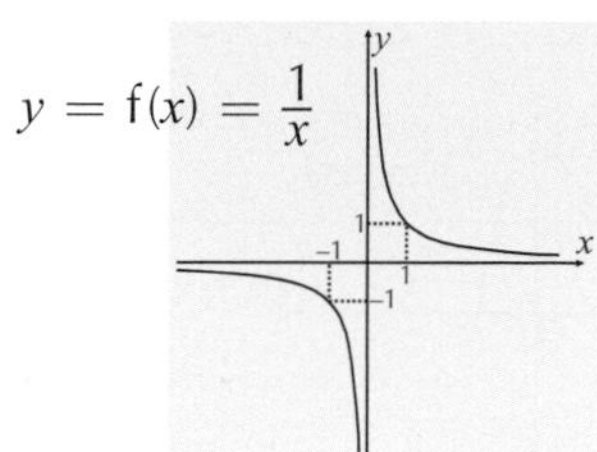

a) Sketch the graph of $y = f(x) + 2$. State the equations of the asymptotes.

- The graph $y = f(x) + 2$ is a translation of the graph upwards by 2.

$y = f(x) + 2$

- For $f(x) = \frac{1}{x}$, the horizontal asymptote is $y = 0$ and the vertical asymptote is $x = 0$.

  So for $y = f(x) + 2$, the horizontal asymptote becomes $y = 2$ (as it has moved up 2) but the vertical asymptote is still $x = 0$.

b) Find the coordinates of the point where $y = f(x) + 2$ crosses a coordinate axis.

- From the sketch we can see that the graph doesn't cross the y-axis, but it does cross the x-axis once, so set $y = 0$:

$$0 = \frac{1}{x} + 2 \quad \Rightarrow -2 = \frac{1}{x} \quad \Rightarrow x = -\frac{1}{2}$$

- So the graph crosses the x-axis, at $(-\frac{1}{2}, 0)$

Tip: This is a reciprocal function. They have the form $y = \frac{k}{x}$ (where k is a constant). Their graphs always have asymptotes. An asymptote of a curve is a line the curve gets infinitely close to, but never touches.

Tip: The vertical asymptote is the same for both as the graph has only moved upwards.

Tip: There's more about graph translations in the section on trig graphs (see p.31-33).

Exercise 2.1

Q1 The diagram shows the graph of $y = f(x)$. The curve has a maximum at (2, 4) and meets the x-axis at (0, 0) and (5, 0).

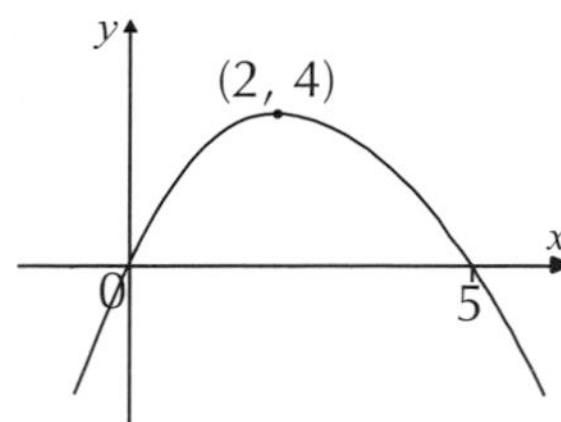

a) Sketch the graph of $y = f(x) + 2$, labelling the coordinates of the maximum and where the curve meets the y-axis.

b) Sketch the graph of $y = f(x + 2)$ labelling the points where the curve meets the x-axis and the maximum.

Q2 The diagram below shows the graph of $y = g(x)$ and two other graphs. Which graph represents $y = g(x - 1)$?

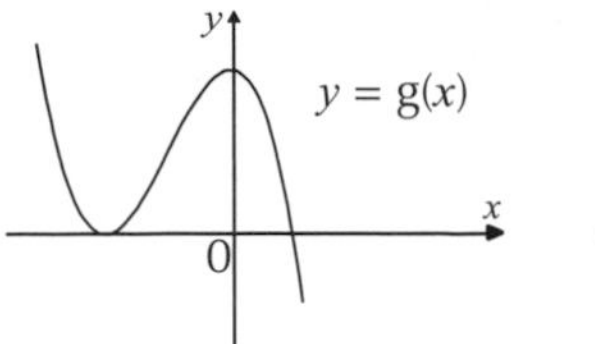

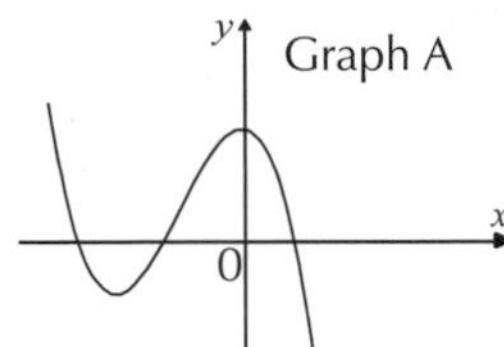

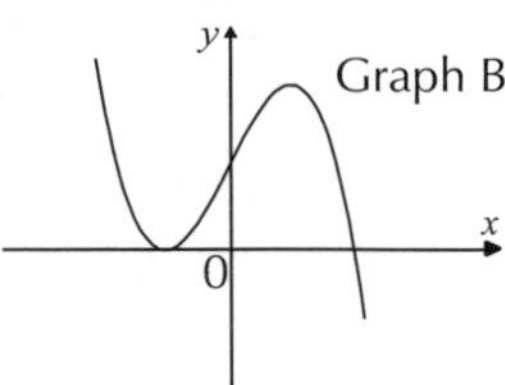

Q3 The diagram on the right shows a sketch of the graph of $y = g(x)$, where $g(x) = -\frac{2}{x}$.

The graph has asymptotes at $y = 0$ and $x = 0$. Sketch these graphs and give the equations of the asymptotes for each.

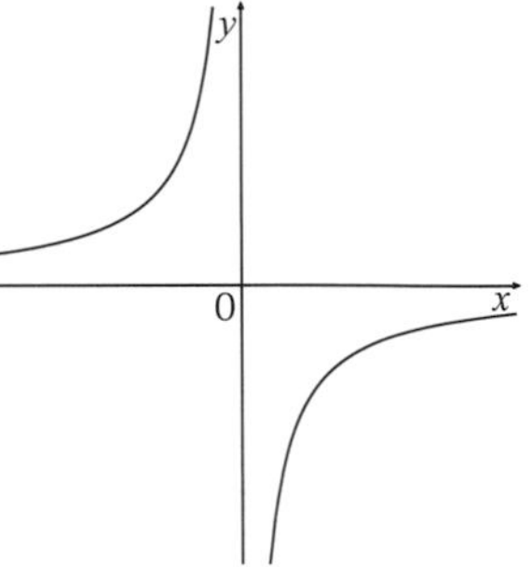

a) $y = g(x + 3)$ b) $y = g(x) + 3$

Q4 Given that $y = x^2(x - 4)$, describe how you would translate the graph to give the graph of $y = (x - 2)^2(x - 6)$.

Q5 a) Explain how the graph of $y = x^3 + 3x + 7$ can be translated to give the graph of $y = x^3 + 3x + 2$.

b) Write this translation in vector form.

Q6 The graph of $y = x^2 - 3x + 7$ is translated 1 unit in the negative x-direction. Write down the equation of the new graph. Give your answer in as simple a form as possible.

Q7 The diagram shows the graph of $y = f(x)$.

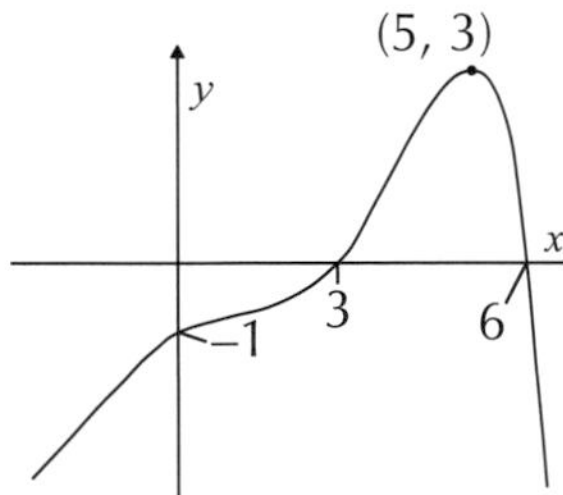

The graph has a maximum at (5, 3), crosses the x-axis at (3, 0) and (6, 0) and crosses the y-axis at (0, –1).

a) Sketch the graph of $y = f(x) - 2$.

b) Label the coordinates of the maximum and the point where the graph meets the y-axis.

Q8 a) Hint: Remember (from C1), to sketch a cubic graph, find the intercepts by setting $x = 0$ and $y = 0$, and use the coefficient of x^3 to tell you the general shape of the curve.

Q8 a) Sketch the graph of $y = (x - 1)(2x - 3)(4 - x)$ and label the points where the graph meets the coordinate axes.

b) The graph in part a) is translated by $\begin{pmatrix} 2 \\ 0 \end{pmatrix}$. Give the equation of the translated graph in its simplest form.

c) On separate axes sketch the graph of the equation from part b), labelling all the points where the graph meets the x-axis.

Stretches and reflections

The graph of a function can be stretched, squashed or reflected by **multiplying** the whole function or the x's in the function by a number. The result you get depends on what you multiply and whether the number is positive or negative.

$y = af(x)$

Multiplying the **whole function** by a **stretches** the graph **vertically** by a scale factor of a.

- If $a > 1$ or $a < -1$ (i.e. $|a| > 1$), the transformed graph will appear **taller** than the original.
- If $-1 < a < 1$ (i.e. $|a| < 1$), the transformed graph will appear **shorter** than the original.
- If a is **negative**, the graph is **also reflected** in the x-axis.

For every point on the graph, the x-coordinate stays the same and the y-coordinate is multiplied by a.

Tip: Remember that all these stretches are in the **vertical** direction. (i.e. parallel to the y-axis).

Tip: When $|a| < 1$, you might find it helpful to think of the stretch as being a 'squash'. You should always use the term 'stretch' in your exam though.

Example 1

The diagram shows the graph of a function f(x).

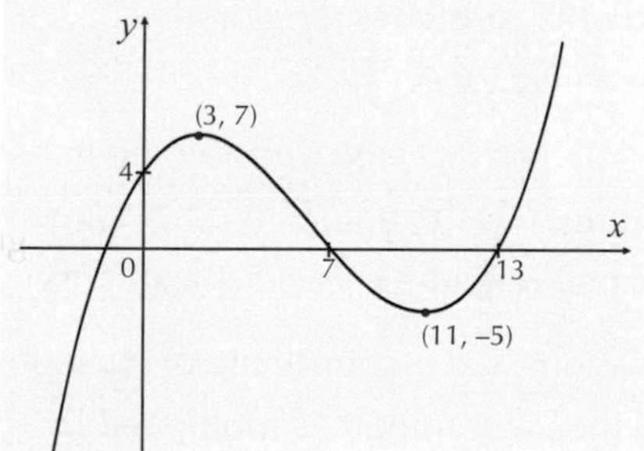

Tip: There are 5 key points marked on the graph that you'll need to keep track of: (0, 4), (3, 7), (7, 0), (11, –5) and (13, 0)

a) Sketch the graph $y = \frac{1}{3}f(x)$.

- The graph above will be stretched vertically by a scale factor of $\frac{1}{3}$.
- As $\frac{1}{3}$ is less than 1, the transformed graph will appear 'flatter' than the original (i.e. it'll be 'squashed').
- The diagram gives a number of key points on the graph — you need to show where each of these points has moved to on the transformed graph:

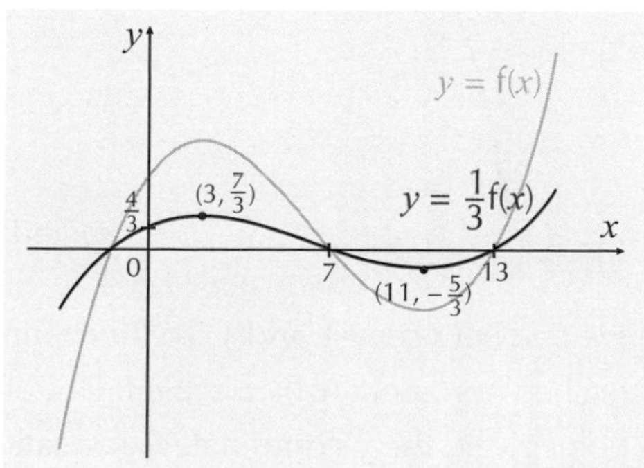

Tip: When finding the new points, remember the x-coordinates don't change, so just multiply the y-coordinates by a.

Tip: The graph still crosses the x-axis at the same points as the original graph — this is true for all $y = af(x)$ transformations.

b) Sketch the graph $y = -2f(x)$.

- Here the **whole function** has been multiplied by –2.
- So the graph will be stretched vertically by a factor of 2, but also reflected in the x-axis because of the minus sign.
- Again, you need to show what has happened to each key point.

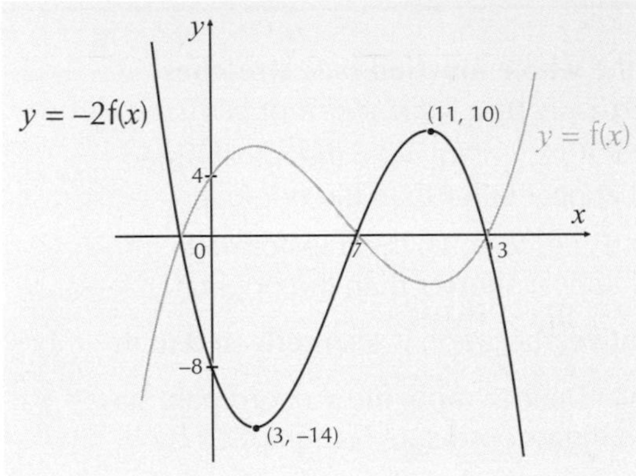

So that's vertical stretches covered. Next up are horizontal stretches:

$y = f(ax)$

Writing 'ax' instead of 'x' **stretches** the graph **horizontally** by a scale factor of $\frac{1}{a}$.

- If $a > 1$ or $a < -1$ (i.e. $|a| > 1$) the transformed graph will be **narrower**.
- If $-1 < a < 1$ (i.e. $|a| < 1$) the transformed graph will be **wider**.
- **Negative** values of a **reflect** the basic shape in the **y-axis**.

For these transformations, the y-coordinate of each point stays the same and the x-coordinate is multiplied by $\frac{1}{a}$.

Tip: Notice that a being bigger or smaller than 1 has the **opposite effect** for horizontal stretches compared to vertical stretches. So here, you can think of the stretch as being a 'squash' when $|a| > 1$.

Example 2

The diagram below shows the graph of $y = f(x)$ again.

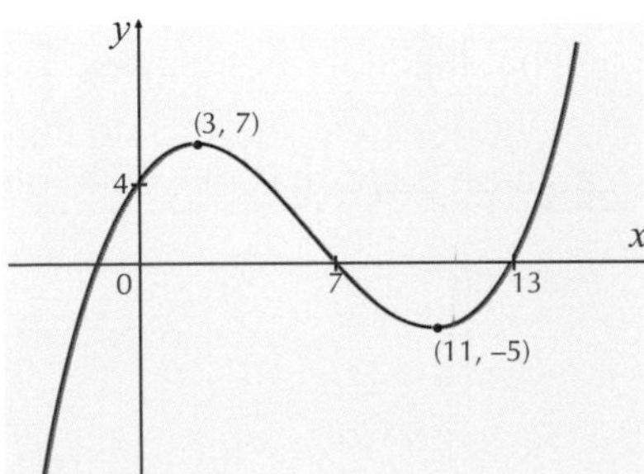

a) Sketch the graph $y = f(\frac{1}{2}x)$.

- $\frac{1}{2}$ is positive and between –1 and 1, so the graph will be stretched horizontally by a scale factor of 2.
- For each point given, the x-coordinate is multiplied by 2 but the y-coordinate doesn't change.

- The graph looks like this. (This time, the y-intercept doesn't change, but the two x-intercepts do.)

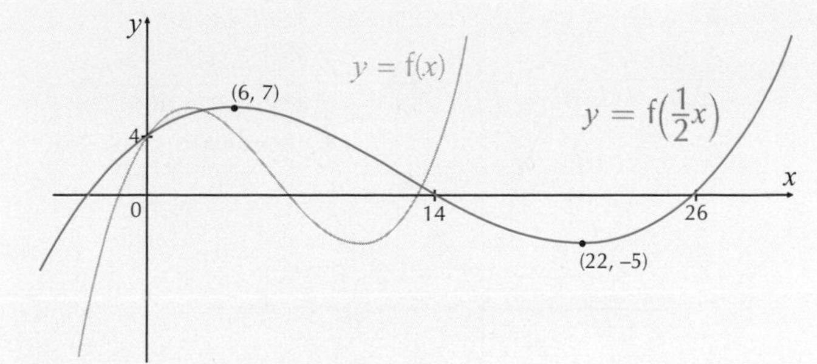

b) Sketch the graph $y = f(-3x)$.

- The transformation has the form $y = f(ax)$, so it's a horizontal stretch.
- $a = -3$, so the graph will be stretched by a scale factor of $\frac{1}{3}$, i.e. the transformed graph will appear narrower than the original.
- The graph will also be **reflected** in the y-axis, since a is negative.
- Find the new position of key points by multiplying their x-coordinate by $-\frac{1}{3}$ (and leaving the y-coordinate the same).
- So the graph looks like this:

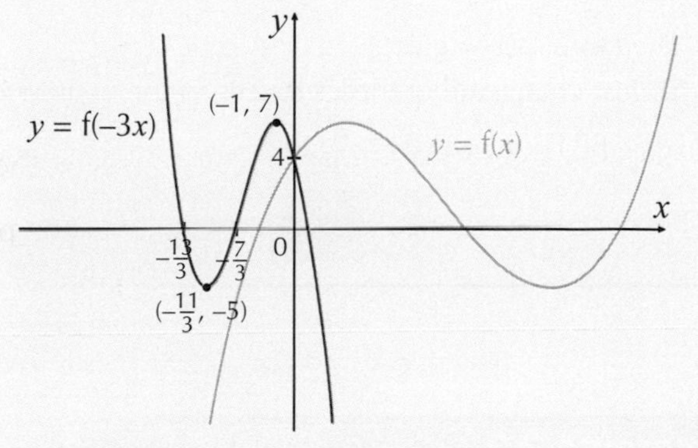

Tip: As always, label any key points, e.g. (3, 7) has become (–1, 7), and (11, –5) has become $(-\frac{11}{3}, -5)$.

Example 3

Below is the graph of the function $g(x) = x - \frac{4}{3}x^3$

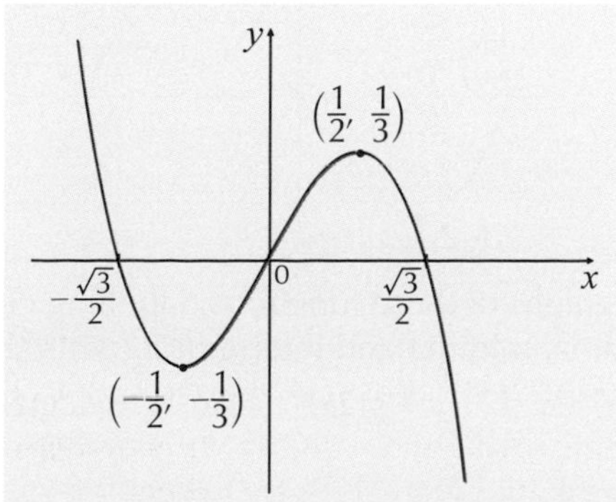

Tip: The key points to keep track of this time are: $(0, 0)$, $\left(-\frac{1}{2}, -\frac{1}{3}\right)$, $\left(\frac{1}{2}, \frac{1}{3}\right)$, $\left(-\frac{\sqrt{3}}{2}, 0\right)$ and $\left(\frac{\sqrt{3}}{2}, 0\right)$.

a) Sketch the graph of $y = -2g(x)$

- It's of the form $ag(x)$, so the graph will be stretched **vertically** by a scale factor of 2, but also reflected in the x-axis:

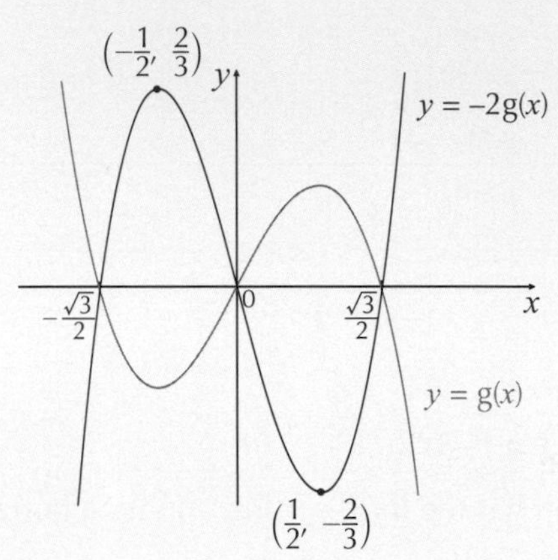

b) The graph of $y = g(x)$ is stretched parallel to the x-axis by a scale factor of $\frac{1}{2}$ to give the function $y = h(x)$. Find an expression for $h(x)$.

- It's a horizontal stretch, so you know that $h(x) = g(ax)$, where $\frac{1}{a}$ is the scale factor of the stretch.
- You're told that the scale factor is $\frac{1}{2}$, so a must be equal to 2.
- Therefore, $h(x) = g(2x)$.
  So just change all of the x's to $2x$'s in the expression for $g(x)$:

$$h(x) = g(2x) = 2x - \frac{4}{3}(2x)^3$$

$$= 2x - \frac{32}{3}x^3$$

Exercise 2.2

Q1 The diagram shows the graph of $y = g(x)$. The graph has a minimum at (–2, –3), a maximum at (2, 3) and crosses the x-axis at (0, 0), (–4, 0) and (4, 0).

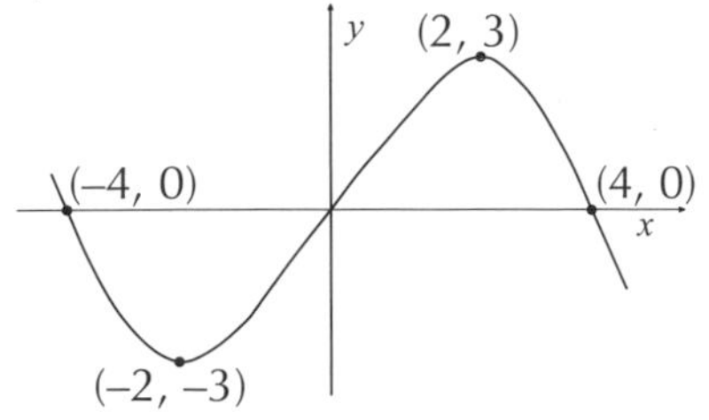

Sketch the graphs of these functions, labelling clearly the coordinates of any maxima, minima and intersections with the axes:

a) $y = 2g(x)$ b) $y = g(2x)$ c) $y = -2g(x)$ d) $y = g(-2x)$

Q2 The diagram shows the graph of f(x) and Graph A of a function that is a transformation of f(x).

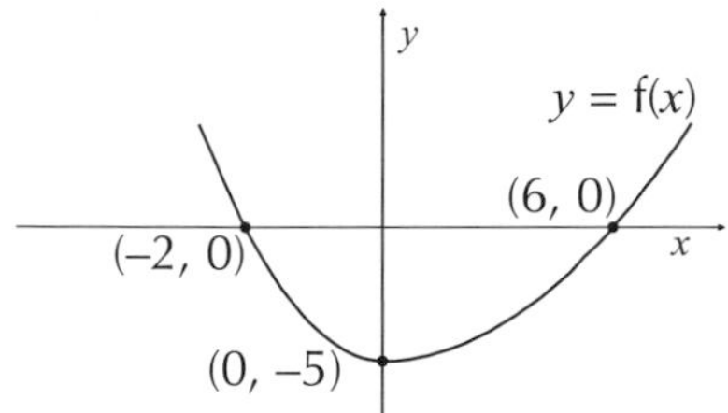

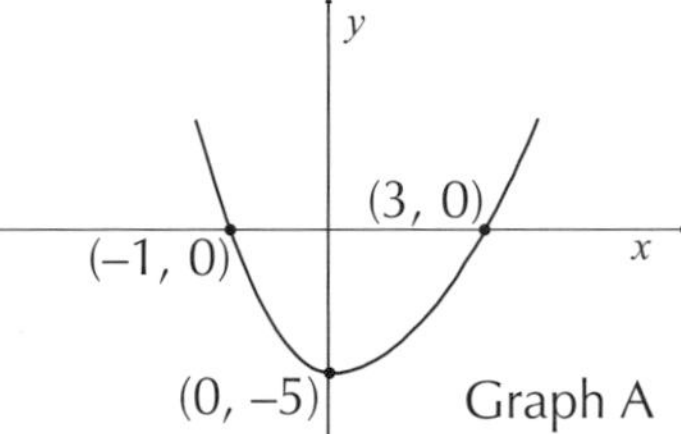

Which of these equations gives the transformed graph?

a) $y = 2\text{f}(x)$ b) $y = \text{f}(2x)$ c) $y = \text{f}(0.5x)$ d) $y = 0.5\text{f}(x)$

Q3 The diagram shows the graph of f(x) and Graph A of a function that is a transformation of f(x).

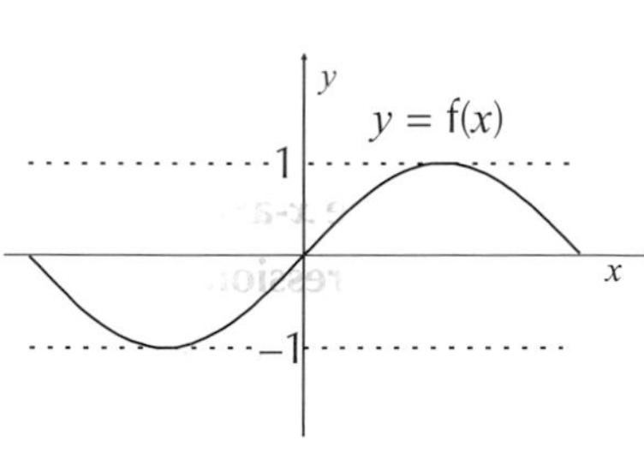

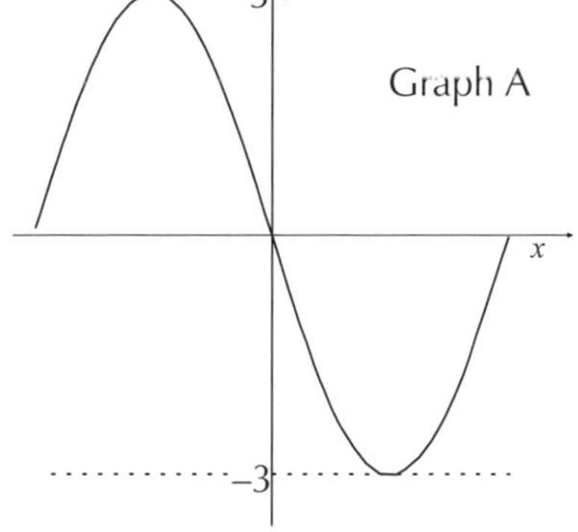

Q3 Hint: There are actually two transformations that could give Graph A, but only one of them is listed.

Which of these equations could give the transformed graph?

a) $y = 3\text{f}(x)$ b) $y = -3\text{f}(x)$ c) $y = \text{f}(-3x)$ d) $y = \text{f}(3x)$

Q4 Given that $\text{f}(x) = x^3 - x$, sketch the graphs of the following functions:

a) $y = \text{f}(x) + 2$ b) $y = \text{f}(x - 2)$ c) $y = \text{f}(-2x)$ d) $y = -2\text{f}(x)$

Q4 Hint: Look back at your C1 notes if you can't remember what graphs like $y = x^3 - x$ should look like.

Q5 Describe clearly the transformation that is required to take the graph of $y = x^3 + 2x + 4$ to the graph of $y = 3x^3 + 6x + 12$.

Q6 Describe clearly the transformation that is required to take the graph of $y = x^2 + x + 4$ to the graph of $y = 4x^2 - 2x + 4$.

Q6 Hint: The terms which contain x's are different to the original, but the constant term is not.

Q7 a) The graph of $y = 5 - 15x - 90x^2$ is stretched vertically by scale factor 0.2 to give the function $y = \text{g}(x)$. Find an expression for g(x).

b) $y = \text{g}(x)$ is stretched horizontally by scale factor 3 to give the function $y = \text{h}(x)$. Find an expression for h(x).

Q8 a) Sketch the graph of $\text{f}(x) = x^2 - 6x - 7$ showing clearly the coordinates of any turning points and where the curve meets the coordinate axes.

Q8 a) Hint: Complete the square.

b) Write down the equation of the graph obtained by stretching the graph of f(x) vertically with a scale factor of –2.

c) Sketch the graph with equation you found in part b) showing clearly the coordinates of any turning points and where the curve meets the coordinate axes.

Review Exercise — Chapter 1

Q1 Simplify these:

a) x^3x^5 b) a^7a^8 c) $\frac{x^8}{x^2}$

d) $(a^2)^4$ e) $(xy^2)(x^3yz)$ f) $\frac{a^2b^4c^6}{a^3b^2c}$

Q2 Work out the following without using a calculator:

a) $16^{\frac{1}{2}}$ b) $8^{\frac{2}{3}}$ c) $16^{\frac{3}{4}}$

d) x^0 e) $49^{-\frac{1}{2}}$

Q3 Use the graph of f(x) below to sketch these transformed graphs:

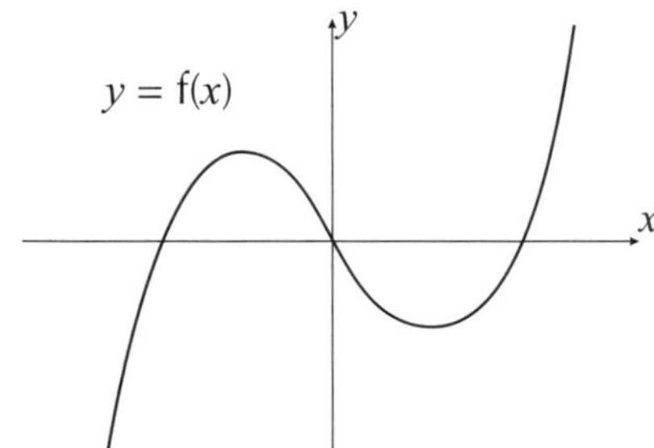

a) $y = \text{f}(ax)$, where (i) $a > 1$,
(ii) $0 < a < 1$.

b) $y = a\text{f}(x)$, where (i) $a > 1$,
(ii) $0 < a < 1$.

c) (i) $y = \text{f}(x + a)$, where $a > 0$,
(ii) $y = \text{f}(x - a)$, where $a > 0$.

d) (i) $y = \text{f}(x) + a$, where $a > 0$,
(ii) $y = \text{f}(x) - a$, where $a > 0$.

Q4 The diagram shows the graph of $y = \text{f}(x)$.
The curve has a maximum at (2, 4) and meets the x-axis at (0, 0) and (5, 0).

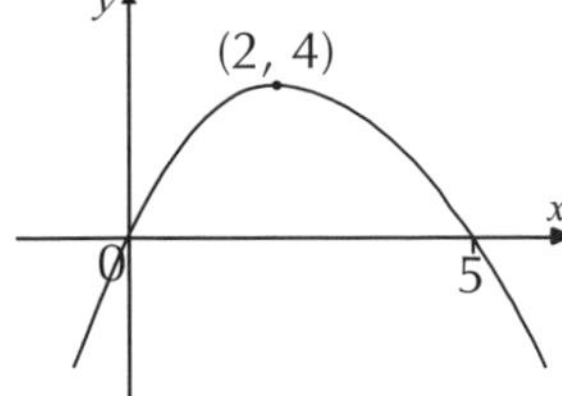

Sketch the graphs of these functions, labelling clearly the coordinates of any maxima or minima and where the curve meets the coordinate axes.

a) $y = \text{f}(-x)$ b) $y = -\text{f}(x)$ c) $y = 2\text{f}(x)$ d) $y = \text{f}(2x)$

Exam-Style Questions — Chapter 1

1 Give the values of a, b and c, such that:

a) $3^a = 27$, *(1 mark)*

b) $3 = 27^b$, *(1 mark)*

c) $27^c = 81$. *(2 marks)*

2 Given that $10000\sqrt{10} = 10^k$, find the value of k. *(3 marks)*

3 Figure 1 shows a sketch of the graph of the function $y = \mathrm{f}(x)$.
The graph crosses the x-axis at $(-1, 0)$, $(1, 0)$ and $(2, 0)$, and crosses the y-axis at $(0, 2)$.

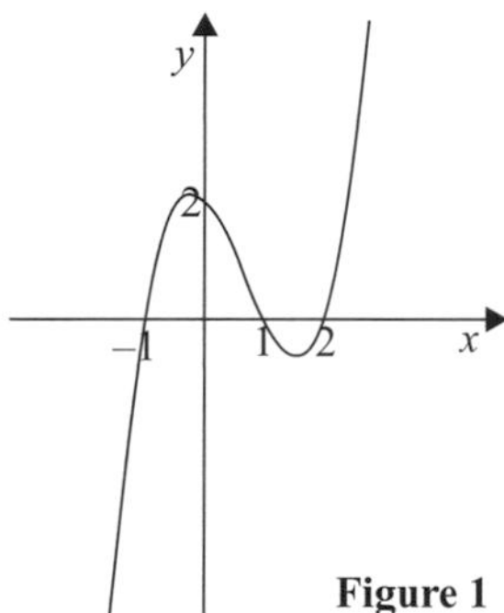

Figure 1

On separate diagrams, sketch the following:

a) $y = \mathrm{f}\left(\frac{1}{2}x\right)$. *(3 marks)*

b) $y = \mathrm{f}(x - 4)$. *(2 marks)*

On each diagram, label any known points of intersection with the x- or y-axes.

4 Write
$$\frac{x + 5x^3}{\sqrt{x}}$$
in the form $x^m + 5x^n$, where m and n are constants. *(2 marks)*

5 a) Sketch the curve $y = \mathrm{f}(x)$, where $\mathrm{f}(x) = x^2 - 4$, showing clearly the points of intersection with the x- and y-axes. *(2 marks)*

b) Describe fully the transformation that transforms the curve $y = \mathrm{f}(x)$ to the curve $y = -2\mathrm{f}(x)$. *(2 marks)*

c) The curve $y = \mathrm{f}(x)$ is translated two units in the positive y-direction.
State the equation of the curve after it has been transformed, in terms of $\mathrm{f}(x)$. *(1 mark)*

Chapter 2 Trigonometry

1. Arcs and Sectors

Learning Objectives:

- Be able to use radians as the measure for the size of an angle.
- Be able to use the formula $l = r\theta$ to work out the arc length of a sector of a circle.
- Be able to use the formula $A = \frac{1}{2}r^2\theta$ to work out the area of a sector.

You'll be familiar with angles being measured in degrees. Radians are another unit of measurement for angles. They can be easier to use than degrees when measuring things like the arc length of a sector of a circle or its area, and they come up a lot in trigonometry and in later core modules.

Radians

A **radian** (rad) is just another unit of measurement for an angle.

1 radian is the angle formed in a **sector** that has an **arc length** that is the same as the **radius**.

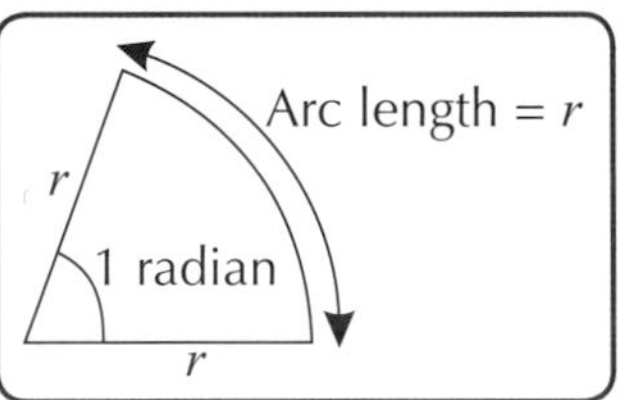

In other words, if you have a **sector** with an angle of **1 radian**, then the **length** of the **arc** will be exactly the **same length** as the **radius** r.

It's important to know how **radians relate to degrees**:

- 360 degrees (a complete circle) = 2π radians
- 180 degrees = π radians
- 1 radian is about 57 degrees

Tip: Radians are sometimes shown by 'rad' after the number, or a '^{c}' (e.g. $4\pi^c$), but most of the time angles in radians are given without a symbol.

You also need to know how to **convert** between the two units. The table below shows you how:

Converting angles	
Radians to degrees: Divide by π, multiply by 180.	**Degrees to radians:** Divide by 180, multiply by π.

Here's a table of some of the **common angles** you're going to need, in degrees and radians:

Degrees	0	30	45	60	90	120	180	270	360
Radians	0	$\frac{\pi}{6}$	$\frac{\pi}{4}$	$\frac{\pi}{3}$	$\frac{\pi}{2}$	$\frac{2\pi}{3}$	π	$\frac{3\pi}{2}$	2π

Tip: It's a good idea to learn these common angles — they come up a lot.

Examples

a) Convert $\frac{\pi}{15}$ into degrees.

- To convert from radians to degrees:
- Divide by π... $$\frac{\pi}{15} \div \pi = \frac{1}{15}$$
- ... then multiply by 180... $$\frac{1}{15} \times 180 = 12°$$

Tip: Notice how the angle was given without a symbol — if this happens, you can just assume it's in radians.

b) Convert 120 degrees into radians.

- You could smugly use the table on the last page to find the answer, but to show that the rule for converting from degrees to radians works...
- ... divide by 180 and then multiply by π. $$\frac{120}{180} \times \pi = \frac{2\pi}{3}$$

c) Convert 297 degrees into radians.

- To convert from degrees to radians, divide by 180 and then multiply by π. $$\frac{297}{180} \times \pi = 1.65\pi \text{ or } 5.18 \text{ rad (3 s.f.)}$$

Tip: In the exam, you can give your answer to part c) in terms of π or as a rounded number, unless the question states otherwise. Generally though, it's better to just keep it in terms of π, and if the question asks for an exact answer you have to do this.

Exercise 1.1

Q1 Convert the angles below into radians. Give your answers in terms of π.

a) 180° b) 135°

c) 270° d) 70°

e) 150° f) 75°

Q2 Convert the angles below into degrees.

a) $\frac{\pi}{4}$ b) $\frac{\pi}{2}$

c) $\frac{\pi}{3}$ d) $\frac{5\pi}{2}$

e) $\frac{3\pi}{4}$ f) $\frac{7\pi}{3}$

g) 1 h) $\frac{7\pi}{10}$

i) $\frac{13\pi}{8}$ j) 1.8

k) $\frac{4\pi}{9}$ l) $\frac{11\pi}{6}$

Arc length and sector area

A **sector** is part of a circle formed by **two radii** and part of the **circumference**. The **arc** of a sector is the **curved** edge of the sector. You can work out the **length** of the **arc**, or the **area** of the sector — as long as you know the **angle** at the **centre** (θ) and the **length** of the **radius** (r). When working out arc length and sector area you **always** work in radians.

Arc length

For a circle with **radius** r, a sector with **angle** θ (measured in **radians**) has **arc length** l, given by:

$$l = r\theta$$

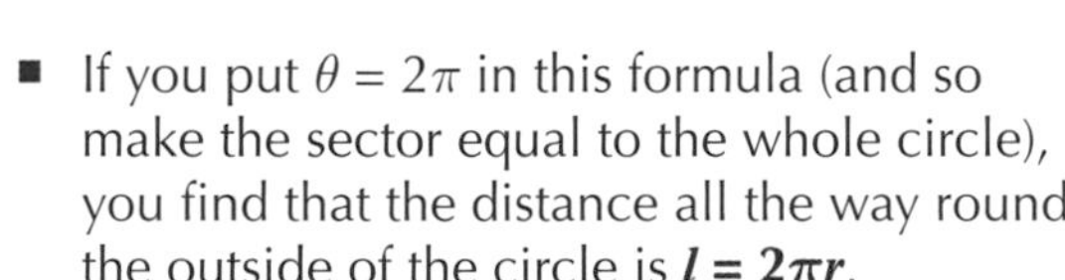

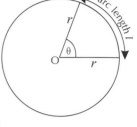

- If you put $\theta = 2\pi$ in this formula (and so make the sector equal to the whole circle), you find that the distance all the way round the outside of the circle is $l = 2\pi r$.

- This is just the normal **circumference** formula.

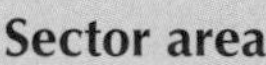

Sector area

For a circle with **radius** r, a sector with **angle** θ (measured in **radians**) has **area** A, given by:

$$A = \frac{1}{2}r^2\theta$$

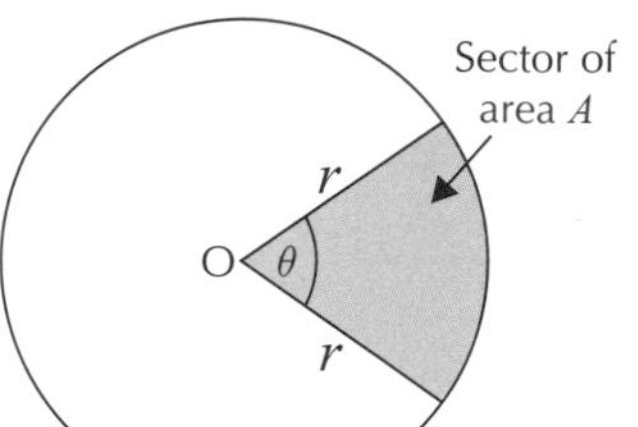

- Again, if you put $\theta = 2\pi$ in the formula, you find that the area of the whole circle is $A = \frac{1}{2}r^2 \times 2\pi = \pi r^2$.
- This is just the normal '**area of a circle**' formula.

Example 1

Find the exact length L and area A in the diagram to the right.

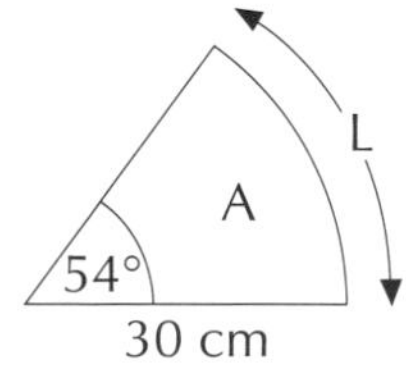

- It's asking for an arc length and sector area, so you need the angle in **radians**.

$$54° = \frac{54 \times \pi}{180} = \frac{3\pi}{10} \text{ radians}$$

- Now put everything in your formulas:

$$\text{L} = r\theta = 30 \times \frac{3\pi}{10} = 9\pi \text{ cm}$$

$$\text{A} = \frac{1}{2}r^2\theta = \frac{1}{2} \times 30^2 \times \frac{3\pi}{10} = 135\pi \text{ cm}^2$$

Example 2

Find the area of the shaded part of the symbol.

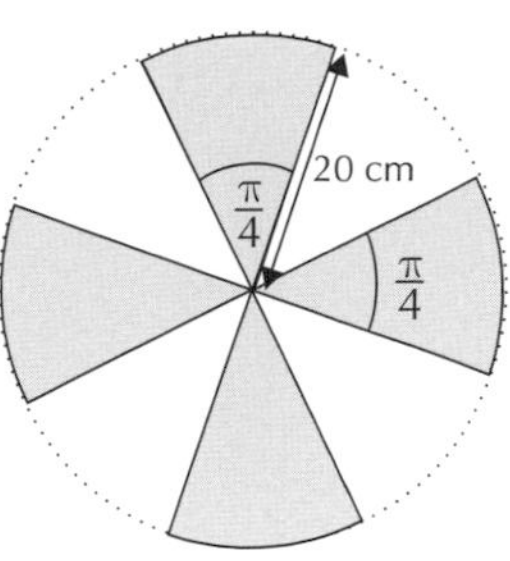

- Each 'leaf' has area:

$$\frac{1}{2} \times 20^2 \times \frac{\pi}{4} = 50\pi \text{ cm}^2$$

- So the area of the whole symbol =

$$4 \times 50\pi = 200\pi \text{ cm}^2$$

Tip: Instead, you could use the total angle of all the shaded sectors (π).

Example 3

The sector shown has an area of 6π cm². Find the arc length, l.

- First, get the angle in **radians**:

$$60° = \frac{60 \times \pi}{180} = \frac{\pi}{3} \text{ radians}$$

Tip: This is one of the common angles from the table on page 16 — it's definitely worth learning them.

- You want to find the arc length, but you don't know the sector's radius.
- But we know its area, so use the area formula to **work out** the **radius**:

$$A = \frac{1}{2}r^2\theta \Rightarrow 6\pi = \frac{1}{2} \times r^2 \times \frac{\pi}{3}$$

$$36 = r^2$$

$$r = 6$$

- Putting this value of r into the equation for arc length gives us:

$$l = r\theta = 6 \times \frac{\pi}{3} = 2\pi \text{ cm}$$

Exercise 1.2

Q1 The diagram below shows a sector OAB. The centre is at O and the radius is 6 cm. The angle AOB is 2 radians.

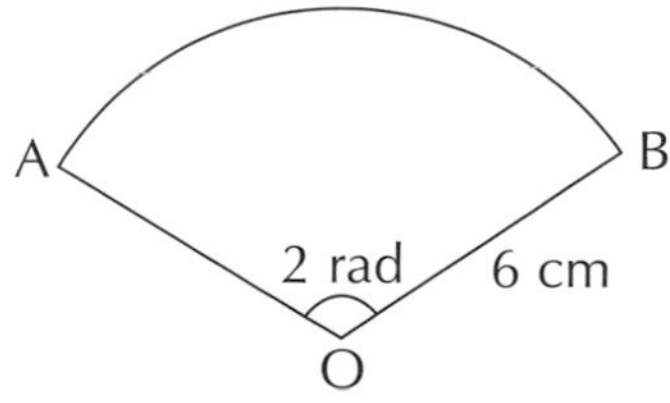

Find the arc length and area of this sector.

Q2 Hint: Remember to convert 46° to radians first.

Q2 The diagram below shows a sector OAB. The centre is at O and the radius is 8 cm. The angle AOB is 46°.

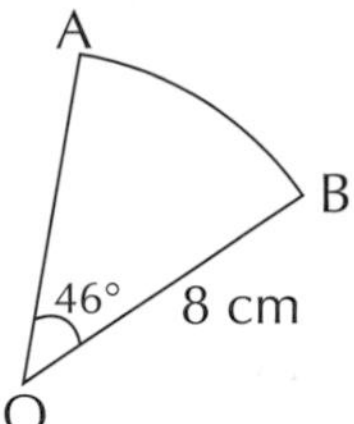

Find the arc length and area of this sector to 1 d.p.

Q3 The diagram below shows a sector of a circle with a centre O and radius r cm. The angle AOB shown is θ.

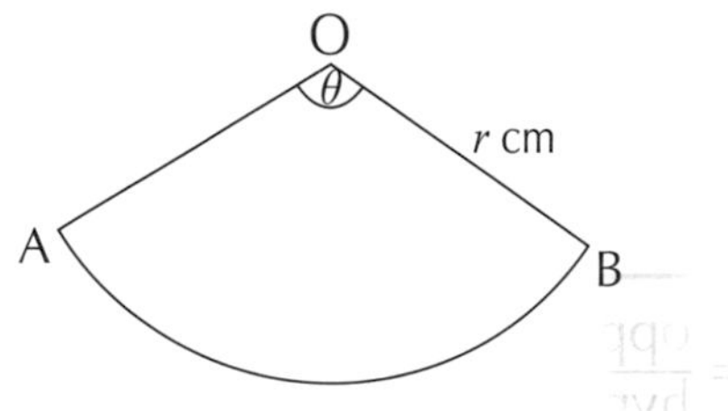

For each of the following values of θ and r, give the arc length and the area of the sector. Where appropriate give your answers to 3 s.f.

a) $\theta = 1.2$ radians, $r = 5$ cm

b) $\theta = 0.6$ radians, $r = 4$ cm

c) $\theta = 80°$, $r = 9$ cm

d) $\theta = \frac{5\pi}{12}$, $r = 4$ cm

Q4 The diagram below shows a sector ABC of a circle, where the angle BAC is 0.9 radians.

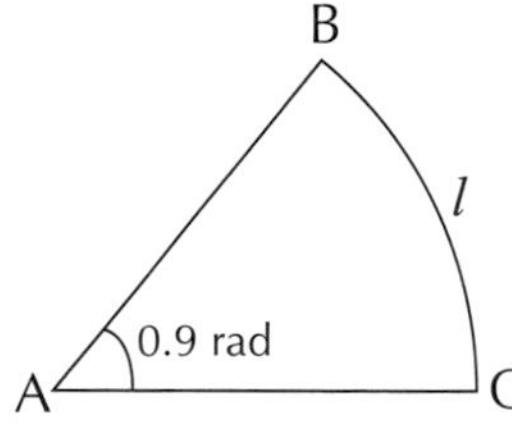

Given that the area of the sector is 16.2 cm², find the arc length l.

Q5 A circle C has a radius of length 3 cm with centre O. A sector of this circle is given by angle AOB which is 20°.

Find the length of the arc AB and the area of the sector. Give your answer in terms of π.

Q6 The sector shown has an arc length of 7 cm. The angle BAC is 1.4 rad. Find the area of the sector.

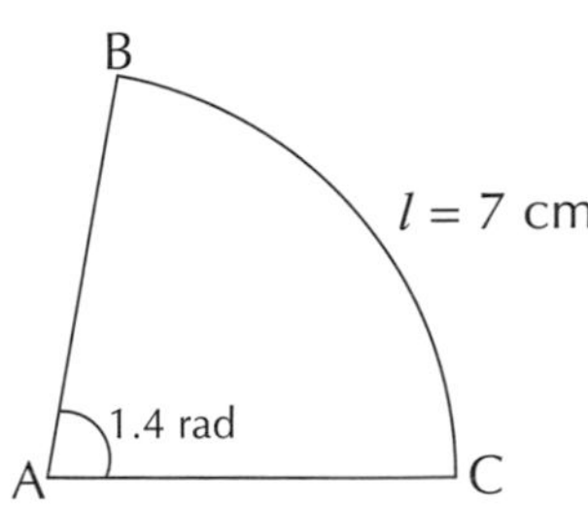

2. The Sine and Cosine Rules

In this section you'll see how SOHCAHTOA and the sine and cosine rules can be used to find the length of each side and the size of each angle in a triangle, as well as its area. You might have seen some of this at GCSE, so parts of this chapter will just be a recap.

Learning Objectives:

- Be able to find the values of sin, cos and tan of 30°, 60° and 45° (and the equivalent angles in radians) without a calculator.
- Know the sine and cosine rules and be able to use them on any triangle.
- Be able to work out the area of a triangle using the formula $\frac{1}{2}ab\sin C$.

Trig values from triangles

You need to know the values of **sin**, **cos** and **tan** at 30°, 60° and 45°, and there are two **triangles** that can help you remember them. It may seem like a long-winded way of doing it, but once you know how to do it, you'll always be able to work them out — even without a calculator.

The idea is you draw the triangles below, putting in their angles and side lengths. Then you can use them to work out special trig values like **sin 45°** or **cos 60°** with exact values instead of the decimals given by calculators.

First, make sure you can remember SOHCAHTOA:

$$\sin = \frac{\text{opp}}{\text{hyp}} \qquad \cos = \frac{\text{adj}}{\text{hyp}} \qquad \tan = \frac{\text{opp}}{\text{adj}}$$

These are the two triangles that you'll use:

Half an equilateral triangle with sides of length 2:

- You can work out the height using Pythagoras' theorem: height = $\sqrt{2^2 - 1^2} = \sqrt{3}$.
- Then you can use the triangle to work out sin, cos and tan of 30° and 60°.

2
30°
$\sqrt{3}$
60°
1

$\sin 30° = \frac{1}{2}$	$\cos 30° = \frac{\sqrt{3}}{2}$	$\tan 30° = \frac{1}{\sqrt{3}}$
$\sin 60° = \frac{\sqrt{3}}{2}$	$\cos 60° = \frac{1}{2}$	$\tan 60° = \sqrt{3}$

Tip: If you're working in radians (see page 16), you just need to replace the angle in degrees with the equivalent angle in radians. So $\sin\frac{\pi}{6} = \sin 30° = \frac{1}{2}$.

Tip: Make sure you're confident with these values as they'll come up a lot in C2-C4.

Right-angled triangle with two sides of length 1:

- You can work out the hypotenuse using Pythagoras' theorem: hypotenuse $= \sqrt{1^2 + 1^2} = \sqrt{2}$.
- Then you can use the triangle to work out sin, cos and tan of 45°.

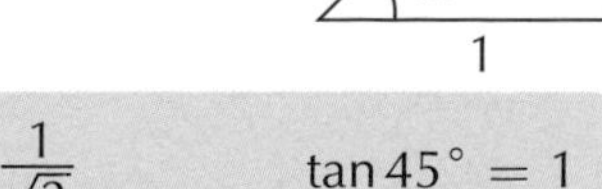

$\sin 45° = \frac{1}{\sqrt{2}}$	$\cos 45° = \frac{1}{\sqrt{2}}$	$\tan 45° = 1$

The sine and cosine rules

There are three useful formulas you need to know for working out information about a triangle. There are **two** for finding the **angles** and **sides** (called the **sine rule** and **cosine rule**) and one for finding the **area**.

> **Tip:** These rules work on any triangle, not just right-angled triangles.

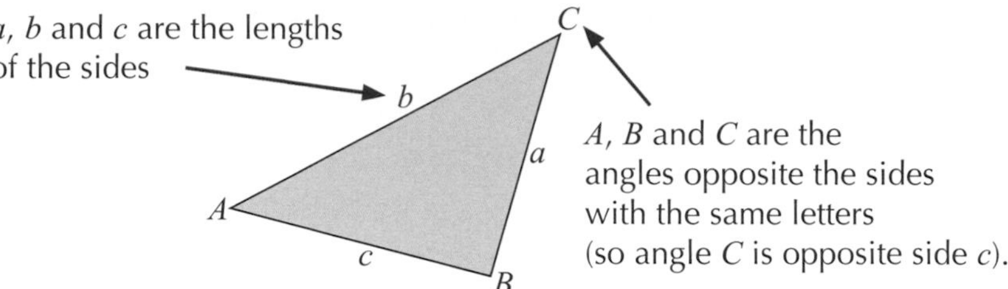

The Sine Rule

$$\frac{a}{\sin A} = \frac{b}{\sin B} = \frac{c}{\sin C}$$

The Cosine Rule

$$a^2 = b^2 + c^2 - 2bc\cos A$$

Area of any triangle

$$\text{Area} = \frac{1}{2}ab\sin C$$

> **Tip:** You can use any two bits of the sine rule to make a normal equation with just one = sign. The sine rule also works if you flip all the fractions upside down: $\frac{\sin A}{a} = \frac{\sin B}{b} = \frac{\sin C}{c}$.

> **Tip:** You can also rearrange the cosine rule into the form $\cos A = \frac{b^2 + c^2 - a^2}{2bc}$ to find an angle.

> **Tip:** Remember, if you know two angles you can work out the third by subtracting them from 180°.

To decide which rule to use, look at what you know about the triangle:

You can use the **sine rule** if:

- You know **any two angles** and a **side**.

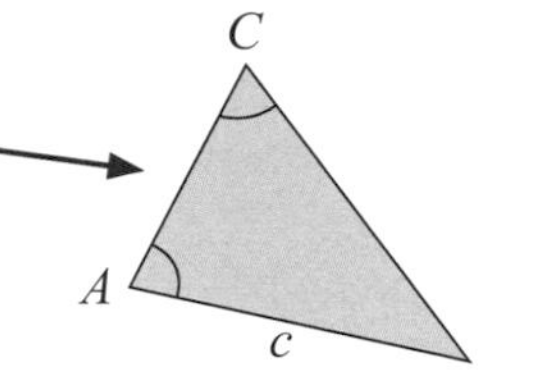

You can **sometimes** use the **sine rule** if:

- You know **two sides** and an **angle that isn't between them**.

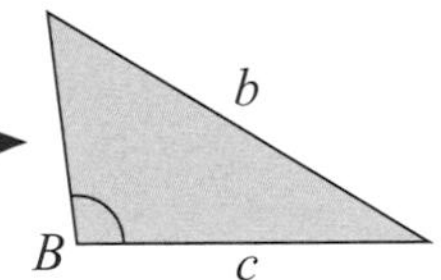

This doesn't always work though — sometimes there are **2 possible** triangles:

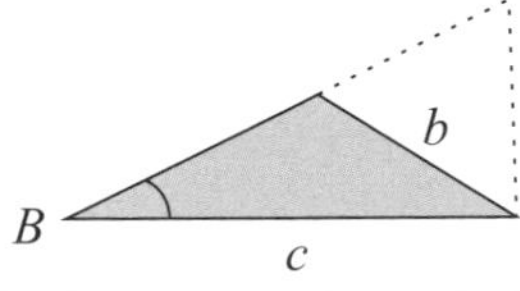

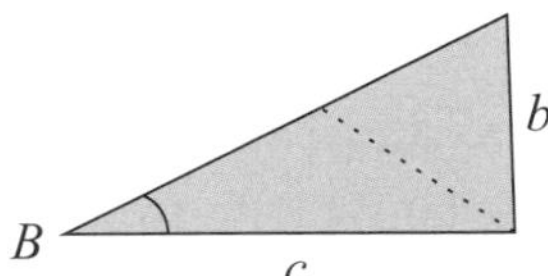

You can use the **cosine rule** if:

- You know **all three** sides...

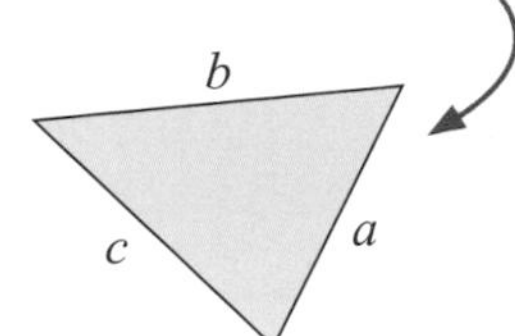

- ...or you know **two sides** and the **angle** that's **between** them.

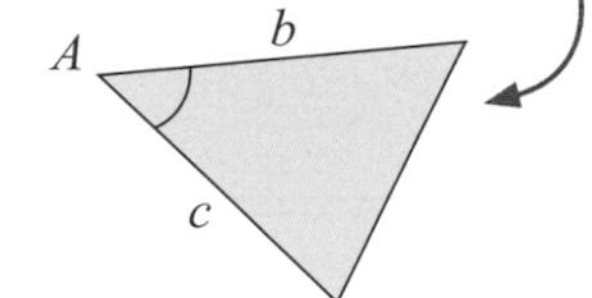

Example 1

Find the missing sides and angles for $\triangle ABC$, in which A = 40°, a = 27 m and B = 73°. Then find the area of the triangle.

- Start by **sketching** the triangle. It doesn't have to be particularly accurate, but it can help you decide which rule(s) you need.
- Here you have 2 angles and a side, so you can use the **sine rule**.
- First, though, start by finding angle C (using the fact that the angles in a triangle add up to 180°).

$$\angle C = 180° - 73° - 40° = 67°$$

- Now use the sine rule to find the other sides one at a time:

$$\frac{a}{\sin A} = \frac{b}{\sin B} \Rightarrow \frac{27}{\sin 40°} = \frac{b}{\sin 73°}$$

$$\Rightarrow b = \frac{27 \times \sin 73°}{\sin 40°}$$

$$= 40.2 \text{ m (1 d.p.)}$$

$$\frac{c}{\sin C} = \frac{a}{\sin A} \Rightarrow \frac{c}{\sin 67°} = \frac{27}{\sin 40°}$$

$$\Rightarrow c = \frac{27 \times \sin 67°}{\sin 40°}$$

$$= 38.7 \text{ m (1 d.p.)}$$

- Now you've found the missing values, you can find the area using the formula:

$$\text{Area of } \triangle ABC = \frac{1}{2}ab\sin C$$

$$= \frac{1}{2} \times 27 \times 40.169... \times \sin 67°$$

$$= 499.2 \text{ m}^2 \text{ (1 d.p.)}$$

Tip: Use the unrounded value for b here (rather than just 40.2).

Example 2

Find the values of X, Y and Z.

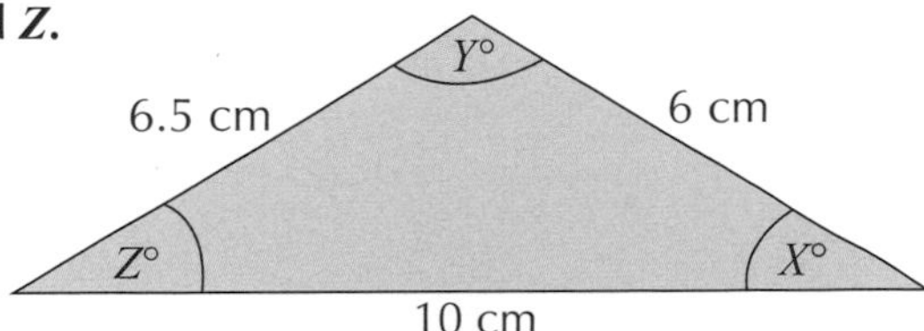

- You've been given all three sides but none of the angles, so start by using the **cosine rule** to find angle Z (you'll have to rearrange the formula a bit first).

$$a^2 = b^2 + c^2 - 2bc\cos A \Rightarrow \cos A = \frac{b^2 + c^2 - a^2}{2bc}$$

$$\Rightarrow \cos Z = \frac{10^2 + 6.5^2 - 6^2}{(2 \times 10 \times 6.5)}$$

$$\Rightarrow \cos Z = 0.817...$$

$$\Rightarrow Z = 35.2° \text{ (1 d.p.)}$$

Tip: One of the hardest things about using the sine and cosine rules is matching the sides and angles given in the question to the ones in the formula. If it helps, label your triangle with A, B, C, a, b and c each time.

Tip: Just use the $\cos^{-1}$ button on your calculator to work out the value of Z from $\cos Z$.

Tip: You could try using the sine rule here, but it would give you a value of 73.8° for Y — and you can see from the diagram that angle Y is obtuse. So here you'd have to subtract 73.8° from 180° to get the actual value of Y — there's more on this later in the chapter.

- Use the cosine rule **again** to find the value of another angle. It doesn't matter which one you go for (using Y here).

$$a^2 = b^2 + c^2 - 2bc\cos A$$

$$\Rightarrow \cos Y = \frac{6^2 + 6.5^2 - 10^2}{2 \times 6 \times 6.5}$$

$$\Rightarrow \cos Y = -0.278...$$

$$\Rightarrow Y = 106.2° \text{ (1 d.p.)}$$

- Now that you have two of the angles, you can find the other by subtracting them from 180°:

$$X = 180° - 35.2° - 106.2°$$

$$= 38.6° \text{ (1 d.p.)}$$

- You can find the areas of more **complicated** shapes by turning them into **multiple triangles** stuck together, then using the **sine** and **cosine rules** on each individual triangle.
- This method can be used for working out angles and sides in real-life problems, such as calculating distances travelled or areas covered. Sometimes you'll see a problem that uses **bearings**.

Example 3

Rasmus the trawlerman has cast his nets between buoys in the North Sea (shown on the diagram below).

a) Find the area of sea his nets cover to 2 s.f.

Tip: Rasmus's boat is called the Sea Beast.

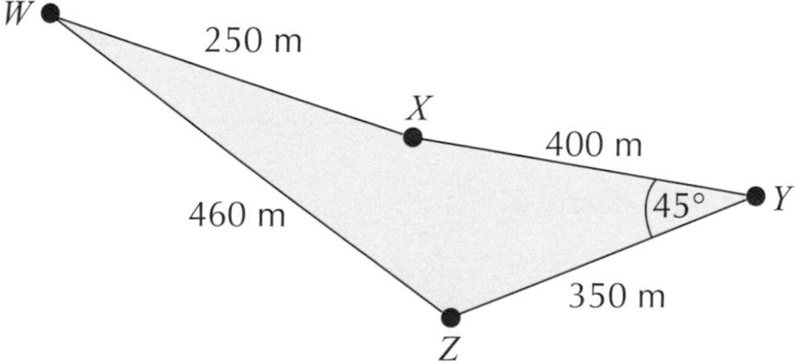

- You can start by finding the distance between X and Z (let's call it y) — this will split the area into 2 triangles. Do this by treating XYZ as a triangle and using the **cosine rule**:

$$a^2 = b^2 + c^2 - 2bc\cos A$$

$$\Rightarrow y^2 = 400^2 + 350^2 - 2(400)(350)\cos 45°$$

$$\Rightarrow y^2 = 84510.1...$$

$$\Rightarrow y = 290.7 \text{ m (1 d.p.)}$$

- Now you have all three sides for the left-hand triangle, so you can find an angle (let's say W) with the **cosine rule**.

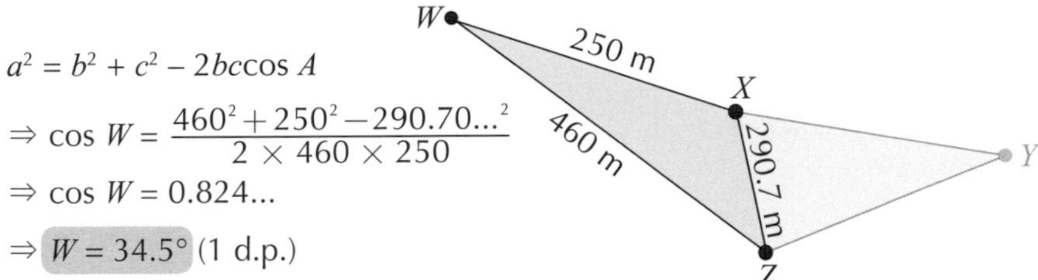

$a^2 = b^2 + c^2 - 2bc\cos A$

$\Rightarrow \cos W = \dfrac{460^2 + 250^2 - 290.70...^2}{2 \times 460 \times 250}$

$\Rightarrow \cos W = 0.824...$

$\Rightarrow W = 34.5°$ (1 d.p.)

- Now you have enough information to find the **area** of each triangle with the formula on page 22.

Left-hand triangle:

$\text{Area} = \frac{1}{2}ab\sin C$

$= \frac{1}{2} \times 250 \times 460 \times \sin 34.48...°$

$= 32\,600 \text{ m}^2$ (3 s.f.)

Right-hand triangle:

$\text{Area} = \frac{1}{2}ab\sin C$

$= \frac{1}{2} \times 400 \times 350 \times \sin 45°$

$= 49\,500 \text{ m}^2$ (3 s.f.)

Tip: You could have found the area of the right-hand triangle at the start as you had all the info you needed.

- So the total area of sea covered is:

$32\,600 + 49\,500 = 82\,000 \text{ m}^2$ (2 s.f.)

b) If X is on a bearing of 100° from W, on what bearing does Rasmus have to sail to get from X to Y (to 3 s.f.)?

- To find the bearing, find all the other angles round X and then subtract them from 360°. The unknown angle marked below is 180° – 100° = 80°.

Tip: This comes from the rules of parallel lines — you did this at GCSE.

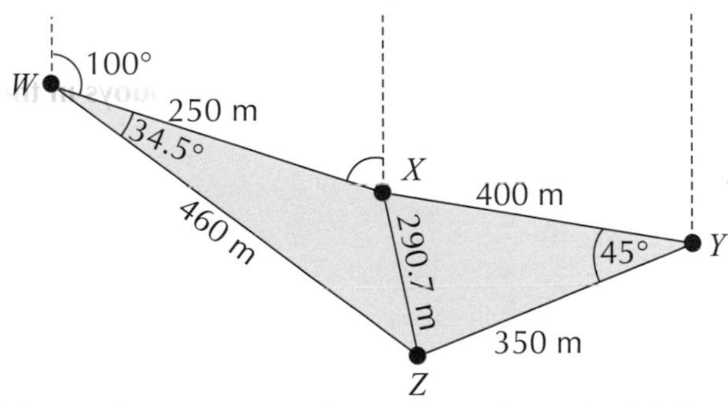

- To find the angle $\angle WXZ$, use the cosine rule on the left-hand triangle:

$a^2 = b^2 + c^2 - 2bc\cos A \quad \Rightarrow \quad \cos\angle WXZ = \dfrac{250^2 + 290.70...^2 - 460^2}{2 \times 250 \times 290.70...}$

$\Rightarrow \quad \angle WXZ = \cos^{-1} -0.444...$

$\Rightarrow \quad \angle WXZ = 116.38°$ (2 d.p.)

- Then do the same for angle $\angle YXZ$, using the right-hand triangle:

$a^2 = b^2 + c^2 - 2bc\cos A \quad \Rightarrow \quad \cos\angle YXZ = \dfrac{400^2 + 290.70...^2 - 350^2}{2 \times 400 \times 290.70...}$

$\Rightarrow \quad \cos\angle YXZ = 0.524...$

$\Rightarrow \quad \angle YXZ = 58.36°$ (2 d.p.)

- Now just subtract all the angles from 360° to find the bearing Rasmus should sail on to get from X to Y:

$360° - 80° - 116.38° - 58.36° = 105.26° = 105°$ (3 s.f.)

Exercise 2.1

Give all answers to 3 significant figures unless otherwise stated.

Q1 Use the cosine rule to find the length QR.

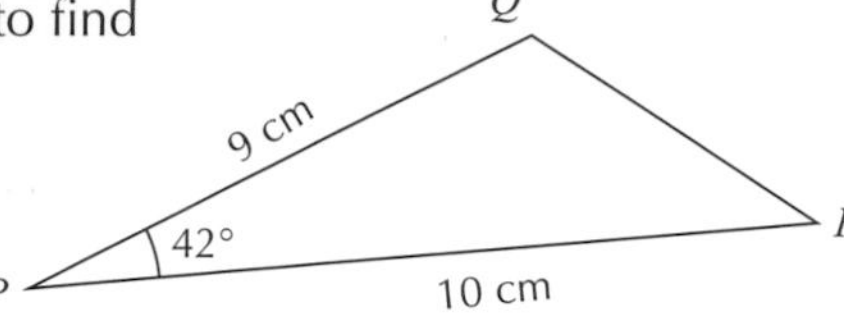

Q2 Use the sine rule to find the length TW.

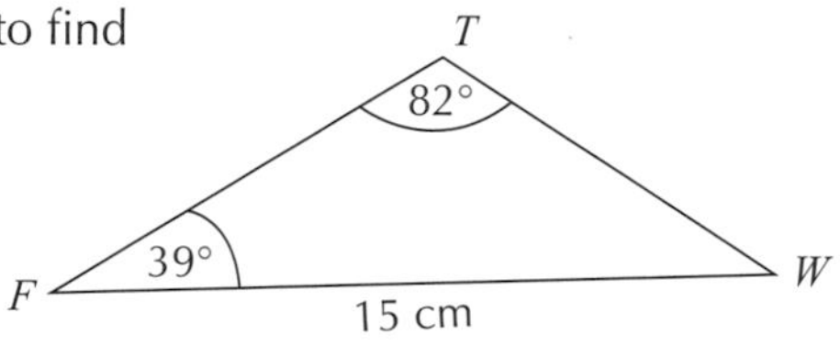

Q3 Find the length AC.

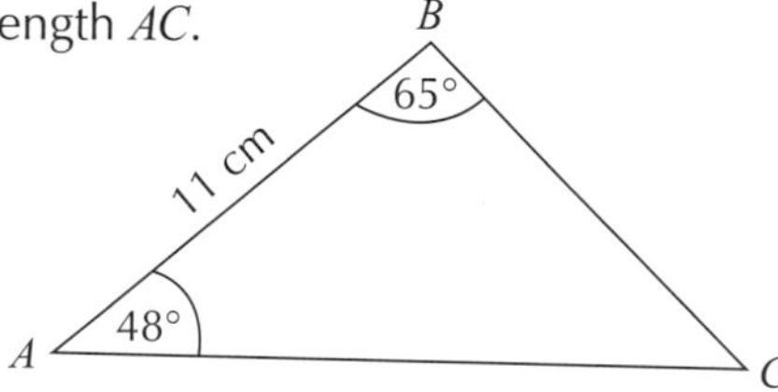

Q4 Find the size of angle D.

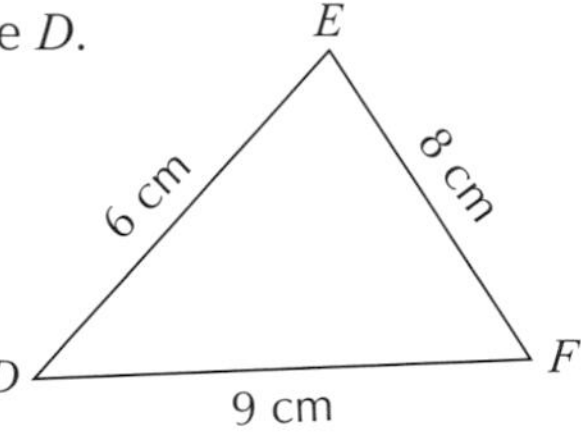

Q5 In triangle JKL: $JL = 24$ cm, $KL = 29$ cm and angle $L = 62°$. Find the length JK.

Q6 Hint: Make sure you set your calculator to radians.

Q6 In triangle GHI: $HI = 8.3$ cm, $GH = 6.4$ cm and angle $H = 2.3$ rad. Find the length GI.

Q7 In triangle BCD: $BC = 14$ cm, $CD = 11$ cm and $BD = 23$ cm. Find the angle C (in degrees) to 1 d.p.

Q8 In triangle PQR: $PR = 48$ m, angle $P = 0.66$ rad and angle $R = 0.75$ rad. Find the length PQ.

Q9 Hint: Sketching the triangle first will make it easier to see which angle you need to find. The smallest angle is opposite the shortest side, so it's easy to identify.

Q9 In triangle DEF: $DE = 8$ cm, $EF = 11$ cm and $DF = 16$ cm. Find the smallest angle (in degrees).

Q10 Find the area of this triangle.

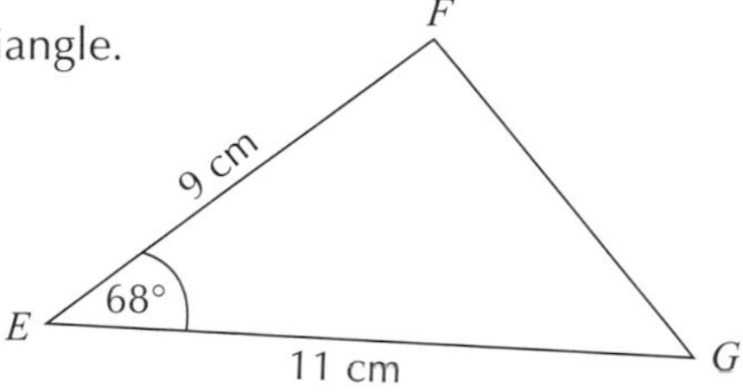

Q11 Find the area of this triangle.

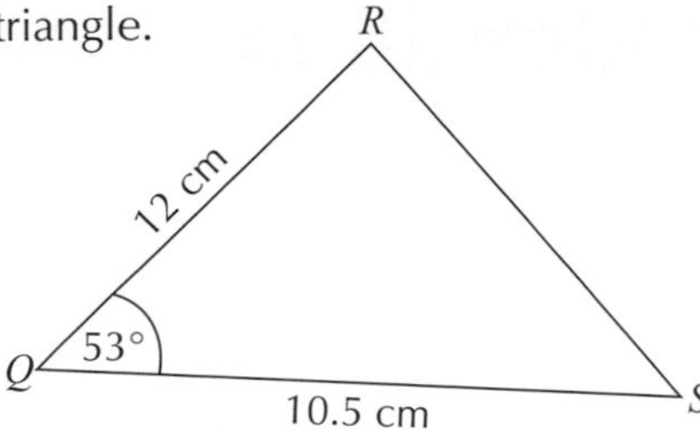

Q12 Find the area of this triangle to 2 d.p.

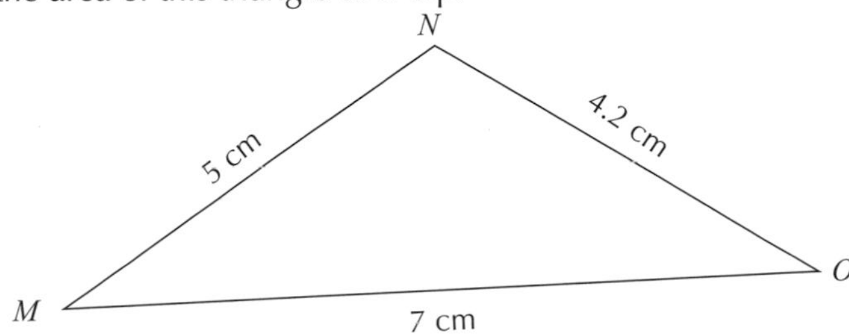

Q13 Two points, A and B, are both at sea level and on opposite sides of a mountain. The distance between them is 5 km. From A, the angle of elevation of the top of the mountain (M) is 21°, and from B, the angle of elevation is 17°.

a) Find the distance BM.

b) Hence find the height of the mountain to the nearest metre.

Q14 A ship sails 8 km on a bearing of 070° and then changes direction to sail 10 km on a bearing of 030°.

a) Draw a diagram to represent the situation.

b) What's the ship's distance from its starting position?

c) On what bearing must it now sail to get back to its starting position?

Q14 Hint: Bearings are measured clockwise from the vertical (North).

Q15 a) Find the length AC.

b) Hence find the area of the quadrilateral $ABCD$.

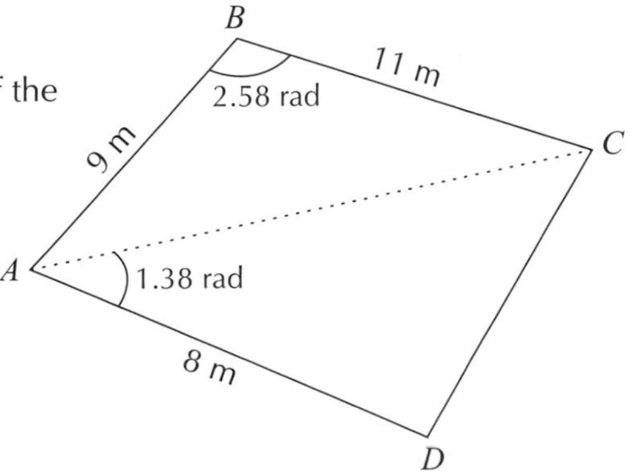

Q16 A children's pirate hat is to be made from 4 identical triangular cardboard faces with sides of 12 cm, 15 cm and 18 cm. What's the total area of cardboard needed?

3. Trig Identities

Learning Objectives:

- Know the trig identities $\tan x \equiv \frac{\sin x}{\cos x}$ and $\sin^2 x + \cos^2 x \equiv 1$.
- Be able to use trig identities to prove other relations.
- Be able to use trig identities to find the values of an expression.

Trig identities are really useful for simplifying expressions — they can make equations easier to solve by replacing one term with another.

Trig identities

There are **two trig identities** you need to know in C2. They're really useful in trigonometry and come up time and time again in C3 and C4, so make sure you learn them.

$$\tan x \equiv \frac{\sin x}{\cos x} \qquad \sin^2 x + \cos^2 x \equiv 1$$

- The second identity can also be rearranged into $\mathbf{\sin^2 x \equiv 1 - \cos^2 x}$ or $\mathbf{\cos^2 x \equiv 1 - \sin^2 x}$.
- You can use them to **prove** that two expressions are equivalent.

Tip: The '$\equiv$' means that the relation is true for all values of x. An identity is just a relation which contains a '$\equiv$' sign.

Example 1

Show that $\frac{\cos^2\theta}{1 + \sin\theta} \equiv 1 - \sin\theta$.

- A good way of doing this kind of question is to play around with **one side** of the equation until it's the same as the other side.
- Start with the left-hand side: $\frac{\cos^2\theta}{1 + \sin\theta}$
- There are usually "clues" that you can pick up to help you decide what to do next. You know there's a trig identity for $\cos^2\theta$, so start by **replacing** it in the fraction:

$$\frac{\cos^2\theta}{1 + \sin\theta} \equiv \frac{1 - \sin^2\theta}{1 + \sin\theta}$$

- The next step isn't quite as obvious, but if you look at the top of the fraction it might remind you of something — it's a **difference of two squares**.

$$\frac{1 - \sin^2\theta}{1 + \sin\theta} \equiv \frac{(1 + \sin\theta)(1 - \sin\theta)}{1 + \sin\theta}$$

- Now you can just cancel the $1 + \sin\theta$ from the top and bottom of the fraction, and you get the expression you were looking for. So:

$$\frac{\cos^2\theta}{1 + \sin\theta} \equiv 1 - \sin\theta$$ — as required.

Tip: The replacements aren't always easy to spot — look out for things like differences of two squares, or 1's that can be replaced by $\sin^2 x + \cos^2 x$.

Example 2

Show that $\cos\theta\tan\theta + 4\sin\theta \equiv 5\sin\theta$.

- Again, start with the left-hand side and see if there are any **replacements** you can easily make. Try putting in the trig identity for $\tan\theta$.

$$\cos\theta\tan\theta + 4\sin\theta \equiv \cos\theta\frac{\sin\theta}{\cos\theta} + 4\sin\theta$$

Tip: Always keep in mind what you're aiming for — here you want your answer in terms of just $\sin\theta$.

- Now you have a term with $\cos\theta$ on the top and bottom. **Cancel** these out and see what you're left with.

$$\cos\theta\frac{\sin\theta}{\cos\theta} + 4\sin\theta \equiv \sin\theta + 4\sin\theta$$

- Now it's just a case of adding the terms together, and you've arrived at the right-hand side. So:

$\cos\theta\tan\theta + 4\sin\theta \equiv 5\sin\theta$ — as required.

Example 3

Find $\sin\theta$ if $\cos\theta = \frac{2}{3}$, given that θ is an acute angle.

- The identity to use here is $\sin^2\theta + \cos^2\theta \equiv 1$
- Rearranging this gives $\sin^2\theta \equiv 1 - \cos^2\theta$
- Then put in the value of $\cos\theta$ in the question and square root each side:

$$\sin\theta = \sqrt{1-\left(\frac{2}{3}\right)^2} = \sqrt{\frac{5}{9}} = \frac{\sqrt{5}}{3}$$

Tip: You're told that θ is acute here, which means that $\sin\theta$ is positive (this is covered on the next two pages), so you can ignore the negative square root.

Exercise 3.1

Q1 Use the identity $\tan\theta \equiv \frac{\sin\theta}{\cos\theta}$ to show that $\frac{\sin\theta}{\tan\theta} - \cos\theta \equiv 0$.

Q2 Use the identity $\sin^2\theta + \cos^2\theta \equiv 1$ to show that $\cos^2\theta \equiv (1 - \sin\theta)(1 + \sin\theta)$.

Q3 Given that x is acute, find $\cos x$ if $\sin x = \frac{1}{2}$.

Q4 Show that $4\sin^2 x - 3\cos x + 1 \equiv 5 - 3\cos x - 4\cos^2 x$.

Q5 Given that x is acute, find $\tan x$ if $\sin^2 x = \frac{3}{4}$.

Q6 Show that $(\tan x + 1)(\tan x - 1) \equiv \frac{1}{\cos^2 x} - 2$.

Q7 Show that $(\sin\theta + \cos\theta)^2 + (\sin\theta - \cos\theta)^2 \equiv 2$.

Q8 Show that $\tan x + \frac{1}{\tan x} \equiv \frac{1}{\sin x\cos x}$.

Q9 Show that $4 + \sin x - 6\cos^2 x \equiv (2\sin x - 1)(3\sin x + 2)$.

Q10 Show that $\sin^2 x\cos^2 y - \cos^2 x\sin^2 y \equiv \cos^2 y - \cos^2 x$.

Q3, 5 Hint: You're told that x is acute, so just ignore the negative roots.

Q4 Hint: If you're not told which identity to use, just play around with the ones you know until something works.

Q8 Hint: $\frac{1}{\tan x} \equiv \frac{\cos x}{\sin x}$

4. Trig Functions

Learning Objectives:

- Be able to sketch the graphs of sin x, cos x and tan x.
- Be able to sketch the common transformations of the graphs of sin x, cos x and tan x.

Being able to sketch the graphs of trig functions and their transformations is really useful — it'll come in handy later in the chapter when you have to solve equations within a given interval.

Graphs of trig functions

You should be able to draw the graphs of **sin x**, **cos x** and **tan x** without looking them up — including all the important points, like where the graphs cross the **axes** and their **maximum** and **minimum** points.

sin x

- The graph of $y = \sin x$ is **periodic** — it repeats itself every 360° (or 2π radians). So $\sin x = \sin (x + 360°) = \sin (x + 720°)$ $= \sin (x + 360°n)$, where n is an integer.
- It bounces between $y = -1$ and 1, and it can **never** have a value outside this range.
- It goes through the **origin** (as $\sin 0° = 0$) and then crosses the x-axis every **180°**.
- $\sin (-x) = -\sin x$. The graph has **rotational symmetry** around the origin, so you could rotate it 180° about (0, 0) and it would look the same.
- The graph of sin x looks like this:

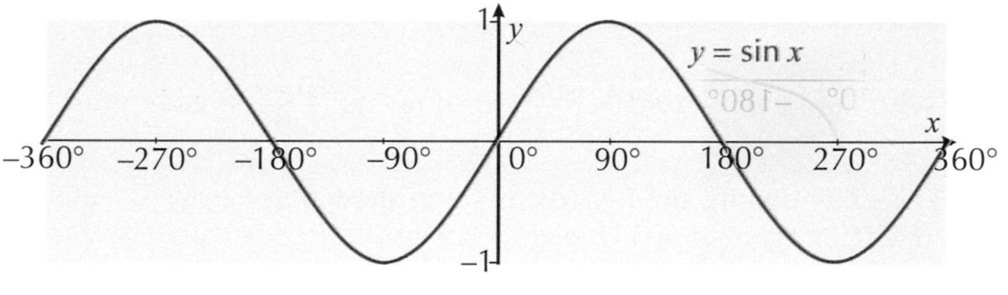

Tip: You say that sin x has a period of 360°.

Tip: Make sure you know the coordinates of the key points in radians as well.

cos x

- The graph of $y = \cos x$ is also **periodic** with period 360° (or 2π radians). $\cos x = \cos (x + 360°) = \cos (x + 720°) = \cos (x + 360°n)$, where n is an integer.
- It also bounces between $y = -1$ and 1, and it can **never** have a value outside this range.
- It crosses the y-axis at $y = 1$ (as $\cos 0° = 1$) and the x-axis at ±90°, ±270° etc.
- $\cos (-x) = \cos x$. The graph is **symmetrical** about the **y-axis**, so you could reflect it in the y-axis and it would look the same.

Tip: The graphs of sin x and cos x are the same shape but shifted 90° along the x-axis. This makes them easier to remember, but make sure you don't get them mixed up.

- The graph of cos x looks like this:

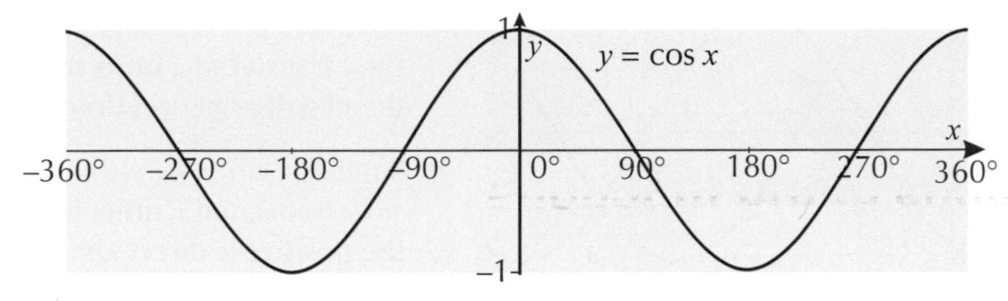

1
y
y = cos x
x
–360°
–270°
–180°
–90°
0°
90°
180°
270°
360°
–1

tan x

- The graph of $y = \tan x$ is also **periodic**, but this time it repeats itself every 180° (or π radians). So $\tan x = \tan(x + 180°) = \tan(x + 180°n)$, where n is an integer.
- It takes values between $-\infty$ and ∞ in each **180° interval**.
- It goes through the **origin** (as $\tan 0° = 0$).
- It's **undefined** at ±90°, ±270°, ±450°...
  — at these points it **jumps** from ∞ to $-\infty$ or vice versa.
- The graph of tan x looks like this:

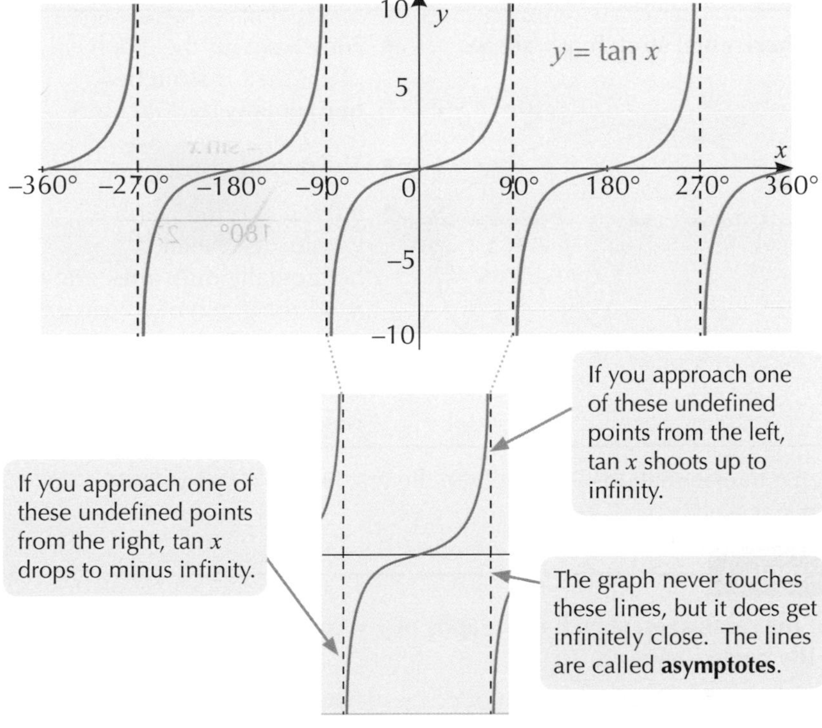

10
y
y = tan x
5
x
–360°
–270°
–180°
–90°
0
90°
180°
270°
360°
–5
–10
If you approach one of these undefined points from the left, tan x shoots up to infinity.
If you approach one of these undefined points from the right, tan x drops to minus infinity.
The graph never touches these lines, but it does get infinitely close. The lines are called asymptotes.

Tip: The best way to learn these functions is to practise sketching them and marking on the key points.

Tip: $y = \tan x$ is undefined at these points because you're dividing by zero. Remember from p.28 that $\tan x = \frac{\sin x}{\cos x}$, so when $\cos x = 0$, $\tan x$ is undefined, and $\cos x = 0$ when $x = 90°$, 270° etc. (see previous page).

Transformations

You came across different types of **transformations** in Chapter 1. A **translation** is a horizontal or vertical **shift** that doesn't change the shape of the graph. A **stretch** is exactly what it says — a horizontal or vertical **stretch** of the graph. Now, you'll need to be able to apply these types of transformation to **trig functions**.

Tip: For $y = \sin(x + c)$, the graph has a maximum where $x + c = 90°, 450°$, etc. — i.e. when $x = 90° - c$, $450° - c$, ... It has a minimum where $x + c = 270°, 630°$ ... and crosses the x-axis at $x + c = 0°, 180°, 360°$ ...

1. A translation parallel to the x-axis: $y = \sin(x + c)$

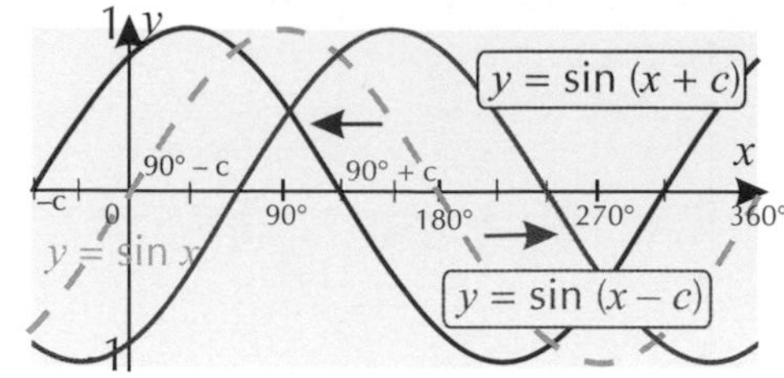

- For $c > 0$, $\sin(x + c)$ is just $\sin x$ **translated c units in the negative x-direction.**
- Similarly, $\sin(x - c)$ is just $\sin x$ **translated c units in the positive x-direction.**

Tip: In the diagram, n is about 2 for the blue curve and about 0.5 for the orange curve.

Tip: When $0 < n < 1$ it looks like a squash, but it's still called a stretch.

2. A vertical stretch: $y = n\sin x$

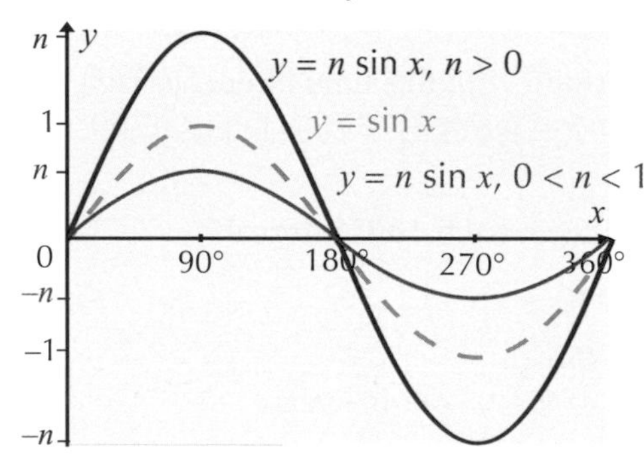

- For $y = n\sin x$, the graph of $y = \sin x$ is **stretched vertically** by a factor of n.
- If $n > 1$, the graph gets taller, and if $0 < n < 1$, the graph gets flatter.
- And if $n < 0$, the graph is also **reflected** in the **x-axis**.

Tip: Make sure you know which way the stretch goes. The larger n is, the more squashed the graph becomes. In the diagram, n is 3 for the blue curve and 0.5 for the orange curve.

3. A horizontal stretch: $y = \sin nx$

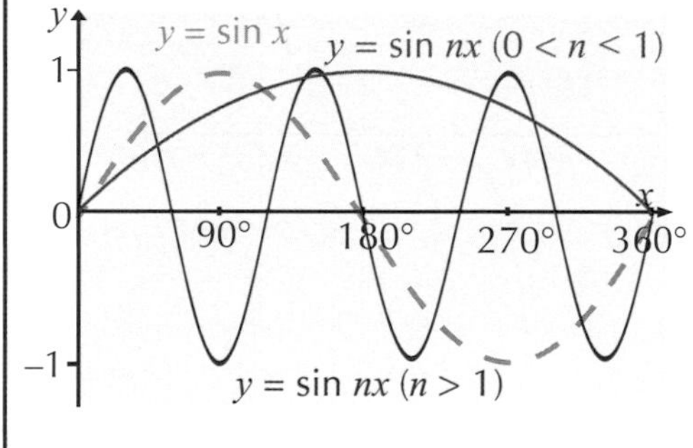

- For $y = \sin nx$, the graph of $y = \sin x$ is **stretched horizontally** by a factor of $\frac{1}{n}$.
- The **period** of $y = \sin nx$ is $\frac{360°}{n}$.
- If $0 < n < 1$, the graph of $y = \sin x$ is stretched horizontally **outwards**, and if $n > 1$ the graph of $y = \sin x$ is 'squashed' **inwards**.
- If $n < 0$, the graph is also **reflected** in the **y-axis**.

The same transformations will apply to the graphs of $\mathbf{y = \cos x}$ and $\mathbf{y = \tan x}$ as well.

Tip: Don't worry that the angles are in radians here — the transformations work in the same way.

Example 1

On the same axes, sketch the graphs of $y = \cos x$ and $y = -2\cos x$ in the range $-2\pi \le x \le 2\pi$.

- Start by **sketching** the graph of cos x — have a look back at pages 30-31 if you need a reminder of how to do this.

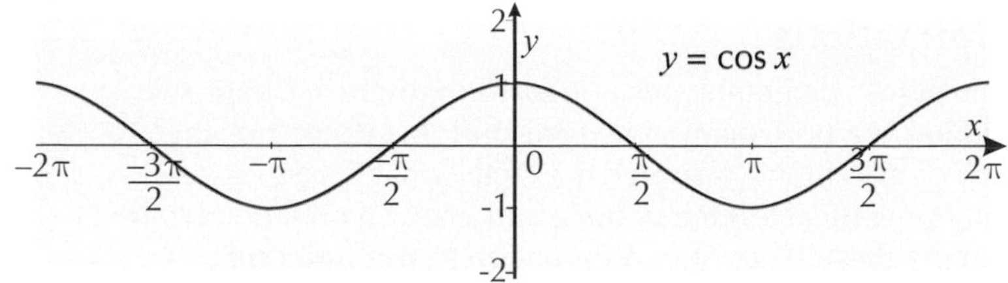

- Next, think about what the **transformed** graph will look like. It's in the form $\boldsymbol{y = n\cos x}$, so it will be **stretched vertically**.
- $n = -2$, so it will be stretched by a factor of **2**. As n is negative, it will also be **reflected** in the x-axis. This is all the information you need to be able to sketch the graph.

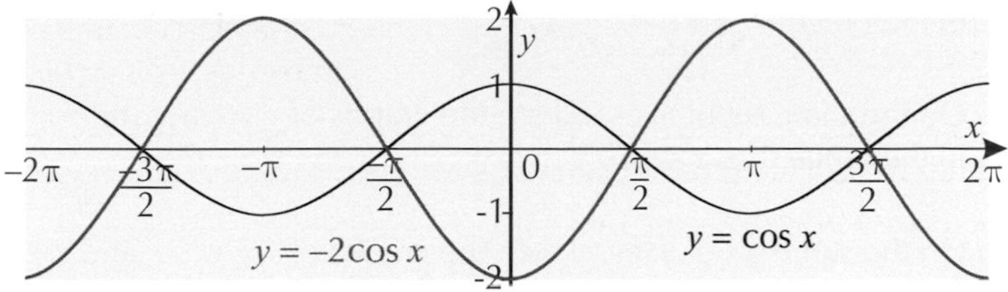

Example 2

On the same axes, sketch the graphs of $y = \tan x$ and $y = \tan 2x$ in the range $-180° \leq x \leq 180°$.

- Again, start by sketching the graph of $y = \tan x$ (see p.31).

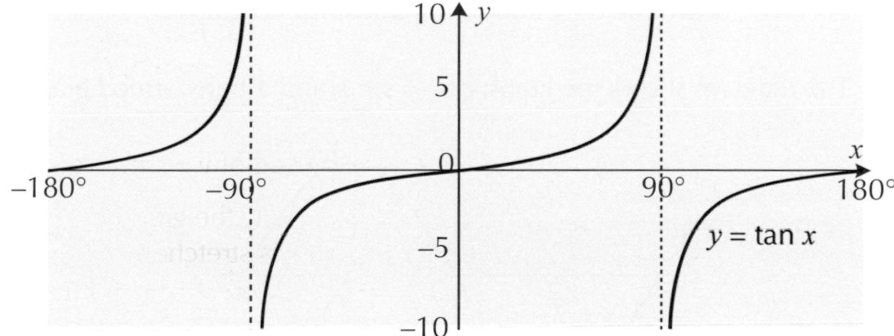

- This time it's in the form $y = \tan nx$, so it will be stretched horizontally. $n > 1$, so the graph will be stretched by a factor of $\frac{1}{2}$.
- To make it easier, draw dotted lines for the new asymptotes (divide the x-values of the old ones by 2) then draw the tan shape between them.

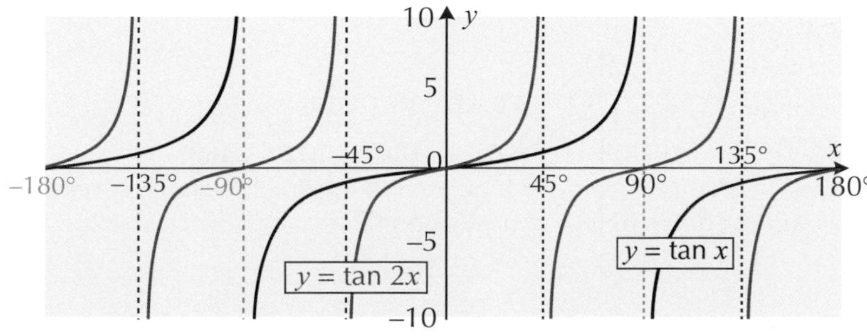

Tip: You'll have double the number of repetitions of the tan shape in the same interval because you've halved the period.

Exercise 4.1

Q1 On the same set of axes, sketch the graphs of $y = \cos x$ and $y = \cos (x + 90°)$ in the range $-180° \le x \le 180°$.

Q2 On the same set of axes, sketch the graphs of $y = \sin x$ and $y = \frac{1}{3}\sin x$ in the range $-\pi \le x \le \pi$.

Q3 On the same set of axes, sketch the graphs of $y = \sin x$ and $y = \sin 3x$ in the range $0° \le x \le 360°$.

Q4 On the same set of axes, sketch the graphs of $y = \cos x$ and $y = -\cos x$ in the range $0 \le x \le 2\pi$.

Q5 c) Hint: Just look at what's happened to the graph, then think about which type of transformation is needed to achieve it.

Q5 a) Sketch the graph of $f(x) = \tan x$ in the range $-90° \le x \le 270°$.

b) Translate this graph 90° in the negative x-direction and sketch it on the same set of axes as part a).

c) Write down the equation of the transformed graph.

Q6 a) Sketch the graph of $y = \sin x$ in the range $-2\pi \le x \le 2\pi$.

b) Stretch the graph horizontally by a factor of 2 and sketch it on the same set of axes as part a).

c) Write down the equation of the transformed graph.

Q7 The diagram shows the graph of $y = \sin x$ and a transformed graph.

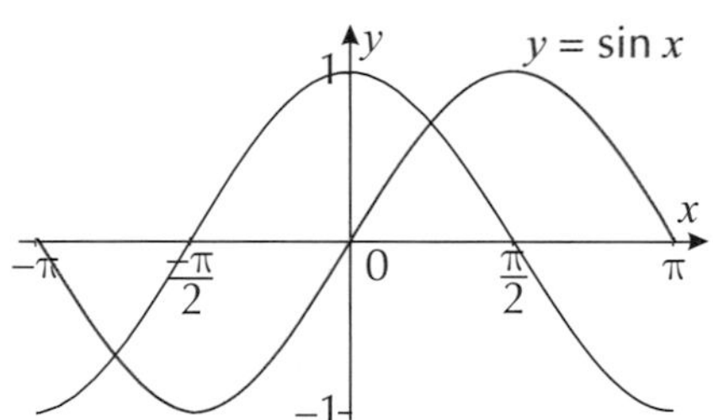

a) Describe the transformation.

b) Write down the equation of the transformed graph.

Q8 The diagram shows the graph of $y = \cos x$ and a transformed graph.

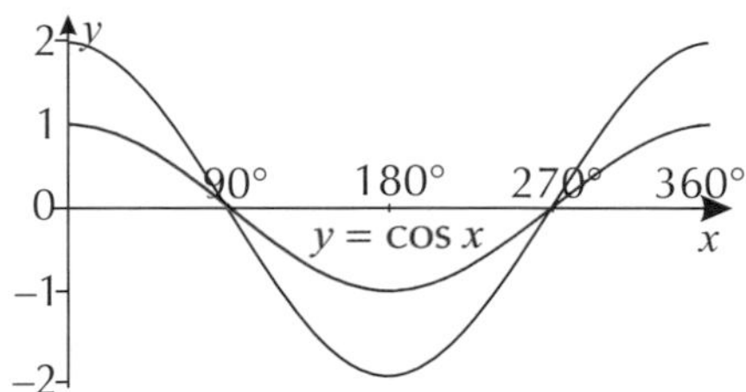

a) Describe the transformation.

b) Write down the equation of the transformed graph.

5. Solving Trig Equations

Once you know how to sketch the graphs of trig functions, you can use them to solve trig equations. Solving a trig equation just means finding the value (or values) of x that satisfies the given equation.

Learning Objectives:

- Be able to solve trig equations by sketching a graph.
- Be able to solve trig equations using a CAST diagram.
- Be able to solve trig equations of the form $\sin kx = n$ and $\sin (x + c) = n$.
- Be able to solve trig equations using trig identities.

Sketching a graph

To solve trig equations in a **given interval** you can use one of two methods. The first involves sketching a **graph** of the function and using its **symmetry** to find the solutions. You'll often find that there's **more than one** solution to the equation — in every **360° interval**, there are usually **two** solutions to an equation, and if the interval is bigger (see example 2 below), there'll be even more solutions.

Example 1

Solve $\cos x = \frac{1}{2}$ for $0° \leq x \leq 360°$.

- Start by using your **calculator** to work out the first value. For $\cos x = \frac{1}{2}$, $x = 60°$.
- Then **sketch a graph** of $\cos x$ in the range you're interested in, and draw a horizontal line across for $y = \frac{1}{2}$. The points where the line and curve **meet** are the solutions of the equation.

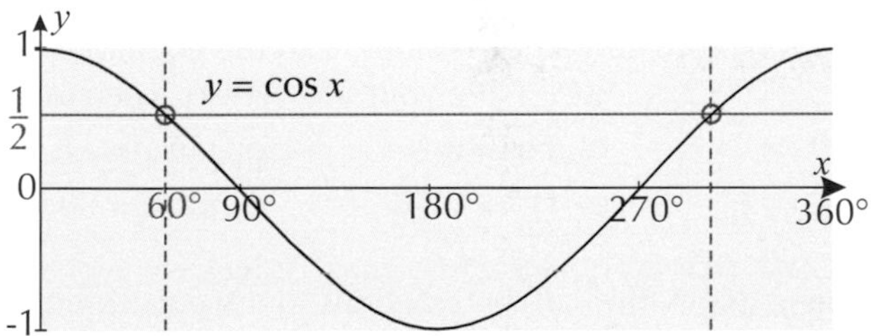

- Each 360° interval of the graph is symmetrical, so the second solution will be the same distance from 360° as the first is from 0°. You know one solution is 60°, so the other solution is 360° – 60° = 300°.
- You now know all of the solutions in this interval: $x = 60°, 300°$

Tip: This is actually one of the common trig angles from page 21.

Tip: If you are dealing with sin or tan instead, use the graphs to work out the solutions in a similar way.

If you had an interval that was **larger** than **one repetition** of the graph (i.e. 360° or 2π for sin and cos, and 180° or π for tan), you'd just add or subtract **multiples** of 360° (for sin and cos) or 180° (for tan) onto the solutions you've found until you have **all** the solutions in the **given range**.

Example 2

Solve $\sin x = -0.3$ for $0 \leq x \leq 4\pi$. Give your answers to 3 s.f.

- Again, use your **calculator** to work out the first value. For $\sin x = -0.3$, $x = -0.3046...$ However, this is **outside** the given range for x, so **add on 2π** to find the first solution in the range: $-0.3046... + 2\pi = 5.978...$
- Now **sketch a graph** of $\sin x$ in the range you're interested in, and draw a horizontal line across at $y = -0.3$. This time, you'll need to draw the graph between $x = 0$ and $x = 4\pi$, so there'll be **2 repetitions** of the sin wave.

Tip: You add on 2π because the curve repeats every 2π radians. If you were working in degrees, you'd add on 360° instead (for tan, it would be π or 180°).

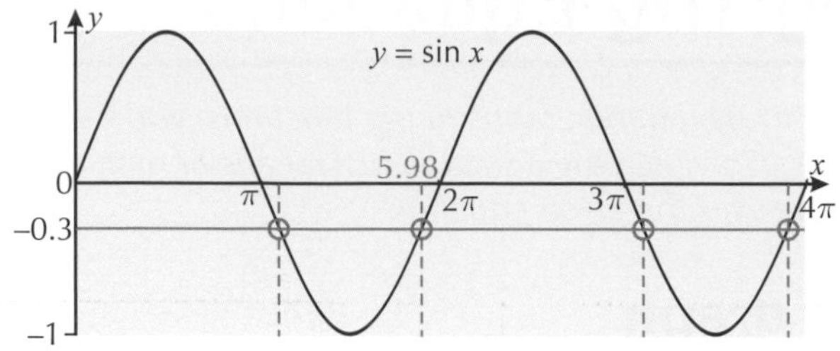

- You can see from the graph that there are **4 solutions** in the given range (because the horizontal line crosses the curve 4 times). You've already found the one at $x = 5.978...$ — to find the next one, you use the **symmetry** of the graph. This first solution is $2\pi - 5.978... = 0.3046...$ away from $\mathbf{2\pi}$. Now, looking at the graph, the other solution between 0 and 2π will be 0.3046... away from $\boldsymbol{\pi}$ — i.e. $\pi + 0.3046... = 3.446...$
- For the other solutions (the ones between 2π and 4π), just **add** $\mathbf{2\pi}$ onto the values you've already found: $3.4462... + 2\pi = 9.729...$ and $5.978... + 2\pi = 12.261...$
- So the solutions to $\sin x = -0.3$ for $0 \leq x \leq 4\pi$, to 3 s.f., are:

$x = 3.45, 5.98, 9.73$ and 12.3.

Tip: If the range was bigger, just keep on adding (or subtracting) lots of 2π until you have all the answers within the required range.

Exercise 5.1

Q1 By sketching a graph, find all the solutions to the equations below in the interval $0° \leq x \leq 360°$. Give your answers to 1 decimal place.

a) $\sin x = 0.75$ b) $\cos x = 0.31$ c) $\tan x = -1.5$

d) $\sin x = -0.42$ e) $\cos x = -0.56$ f) $\tan x = -0.67$

Q2 By sketching a graph, find all the solutions to the equations below in the interval $0 \leq x \leq 2\pi$. Give your answers as exact values.

a) $\cos x = \frac{1}{\sqrt{2}}$ b) $\tan x = \sqrt{3}$ c) $\sin x = \frac{1}{2}$

d) $\tan x = \frac{1}{\sqrt{3}}$ e) $\tan x = 1$ f) $\cos x = \frac{\sqrt{3}}{2}$

Q2 Hint: All of these values relate to the common angles on p.21.

Q3 One solution of $\cos x = -0.8$ is 143.1° (1 d.p.). Use the graph below to find all the solutions in the interval $0° \leq x \leq 360°$.

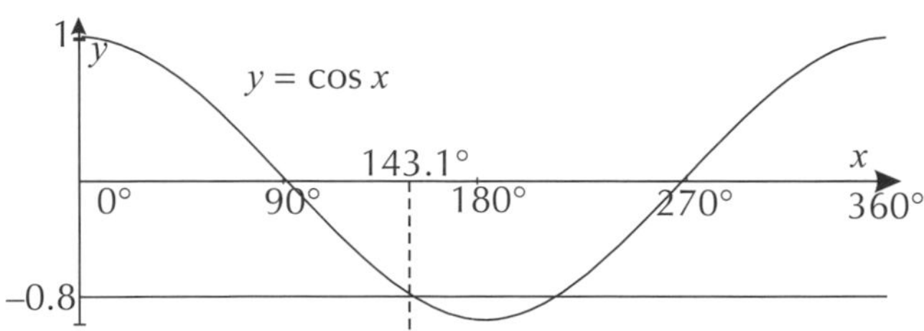

Q4 Find all the solutions of the equation $\tan x = 2.5$ in the interval $0° \leq x \leq 1080°$. Give your answers to 1 decimal place.

Q5 Find all the solutions of the equation $\sin x = 0.81$ in the interval $-2\pi \leq x \leq 2\pi$. Give your answers to 3 significant figures.

Q4-5 Hint: Be careful with the ranges here — and remember that tan repeats every 180°.

Using a CAST diagram

The second way of finding the solutions to a trig equation is by using a **CAST diagram**. CAST stands for Cos, All, Sin, Tan, and it shows you where each of these functions is **positive** by splitting a 360° period into **quadrants**.

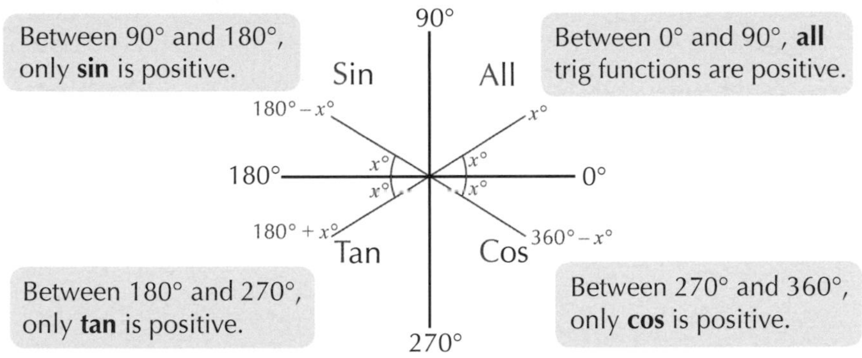

90°
Between 90° and 180°, only **sin** is positive.
Sin
All
Between 0° and 90°, **all** trig functions are positive.
$180° - x°$
$x°$
180°
0°
$180° + x°$
Tan
Cos
$360° - x°$
Between 180° and 270°, only **tan** is positive.
Between 270° and 360°, only **cos** is positive.
270°

Tip: You can use a CAST diagram if you're working in radians too — the axes are just labelled with 0, $\frac{\pi}{2}$, π and $\frac{3\pi}{2}$ radians instead.

- To use a CAST diagram, you need to use your **calculator** to find the first solution of the trig function (or, if it's a common angle, you might just be able to recognise it).
- You then make the **same angle** from the **horizontal** in each of the four quadrants (shown in the diagram above), then measure each angle **anticlockwise** from 0°. So if the first solution was 45°, the solution in the sin quadrant would be 135° (180° – 45°) measured anticlockwise from 0°, and so on.
- **Ignore** the ones that give a **negative** result (unless the given value is negative — in which case you want the two quadrants in which the trig function is **negative**).

Tip: The angle you put into the CAST diagram should be acute (i.e. between 0° and 90°) — if you get a negative value, just put the positive value into the diagram. Or you can measure **clockwise** from 0° for negative angles.

Example 1

Find all the solutions of $\sin x = \frac{1}{2}$ for $0° \leq x \leq 360°$.

- Use a **calculator** to find the **first solution** (30°), and put this in your CAST diagram.
- Then add the **same angle** to each **quadrant**, measuring from the **horizontal** in each case.

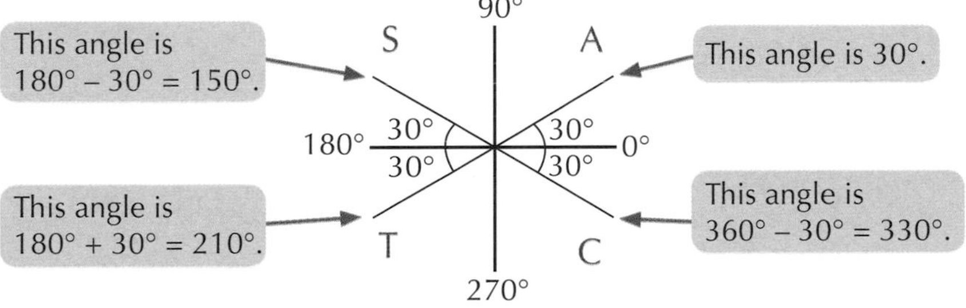

90°
S
A
This angle is 180° – 30° = 150°.
This angle is 30°.
180°
30°
30°
30°
30°
0°
This angle is 180° + 30° = 210°.
This angle is 360° – 30° = 330°.
T
C
270°

- You need a **positive** value of $\sin x$ (because $\frac{1}{2}$ is positive), so you're only interested in the quadrants where $\sin x$ is positive — i.e. the first and second quadrants. There are two solutions: 30° and 150°.

Tip: This value is also a common angle — you don't need to use a calculator if you can remember it.

Tip: Remember, each line you mark on the diagram represents the angle being measured anticlockwise from 0°.

- For values **outside** the range $0° \leq x \leq 360°$, just find solutions between 0° and 360° and then **add** or **subtract multiples of 360°** to find solutions in the correct range (there's an example of this on the next page). If the range is in **radians**, add or subtract multiples of 2π instead.

Tip: Don't be put off by the fact that this example uses radians — the method is just the same.

Tip: Adding or subtracting 2π (or 360°) is the same as going round a full circle on the CAST diagram (so you end up back at the same position).

Q2 Hint: You might have to rearrange some of the equations first.

Example 2

Find all the solutions of $\tan x = -4$ for $0 \le x \le 4\pi$. Give your answers to 3 s.f.

- Using a **calculator**, you'll find that the first solution is $x = -1.33$ (3 s.f.). **Ignore** the negative and just put the value 1.33 into the CAST diagram.
- Add the **same angle** to each **quadrant**, measuring from the **horizontal** in each case. Remember that you're working in **radians** here.

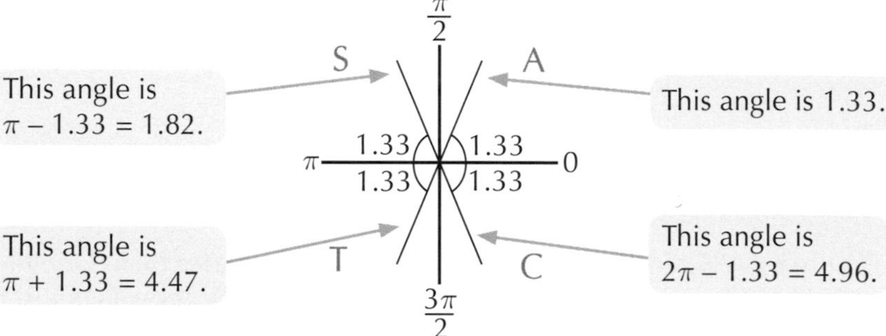

- You need a **negative** value of $\tan x$ (as –4 is negative), so just look at the quadrants where $\tan x$ is negative (i.e. the 'S' and 'C' quadrants). There are two solutions: 1.82 and 4.96 (as the first value was **negative**, you could have measure **clockwise** from 0 to find the solution 4.96).
- To find the solutions between 2π and 4π, just **add 2π** to the solutions you've already found.
- The solutions of $\tan x = -4$ for $0 \le x \le 4\pi$ are $x = 1.82, 4.96, 8.10$ and 11.2 (3 s.f.).

Exercise 5.2

Q1 One solution of $\sin x = 0.45$ is $x = 26.7°$ (1 d.p.). Use a CAST diagram to find all the solutions in the interval $0° \le x \le 360°$.

Q2 Use a CAST diagram to find the solutions of the following equations in the interval $0° \le x \le 360°$. Give your answers to 1 d.p.

a) $\cos x = 0.8$ b) $\tan x = 2.7$ c) $\sin x = -0.15$

d) $\tan x = 0.3$ e) $\tan x = -0.6$ f) $\sin x = -0.29$

g) $4\sin x - 1 = 0$ h) $4\cos x - 3 = 0$ i) $5\tan x + 7 = 0$

Q3 Use a CAST diagram to find all the solutions to $\tan x = -8.4$ in the interval $0 \le x \le 2\pi$. Give your answers to 3 s.f.

Q4 Use a CAST diagram to find all the solutions to $\sin x = 0.75$ in the interval $0° \le x \le 720°$. Give your answers to 1 d.p.

Q5 Use a CAST diagram to find all the solutions to $\cos x = 0.31$ in the interval $-180° \le x \le 180°$. Give your answers to 1 d.p.

Q6 Use a CAST diagram to find all the solutions to $\sin x = 0.82$ in the interval $0 \le x \le 4\pi$. Give your answers to 3 s.f.

Changing the interval

Sometimes you'll have to solve equations of the form **sin $kx = n$** or **sin $(x + c) = n$** (where n, k and c are numbers). In these situations it's usually easiest to **change the interval** you're solving for, then **solve as normal** for kx or $x + c$. You'll then need to remember to get the final solutions either by **dividing by k** or **subtracting c** at the end.

Solving equations of the form sin $kx = n$

Let's start by looking at how to solve equations of the form **sin $kx = n$**.

- First, **multiply** the **interval** you're looking for solutions in by k. E.g. for the equation $\sin 2x = n$ in the interval $0 \leq x \leq 2\pi$, you'd look for solutions in the interval $0 \leq 2x \leq 4\pi$. Then **solve** the equation over the new interval.
- However, this gives you solutions for kx, so you then need to **divide** each solution by k to find the values of x.

You can either **sketch the graph** over the new interval (this will show you **how many** solutions there are) or you can use the **CAST method** to find solutions between 0° and 360° then add on multiples of 360° until you have all the solutions in the new interval — use whichever method you prefer.

Example 1

Solve $\cos 4x = 0.6$ for $0° \leq x \leq 360°$. Give your answers to 1 d.p.

- First, **change** the **interval**. The interval is $0° \leq x \leq 360°$, and the value of k is 4, so **multiply** the whole interval by **4**: $0° \leq 4x \leq 1440°$.
- Then **solve** the equation to find the solutions for $4x$. I'm going to use a **CAST diagram**, but you could sketch a graph if you prefer.
- Find the **first solution** using a calculator: $\cos 4x = 0.6$
  $\Rightarrow 4x = 53.13°$ (2 d.p.)

90°
S A
180° 53.13° 53.13° 0°
53.13° 53.13°
T C
270°

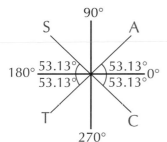

You want the quadrants where cos is **positive**, so the other solution between 0° and 360° is:
$4x = 360° - 53.13° = 306.87°$ (2 d.p.)

- Now **add on** multiples of 360° to find **all** the solutions in the interval $0° \leq 4x \leq 1440°$ (to 2 d.p.):
  53.13°, 306.87°, 413.13°, 666.87°, 773.13°, 1026.87°, 1133.13°, 1386.87°.
- Remember, these are solutions for $4x$. To find the solutions for x, **divide** through by **4**. So the solutions to $\cos 4x = 0.6$ in the interval $0° \leq x \leq 360°$ (to 1 d.p.) are:
  13.3°, 76.7°, 103.3°, 166.7°, 193.3°, 256.7°, 283.3°, 346.7°.
- It's a good idea to **check** your answers — just put your values of x into $\cos 4x$ and check that they give you 0.6. You can make sure you've got the **right number** of solutions too — there are 2 solutions to $\cos x = 0.6$ in the interval $0° \leq x \leq 360°$, so there'll be 8 solutions to $\cos 4x = 0.6$ in the same interval.

Tip: If you'd sketched a graph, you could just see how many times the graph and line crossed — there's an example of this on the next page.

Example 2

Solve $\sin 3x = -\frac{1}{\sqrt{2}}$ for $0° \leq x \leq 360°$.

- This time you've got $3x$ instead of x, which means the **interval** you need to find solutions in is $0° \leq 3x \leq 1080°$. So sketch the graph of $y = \sin x$ between 0° and 1080°.

- Use your **calculator** to find the **first solution**. You'll get $3x = -45°$, but this is outside the interval for $3x$, so use the pattern of the graph to find a solution in the interval. As the sin curve **repeats every 360°**, there'll be a solution at $-45° + 360° = 315°$.

Tip: This is actually one of the common angles from p.21 — so you could have found it without using a calculator.

- Now you can use the **symmetry** of the graph to find the other solution between 0° and 360° — the graph is symmetrical in each interval of 180°, so the other solution is at $180° + 45° = 225°$.

- You know the graph repeats every 360°, so **add on** lots of 360° to the answers you've just found to find the other solutions between 0° and 1080°: $3x = 585°, 675°, 945°, 1035°$.

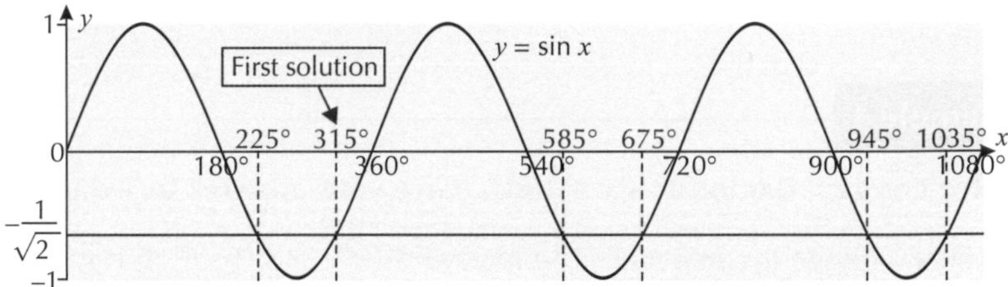

- Now you have 6 solutions for $3x$, so **divide them all by 3** to get the solutions for x: $x = 75°, 105°, 195°, 225°, 315°, 345°$.

Tip: Again, you can check your answers using a calculator — and make sure they're in the right interval.

Example 3

Find all the solutions of $\tan 2x = 1.4$ for $0 \leq x \leq 2\pi$. Give your answers to 3 s.f.

- Here, the interval needs to be multiplied by 2: $0 \leq 2x \leq 4\pi$.
- Use a calculator to work out the first solution: $2x = 0.9505$ (4 s.f.).
- Then use a CAST diagram to find the other solution between 0 and 2π:

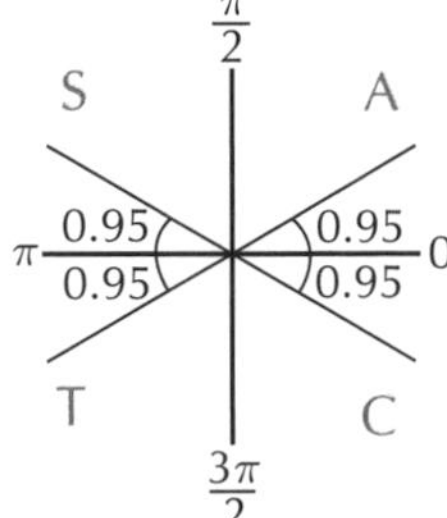

You want the quadrants where tan is **positive**, so the other solution between 0 and 2π is:
$2x = \pi + 0.9505 = 4.092$ (4 s.f.).

- To find the solutions between 2π and 4π, just **add 2π** to the solutions you've already found: $2x = 7.234, 10.38$ (4 s.f.).
- Finally, to find the solutions for x between 0 and 2π, just divide by 2: $x = 0.475, 2.05, 3.62, 5.19$ (3 s.f.)

Solving equations of the form sin $(x + c) = n$

The method for solving equations of the form **sin $(x + c) = n$** is similar — but instead of multiplying the interval, you have to add or subtract the value of c.

- **Add** (or **subtract**) the value of c to the **whole interval** — so the interval $0° \le x \le 360°$ becomes $c \le x + c \le 360° + c$ (you add c onto each bit of the interval).
- Now **solve** the equation over the **new interval** — again, you can either sketch a graph or use a CAST diagram.
- Finally, **subtract** (or **add**) c from your solutions to give the values for x.

Example 1

Solve $\cos(x + 60°) = \frac{3}{4}$ for $-360° \le x \le 360°$, giving your answers to 1 d.p.

- You've got $\cos(x + 60°)$ instead of $\cos x$ — so **add 60°** to each bit of the interval. The new range is: $-300° \le x + 60° \le 420°$.
- Use your **calculator** to get the **first solution**:

$$\cos(x + 60°) = \frac{3}{4} \Rightarrow x + 60° = 41.4° \text{ (1 d.p.)}$$

- Use the **symmetry** of the graph to find the other solution between 0° and 360°. The first solution is 41.4° away from 0°, so the next solution will be 41.4° away from 360° — i.e. at $360° - 41.4° = 318.6°$ (1 d.p.).
- The cos graph **repeats** every 360°, so to find the other solutions, **add and subtract 360°** from the answers you've just found, making sure they're still within the interval you want:
$x + 60° = 401.4°$, $678.6°$ (not in interval), $-41.4°$, $-318.6°$ (not in interval).

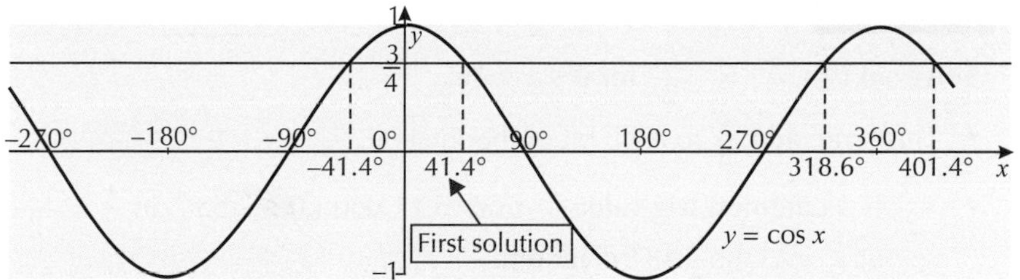

- These solutions are for $\cos(x + 60°)$ so you need to **subtract 60° from each value** to find the solutions for x (to 1 d.p.):
$x = -101.4°, -18.6°, 258.6°$ and $341.4°$
- So there are **4 solutions**, and they're all in the required interval ($-360° \le x \le 360°$). Again, you can **check** your answers by putting them back into $\cos(x + 60°)$ and making sure you get $\frac{3}{4}$.

Tip: Be careful with the interval here — the original interval isn't $0° \le x \le 360°$.

Tip: You can see from the graph that there should be 4 solutions in this interval, but be careful — if your graph wasn't accurate, it would be easy to miss a solution.

Example 2

Solve tan $(x - 75°) = 2$ for $0° \leq x \leq 360°$. Give your answers to 1 d.p.

- First, find the new interval. This time you want to **subtract 75°** from each bit of the interval, so the new interval is $-75° \leq x - 75° \leq 285°$. You'll need to sketch the graph of tan x over this interval.
- Use your **calculator** to find the **first solution**: tan $(x - 75°) = 2 \Rightarrow x - 75° = 63.4°$ (1 d.p.)
- Now you can use the **pattern** of the graph to find the other solution in the interval — the tan graph **repeats** every **180°**, so add on 180° to the solution you've already found: $63.4° + 180° = 243.4°$ (1 d.p.)

Tip: To see if there are any other solutions within the interval, add and subtract 180° to the values you've just found: $x - 75° = -116.6°$, $423.4°$. Both of these values are outside the required interval, so there are only 2 solutions.

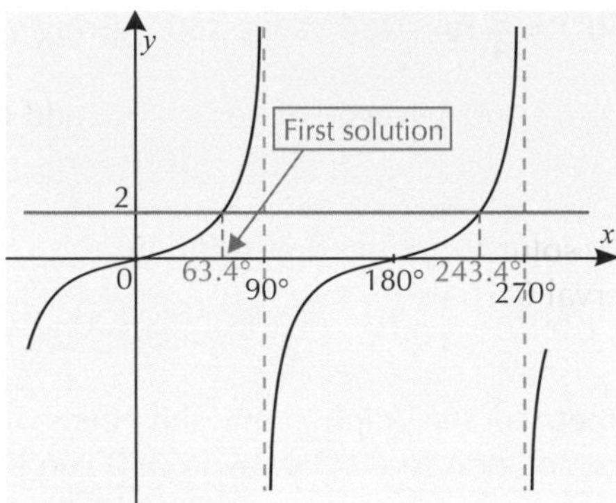

- Finally, **add on 75°** to find the solutions in the interval $0° \leq x \leq 360°$ (to 1 d.p.): $x = 138.4°, 318.4°$.

Example 3

Solve sin $(x + \frac{\pi}{3}) = -\frac{\sqrt{3}}{2}$ for $0 \leq x \leq 4\pi$.

- This time, **add $\frac{\pi}{3}$** to each bit of the interval: $\frac{\pi}{3} \leq x + \frac{\pi}{3} \leq \frac{13\pi}{3}$
- $\frac{\sqrt{3}}{2}$ is a **common trig value** — from p.21 you know that: sin $\frac{\pi}{3} = \frac{\sqrt{3}}{2}$, so put $\frac{\pi}{3}$ into the **CAST diagram**:

Tip: Have a look back at the example on p.38 to see how to deal with negative values.

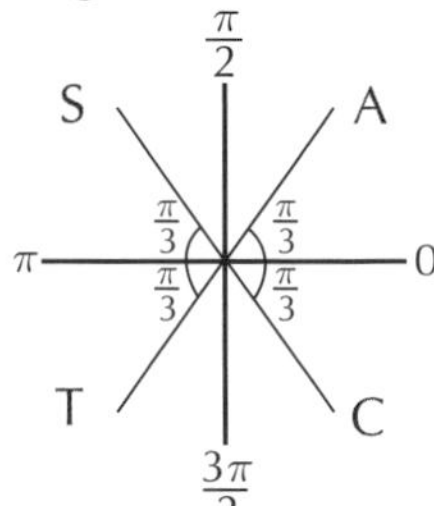

As you're finding solutions for $-\frac{\sqrt{3}}{2}$, you want the quadrants where sin is **negative** (the 3rd and 4th quadrants), so the solutions between 0 and 2π are:

$x + \frac{\pi}{3} = \pi + \frac{\pi}{3} = \frac{4\pi}{3}$ and

$x + \frac{\pi}{3} = 2\pi - \frac{\pi}{3} = \frac{5\pi}{3}$

- To find the other solutions (between 2π and 4π), just **add 2π** to the solutions you've already found: $x + \frac{\pi}{3} = \frac{10\pi}{3}, \frac{11\pi}{3}$
- Finally, **subtract $\frac{\pi}{3}$** from each solution to find the values of x: $x = \pi, \frac{4\pi}{3}, 3\pi, \frac{10\pi}{3}$

Exercise 5.3

In this exercise, where appropriate, you should give answers in degrees to 1 d.p. and answers in radians to 3 s.f.

Q1 Solve $\sin 2x = 0.6$ in the interval $0° \leq x \leq 360°$.

Q2 Solve $\tan 4x = 4.6$ in the interval $0° \leq x \leq 360°$.

Q3 Solve $\cos 3x = -0.24$ in the interval $0° \leq x \leq 360°$.

Q4 Find all the solutions to $\cos 2x = 0.72$ in the interval $0 \leq x \leq 2\pi$.

Q5 Find all the solutions to $\sin 3x = -0.91$ in the interval $0 \leq x \leq 2\pi$.

Q6 Solve $\tan \frac{x}{2} = 2.1$ in the interval $0° \leq x \leq 360°$.

Q6 Hint: Don't let the ½ throw you — it's exactly the same method as before, except you divide the interval by 2 instead of multiplying.

Q7 Find all the solutions to $\cos (x - 27°) = 0.64$ in the interval $0° \leq x \leq 360°$.

Q8 Solve $\tan (x - 140°) = -0.76$ in the interval $0° \leq x \leq 360°$.

Q9 Find all the solutions to $\sin (x + 36°) = 0.45$ in the interval $0° \leq x \leq 360°$.

Q10 Find all the solutions to $\tan (x + 73°) = 1.84$ in the interval $0° \leq x \leq 360°$.

Q11 Find all the solutions to $\sin (x - \frac{\pi}{4}) = -0.25$ in the interval $0 \leq x \leq 2\pi$.

Q12 Solve $\cos (x + \frac{\pi}{8}) = 0.13$ in the interval $0 \leq x \leq 2\pi$.

Q13 Solve $\sin (x + 12°) = \sin 62°$ in the interval $0° \leq x \leq 360°$.

Q13 Hint: $x + 12° = 62°$ gives you the first solution, then you can use a CAST diagram or the sin graph to find any other solutions.

Q14 Solve $\cos 3x = \cos 39°$ in the interval $0° \leq x \leq 360°$.

Using trig identities to solve equations

Sometimes you'll be asked to find solutions to an equation that has a **tan** term as well as a sin or cos term in it.
In these situations you might need to use the **trig identity** for $\tan x$ (p.28):

$$\tan x \equiv \frac{\sin x}{\cos x}$$

This will **eliminate** the tan term, and you'll be left with an equation just in terms of sin or cos.

Tip: Don't make the mistake of cancelling $\sin x$ from the equation instead of factorising — you'll lose the solutions to $\sin x = 0$ if you do.

Tip: Remember $\sin x = 0$ every π radians. Have a look back at the graph on p.30 to see why.

Example

Solve $3\sin x - \tan x = 0$ for $0 \le x \le 2\pi$.

- The equation has both $\sin x$ and $\tan x$ in it, so writing $\tan x$ as $\frac{\sin x}{\cos x}$ would be a good place to start.

$$3\sin x - \tan x = 0 \quad \Rightarrow \quad 3\sin x - \frac{\sin x}{\cos x} = 0$$

- Next get rid of the $\cos x$ on the bottom by multiplying the whole equation by $\cos x$.

$$3\sin x - \frac{\sin x}{\cos x} = 0 \quad \Rightarrow \quad 3\sin x\cos x - \sin x = 0$$

- You now have a common factor of $\sin x$ so factorise:

$$3\sin x\cos x - \sin x = 0 \quad \Rightarrow \quad \sin x(3\cos x - 1) = 0$$

- Now you've got two things multiplying together to make zero. That means **one** of them must be equal to zero.

$$\sin x(3\cos x - 1) = 0 \quad \Rightarrow \quad \sin x = 0 \text{ or } 3\cos x - 1 = 0$$

- If $\sin x = 0$, then the solutions in the required interval are $x = 0, \pi$ and 2π.
- If $3\cos x - 1 = 0$, start by rearranging into $\cos x = \frac{1}{3}$. Use your calculator to find the first solution ($x = 1.2309...$).
- You can then use a CAST diagram to find the other solutions:

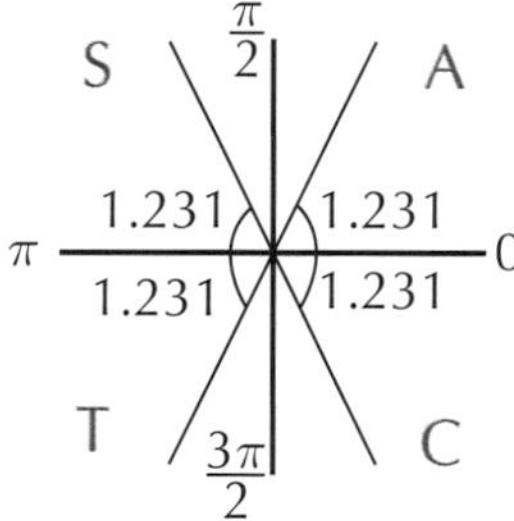

- You need a positive solution for $\cos x$, so look at the 1st and 4th quadrants: 1.2309... and $2\pi - 1.2309... = 5.0522...$ radians.
- You now have all the solutions:
  $x = 0$, 1.231 (4 s.f.), π, 5.052 (4 s.f.) and 2π radians

Similarly, if you have a $\sin^2 x$ or $\cos^2 x$, you can use the other identity from p.28 to rewrite one trig function in terms of the other.

$$\sin^2 x + \cos^2 x \equiv 1$$

Example

Solve $2\sin^2 x + 5\cos x = 4$ for $0° \le x \le 360°$.

- You can't do much while the equation's got both $\sin x$ and $\cos x$ in it. So **replace** the $\sin^2 x$ with $1 - \cos^2 x$:

$$2\sin^2 x + 5\cos x = 4 \quad \Rightarrow \quad 2(1 - \cos^2 x) + 5\cos x = 4$$

- **Multiply out** the bracket and **rearrange** it so that you've got zero on one side — you get a **quadratic** in $\cos x$:

$$2(1 - \cos^2 x) + 5\cos x = 4 \quad \Rightarrow \quad 2\cos^2 x - 5\cos x + 2 = 0$$

- It's easier to **factorise** the quadratic if you make the **substitution** $y = \cos x$:

$$2y^2 - 5y + 2 = 0 \Rightarrow (2y - 1)(y - 2) = 0 \Rightarrow (2\cos x - 1)(\cos x - 2) = 0$$

- One of the brackets must be 0. So you get 2 equations:

$$2\cos x - 1 = 0 \Rightarrow \cos x = \frac{1}{2} \quad \text{or} \quad \cos x - 2 = 0 \Rightarrow \cos x = 2$$

- $\cos x$ is always between -1 and 1, so $\cos x = 2$ has **no solutions**. This means the only solutions are those for $\cos x = \frac{1}{2}$: $x = 60°$ and $300°$.

Tip: Now $\cos x$ is the only trig function you need to deal with.

Tip: The solutions to $\cos x = \frac{1}{2}$ were found on page 35.

Exercise 5.4

In this exercise, give all non-exact answers in degrees to 1 d.p. and all non-exact answers in radians to 3 s.f.

Q1 Solve each of the following equations for values of x in the interval $0° \le x \le 360°$:

a) $(\tan x - 5)(3\sin x - 1) = 0$ b) $5\sin x \tan x - 4\tan x = 0$

c) $\tan^2 x = 9$ d) $4\cos^2 x = 3\cos x$

e) $3\sin x = 5\cos x$ f) $5\tan^2 x - 2\tan x = 0$

g) $6\cos^2 x - \cos x - 2 = 0$ h) $7\sin x + 3\cos x = 0$

Q1 Hint: You might not need to use any trig identities to answer some of these. Think about whether or not each equation can be factorised.

Q2 Find the solutions to each of the following equations in the given interval:

a) $\tan x = \sin x \cos x$ $\quad 0 \le x \le 2\pi$

b) $5\cos^2 x - 9\sin x = 3$ $\quad -2\pi \le x \le 4\pi$

c) $2\sin^2 x + \sin x - 1 = 0$ $\quad -2\pi \le x \le 2\pi$

Q3 a) Show that the equation $4\sin^2 x = 3 - 3\cos x$ can be written as $4\cos^2 x - 3\cos x - 1 = 0$.

b) Hence solve the equation $4\sin^2 x = 3 - 3\cos x$ in the interval $0 \le x \le 2\pi$.

Q4 Find all the solutions of the equation $9\sin^2 2x + 3\cos 2x = 7$ in the interval $0° \le x \le 360°$.

Q4 Hint: Watch out — there are 8 solutions for this one.

Review Exercise — Chapter 2

Q1 The diagram on the right shows a sector ABC of a circle, with centre A and a radius of 10 cm. The angle BAC is 0.7 radians.

Find the arc length BC and area of this sector.

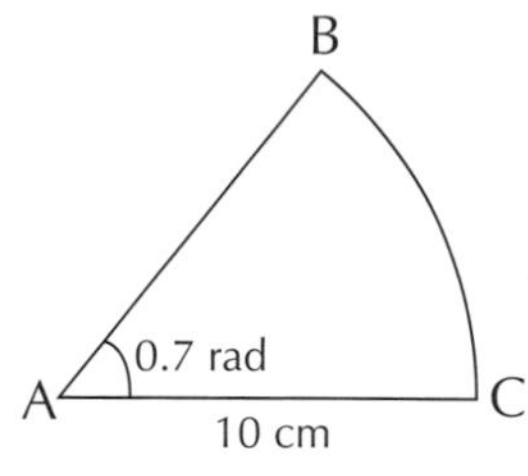

Q2 The sector ABC shown on the right is part of a circle, where the angle BAC is 50°.

Given that the area of the sector is 20π cm^2, find the arc length BC.

Give your answer in terms of π.

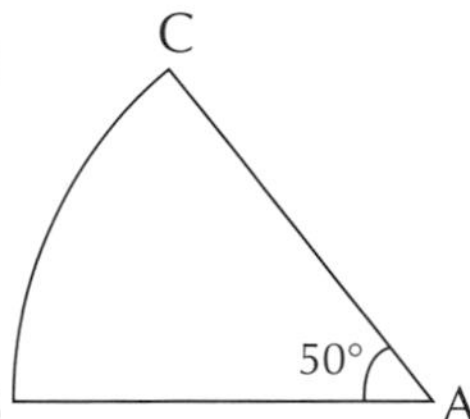

Q3 Write down the exact values of cos 30°, sin 30°, tan 30°, cos 45°, sin 45°, tan 45°, cos 60°, sin 60° and tan 60°.

Q4 For triangle ΔABC, in which $A = 30°$, $C = 25°$ and $b = 6$ m:

a) Find all the sides and angles of the triangle.

b) Find the area of the triangle.

Q5 For triangle ΔPQR, in which $p = 13$ km, $q = 23$ km and $R = 20°$:

a) Find all the sides and angles of the triangle.

b) Find the area of the triangle.

Q6 Find all the angles in the triangle on the right, in degrees to 1 d.p.

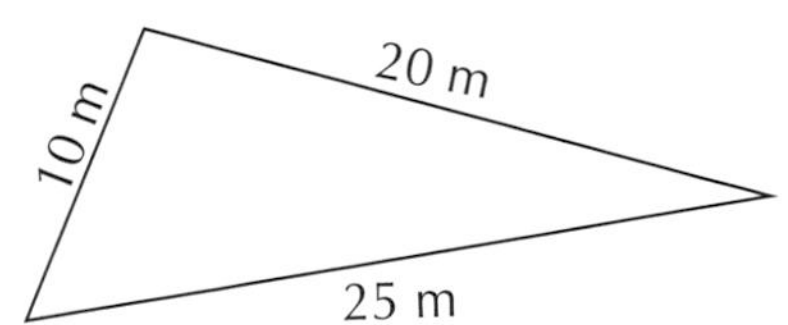

Q7 Find the missing sides and angles for the 2 possible triangles ΔABC which satisfy $b = 5$, $a = 3$, $A = 35°$.

Q7 Hint: This is tricky — sketch it first and try to think how you could make 2 triangles from the numbers given.

Q8 Show that $\tan x - \sin x \cos x \equiv \sin^2 x \tan x$.

Q9 Show that $\tan^2 x - \cos^2 x + 1 \equiv \tan^2 x(1 + \cos^2 x)$.

Q10 Simplify: $(\sin y + \cos y)^2 + (\cos y - \sin y)^2$.

Q11 Show that $\dfrac{\sin^4 x + \sin^2 x \cos^2 x}{\cos^2 x - 1} \equiv -1$.

Q12 Sketch the following graphs in the range $-360° \leq x \leq 360°$, making sure you label all of the key points.

a) $y = \cos x$ b) $y = \sin x$ c) $y = \tan x$

Q13 Below is the graph of $y = \cos x$ and a transformation of the graph. What is the equation of the transformed graph?

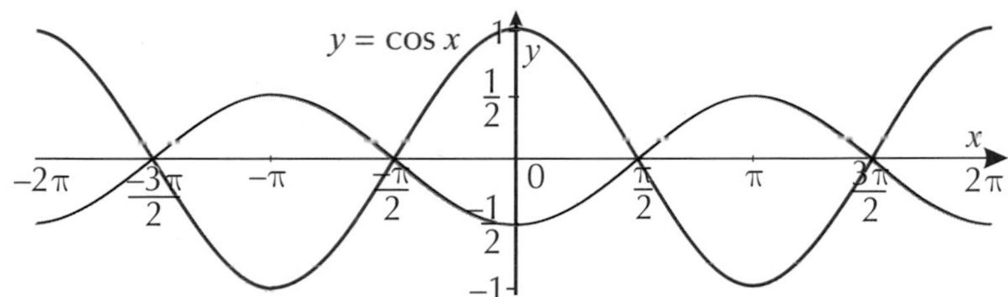

Q14 Below is a graph of $y = \sin x$ and a transformation of the graph. What is the equation of the transformed graph?

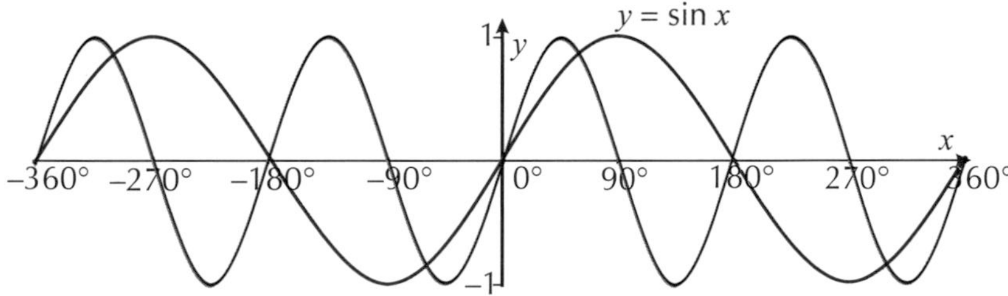

Q15 Sketch the following pairs of graphs on the same axes:

a) $y = \cos x$ and $y = \frac{1}{2}\cos x$ (for $0° \leq x \leq 360°$)

b) $y = \sin x$ and $y = \sin(x + 30°)$ (for $0° \leq x \leq 360°$)

c) $y = \tan x$ and $y = \tan 3x$ (for $0° \leq x \leq 180°$)

Q16 a) Solve each of these equations for $0° \leq \theta \leq 360°$:

(i) $\sin\theta = \frac{\sqrt{3}}{2}$ (ii) $\tan\theta = -1$ (iii) $\cos\theta = -\frac{1}{\sqrt{2}}$

b) Solve each of these equations for $-180° \leq \theta \leq 180°$ (giving your answers to 1 d.p.):

(i) $\cos 4\theta = -\frac{2}{3}$ (ii) $\sin(\theta + 35°) = 0.3$ (iii) $\tan\frac{\theta}{2} = 500$

Q17 Find all the solutions to $6\sin^2 x = \cos x + 5$ in the interval $0 \leq x \leq 2\pi$ (exact answers or to 3 s.f.).

Q18 Solve $3\tan x + 2\cos x = 0$ for $-90° \leq x \leq 90°$.

Q19 Find all the solutions of the equation $6\sin^2 x + \sin x - 1 = 0$ in the interval $0 \leq x \leq 2\pi$, giving your answers to 3 s.f. where appropriate.

Q20 Find all the solutions of the equation $\tan x - 3\sin x = 0$ in the interval $0° \leq x \leq 720°$, giving your answers to 1 d.p.

Exam-Style Questions — Chapter 2

1 The diagram shows the locations of two walkers, X and Y, after walking in different directions from the same start position.
X walked due south for 150 m. Y walked 250 m on a bearing of 100°.

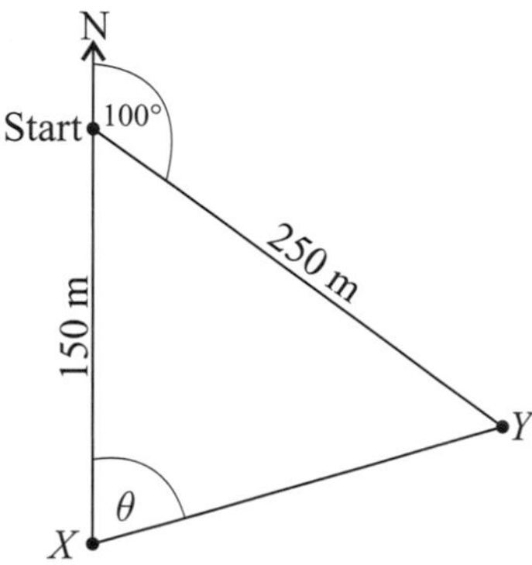

a) Calculate the distance between the two walkers, in m to the nearest m. *(2 marks)*

b) Show that $\frac{\sin\theta}{\sin 80^\circ} = 0.93$ to 2 decimal places. *(2 marks)*

2 The diagram below shows the dimensions of a child's wooden toy.
The toy is a prism with height 10 cm.
Its cross-section is a sector of a circle with radius 20 cm and angle $\frac{\pi}{4}$ radians.

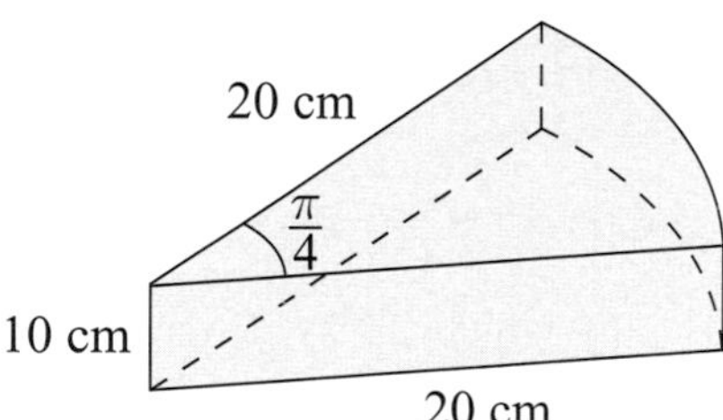

a) Show that the volume of the toy, $V = 500\pi$ cm³. *(3 marks)*

b) Show that the surface area of the toy, $S = (150\pi + 400)$ cm². *(5 marks)*

3 Solve the following equations, for $-\pi \leq x \leq \pi$:

a) $(1 + 2\cos x)(3\tan^2 x - 1) = 0$ *(6 marks)*

b) $3\cos^2 x = \sin^2 x$ *(4 marks)*

4 For an angle x, $3\cos x = 2\sin x$.

a) Find $\tan x$. *(2 marks)*

b) Hence, or otherwise, find all the values of x in the interval $0 \leq x \leq 360°$ for which $3\cos x = 2\sin x$, giving your answers to 1 d.p. *(2 marks)*

5 a) (i) Sketch, for $0 \leq x \leq 360°$, the graph of $y = \cos(x + 60°)$. *(2 marks)*

(ii) Write down all the values of x, for $0 \leq x \leq 360°$, where $\cos(x + 60°) = 0$. *(2 marks)*

b) Sketch, for $0 \leq x \leq 180°$, the graph of $y = \sin 4x$. *(2 marks)*

c) Solve, for $0 \leq x \leq 180°$, the equation: $\sin 4x = 0.5$, giving your answers in degrees. *(4 marks)*

6 Solve, for $0 \leq x \leq 2\pi$:

a) $\tan\left(x + \frac{\pi}{6}\right) = \sqrt{3}$ *(4 marks)*

b) $2\cos\left(x - \frac{\pi}{4}\right) = \sqrt{3}$ *(4 marks)*

c) $\sin 2x = -\frac{1}{2}$ *(6 marks)*

7 Find all the values of x, in the interval $0 \leq x \leq 2\pi$, for which:

$$2 - \sin x = 2\cos^2 x$$

Give your answers in terms of π. *(6 marks)*

8 a) Show that the equation:

$$2(1 - \cos x) = 3\sin^2 x$$

can be written as

$$3\cos^2 x - 2\cos x - 1 = 0$$

(2 marks)

b) Use this to solve the equation

$$2(1 - \cos x) = 3\sin^2 x$$

for $0 \leq x \leq 360°$, giving your answers to 1 d.p. *(6 marks)*

Chapter 3 Logarithms and Exponentials

1. Logs

Learning Objectives:

- Be able to convert between index and log notation.
- Know and be able to use the laws of logs.
- Know and be able to use the change of base formula for logs.

Logarithm might sound scary, but it's just a fancy way of describing the power that something has been raised to. Once you know how to use logs, you can solve all sorts of equations that involve powers.

Logs

A **logarithm** is just the power that a number needs to be **raised to** to produce a given value.

Before now, you've used **index notation** to represent powers, but sometimes it's easier to work with **log notation**.

In **index notation**, $\mathbf{3^5}$ means that **5** lots of **3** are multiplied together. **3** is known as the **base**. You now need to be able to **switch** from index notation into **log notation**, and vice versa.

Tip: If you're struggling to get your head round this, try putting in some numbers — e.g. $\log_3 9 = 2$ is the same as $3^2 = 9$.

Log notation looks like this:

$\log_a b = c$ ... which means the **same** as the **index notation**...

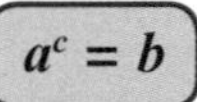

- The little number 'a' after 'log' is the **base**.
- 'c' is the **power** the base is being **raised** to.
- 'b' is the answer you get when a is raised to the power c.
- Log means '**power**', so the log above really just means: "what is the power you need to raise a to if you want to end up with b?"

As $\log_a b = c$ is the same as $a^c = b$, it means that:

$\log_a a = 1$ and $\log_a 1 = 0$

Tip: In index notation, this is saying that $a^1 = a$, and $a^0 = 1$ (you know this from Chapter 1).

- The **base** of a log must always be a **positive integer** (otherwise the log isn't defined for some values).
- So you **can't** take a log of a **negative number** (there's no power you can raise a positive number to to make it negative — this is more obvious if you look at the graphs on p.55).

You can get logs to any base, but **base 10** is the **most common**. The button marked 'log' on your calculator uses base 10.

Here's an example of a log with a base 10:

Tip: Some calculators allow you to find logs to any base.

Index notation: $10^2 = 100$

or

log notation: $\log_{10} 100 = 2$

- So the **logarithm** of 100 to the **base 10** is 2, because 10 raised to the **power** of 2 is 100.
- The base goes here but it's usually left out if it's 10.

Example 1

Write down the values of the following:

a) $\log_2 8$

- **Compare** to $\log_a b = c$. Here the **base** (a) is 2. And the answer (b) is 8.
- So think about the **power** (c) that you'll need to raise 2 to to get 8.
- 8 is 2 raised to the power of 3, so $2^3 = 8$ and $\log_2 8 = 3$

b) $\log_9 3$

- Work out the **power** that 9 needs to be raised to to get 3.
- 3 is the square root of 9, or $9^{\frac{1}{2}} = 3$, so $\log_9 3 = \frac{1}{2}$

Tip: Don't get caught out here — the power is actually a fraction.

c) $\log_5 5$

- Remember that anything to the power of 1 is itself ($a^1 = a$), so $\log_5 5 = 1$

Tip: So $\log_a a = 1$ for any value of a.

Example 2

Write the following using log notation:

a) $5^3 = 125$

- You just need to make sure you get things in the **right place**.
- 3 is the **power** (c) or logarithm that 5 (a, the **base**) is raised to to get 125 (b).
- So sub into $\log_a b = c$ to get: $\log_5 125 = 3$

b) $3^0 = 1$

- You'll need to remember this one: $\log_3 1 = 0$

Tip: This is true for any base a. Any logarithm of 1 is always 0 because a^0 is always 1 (p.50):

$$\log_a 1 = 0$$

Example 3

Find the value of p such that $\log_5 p = -2$.

- $a = 5$, $b = p$ and $c = -2$.
- So sub into $a^c = b$ to get: $5^{-2} = p \Rightarrow \frac{1}{5^2} = p \Rightarrow p = \frac{1}{25}$ or 0.04

Exercise 1.1

Q1 Write the following using log notation:

a) $2^3 = 8$ b) $5^4 = 625$ c) $49^{\frac{1}{2}} = 7$

d) $8^{\frac{2}{3}} = 4$ e) $10^{-2} = \frac{1}{100}$ f) $2^{-3} = 0.125$

Q1 Hint: If you're finding these tricky to get your head around, work out what a, b and c are first, and then substitute them into $\log_a b = c$.

Q2 Write the following using log notation:

a) $4^x = 9$ b) $x^3 = 40$ c) $8^{11} = x$

For questions 3-4, log means $\log_{10}$.

Q3 Write the following using index notation (you don't need to work out any unknowns):

a) $\log_5 125 = 3$ b) $\log 10\,000 = 4$ c) $\log_{\frac{1}{2}} 4 = -2$

d) $\log_7 a = 6$ e) $\log_5 t = 0.2$ f) $\log_4 m = 1$

g) $\log_{\frac{1}{4}} p = \frac{1}{2}$ h) $\log k = 5$ i) $\log_x a = m$

Q4 Find the value of the following.
Give your answer to 3 d.p. where appropriate.

a) $\log 1000$ b) $\log 0.01$ c) $\log 1$

d) $\log 2$ e) $\log 3$ f) $\log 6$

Q5 Find the value of:

a) $\log_2 4$ b) $\log_3 27$ c) $\log_5 0.2$

Q6 Find the value of x, where $x \geq 0$, by writing the following in index notation:

a) $\log_x 49 = 2$ b) $\log_x 8 = 3$ c) $\log_x 100\,000 = 5$

d) $\log_x 3 = \frac{1}{2}$ e) $\log_x 7 = \frac{1}{3}$ f) $\log_x 2 = \frac{1}{5}$

g) $\log_3 x = 4$ h) $\log_2 x = 6$ i) $\log_7 x = 1$

j) $\log_9 x = \frac{1}{2}$ k) $\log_{64} x = \frac{1}{3}$ l) $\log_{27} x = \frac{2}{3}$

Q7 In each part, use index notation to write y in terms of x, given that:

a) $\log_a x = 2$ and $\log_a y = 4$. b) $\log_a x = 3$ and $\log_{2a} y = 3$.

c) $\log_a x = 5$ and $\log_a y = 20$.

Laws of logs

You'll need to be able to **simplify** expressions containing logs in order to answer trickier questions — e.g. to **add** or **subtract** two logs you can combine them into one log. To answer these questions, you'll need to use the **laws of logarithms.** These **only work** if the **base** of each log is the same:

Tip: These laws are really useful, so make sure you know them off by heart.

Laws of Logarithms

$\log_a x + \log_a y = \log_a (xy)$

$\log_a x - \log_a y = \log_a \left(\frac{x}{y}\right)$

$\log_a x^k = k \log_a x$

So $\log_a \frac{1}{x} = \log_a (x^{-1}) = -\log_a x$

Example 1

Simplify the following:

a) $\log_3 4 + \log_3 5$

- First check that the logs you're **adding** have the same base. They do (it's 3) so it's OK to combine them.

- You need to use the law $\log_a x + \log_a y = \log_a (xy)$.
- So here, $a = 3$ (the base), $x = 4$ and $y = 5$.

$$\log_3 4 + \log_3 5 = \log_3 (4 \times 5) = \log_3 20$$

b) $\log_3 4 - \log_3 5$

- You're **taking** one log from another here, and the bases are the same (both 3).
- You need to use the law $\log_a x - \log_a y = \log_a \left(\frac{x}{y}\right)$.
- So here, $a = 3$ (the base), $x = 4$ and $y = 5$.

$$\log_3 4 - \log_3 5 = \log_3 \left(\frac{4}{5}\right)$$

c) $3 \log_4 2 + 2 \log_4 5$

- The logs are being **added**, but first you must use the law $\log_a x^k = k \log_a x$ to get rid of the 3 and 2 in front of the logs.
- Using the law, the logs become:

$$3 \log_4 2 = \log_4 (2^3) = \log_4 8$$

$$2 \log_4 5 = \log_4 (5^2) = \log_4 25$$

- The logs both have the same base (4) so the expression becomes:

$$\log_4 8 + \log_4 25 = \log_4 (8 \times 25) = \log_4 200$$

Tip: It's a good idea to split this into separate steps so you don't make a mistake.

You might be asked to simplify expressions that contain unknown variables too.

Example 2

a) Write the expression $2 \log_a 6 - \log_a 9$ in the form $\log_a n$, where n is a number.

- Use $\log_a x^k = k \log_a x$ to **simplify** $2 \log_a 6$:

$$2 \log_a 6 = \log_a 6^2 = \log_a 36$$

- Then use $\log_a x - \log_a y = \log_a \left(\frac{x}{y}\right)$:

$$\log_a 36 - \log_a 9 = \log_a (36 \div 9) = \log_a 4$$

b) Write the expression $\log_{10}\left(\frac{100x^2}{y^3}\right)$ in terms of $\log_{10} x$ and $\log_{10} y$.

- Use the laws of logs to **break up** the expression:

$$\begin{aligned}\log_{10}\left(\frac{100x^2}{y^3}\right) &= \log_{10} 100x^2 - \log_{10} y^3 \\ &= \log_{10} 100 + \log_{10} x^2 - \log_{10} y^3 \\ &= \log_{10} 10^2 + \log_{10} x^2 - \log_{10} y^3 \\ &= 2 \log_{10} 10 + 2 \log_{10} x - 3 \log_{10} y \\ &= 2 + 2 \log_{10} x - 3 \log_{10} y\end{aligned}$$

Tip: All three of the laws are used here. And if you're not sure where the 2 in the final answer has come from, remember that $\log_a a = 1$.

Changing the base

Your calculator can work out $\log_{10}$ for you — but most calculators can't do any old log, so if you needed to calculate logs with a **different base**, you'd be stuck. Luckily you can **change the base** of any log to base 10 using this formula and then just pop it into your calculator:

Change of Base: $\log_a x = \frac{\log_b x}{\log_b a}$

Tip: You're trying to work out what power you'd need to raise 7 to to get 4.

Examples

a) Find the value of $\log_7 4$ to 4 d.p.

- This is too tricky to work out without a calculator. So **change** the **base** of the log to **10**.
- Here, $a = 7$ and $x = 4$. And we want $b = 10$. So:

$$\log_7 4 = \frac{\log_{10} 4}{\log_{10} 7} = 0.7124 \quad \text{(4 d.p.)}$$

- You can check this on your calculator by doing: $7^{0.7124...} = 4$

b) Find the value of $\log_3 2$ to 4 d.p.

- **Change** the **base** of the log to **10**.
- Here, $a = 3$ and $x = 2$. And we want $b = 10$. So:

$$\log_3 2 = \frac{\log_{10} 2}{\log_{10} 3} = 0.6309 \quad \text{(4 d.p.)}$$

Exercise 1.2

Q1 Simplify the following, where possible:

a) $\log_a 2 + \log_a 5$ b) $\log_m 8 + \log_m 7$ c) $\log_b 8 - \log_b 4$
d) $\log_m 15 - \log_m 5$ e) $3 \log_n 4$ f) $2 \log_a 7$
g) $\frac{1}{2} \log_b 16$ h) $\frac{2}{3} \log_a 125$ i) $\log_3 a - \log_2 a$

Q2 Write each of the following expressions as a single log:

a) $2 \log_a 5 + \log_a 4$ b) $3 \log_m 2 - \log_m 4$ c) $3 \log_n 4 - 2 \log_n 8$
d) $\frac{2}{3} \log_b 216 - 2 \log_b 3$ e) $1 + \log_a 6$ f) $2 - \log_b 5$

Q3 Hint: Rewrite the numbers as products of their prime factors.

Q3 If $\log_a 2 = x$, $\log_a 3 = y$ and $\log_a 5 = z$, write in terms of x, y and z:

a) $\log_a 6$ b) $\log_a 16$ c) $\log_a 60$

Q4 Simplify each of the following as much as possible:

a) $\log_b b^3$ b) $\log_a \sqrt{a}$
c) $\log_m 4m - 2 \log_m 2$ d) $\log_{2b} 4 + \log_{2b} b - \log_{2b} 2$

Q5 Prove that:

a) $\log_2 4^x = 2x$ b) $\frac{\log_a 54 - \log_a 6}{\log_a 3} = 2$

Q6 Find the value of the following logs to 3 s.f.:

a) $\log_6 3$ b) $\log_9 2$ c) $\log_3 13$ d) $\log_5 4$

Q7 Hint: Rewrite the right-hand side as a single logarithm.

Q7 If $\log_m x = 2 + 3 \log_m 2 - \log_m 5$, find an expression for x in terms of m.

2. Exponentials

Over the last few pages, you met logarithms — now it's time to deal with exponentials. An exponential has the effect of reversing a log (it's actually called an inverse — you'll do more on inverses in C3). You can use exponentials to solve equations involving logs and vice versa.

Learning Objectives:
- Know that an exponential function takes the form $y = a^x$.
- Know the shape of the graph $y = a^x$.
- Be able to solve equations of the form $a^x = b$.

Exponentials

Exponentials are functions of the form $y = a^x$ (or $f(x) = a^x$), where $\boldsymbol{a > 0}$. **All** graphs of exponential functions have the **same basic shape**.

$y = a^x$ for $a > 1$

- All the graphs go through **1** at $\boldsymbol{x = 0}$ since $\boldsymbol{a^0 = 1}$ for any a.
- $a > 1$ — so $\boldsymbol{y}$ **increases as** $\boldsymbol{x}$ **increases**.
- The **bigger** a is, the **quicker** the graph increases (so the curve is **steeper**).

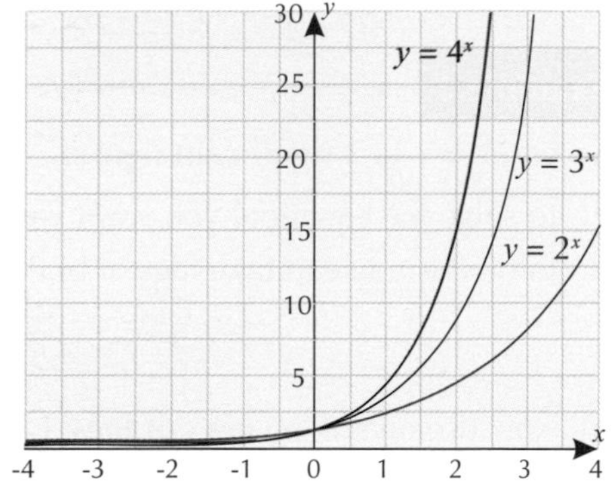

- As x **decreases**, y **decreases** at a **smaller and smaller rate** — y will approach zero, but never actually get there.
- This means as $\boldsymbol{x \to \infty}$, $\boldsymbol{y \to \infty}$ and as $\boldsymbol{x \to -\infty}$, $\boldsymbol{y \to 0}$.

Tip: Notice that the graph of $y = a^x$ is always positive. This is why you can't take the log of a negative number (remember, $y = a^x$ means $\log_a y = x$).

Tip: The notation $x \to \infty$ just means 'x tends to ∞' (i.e. x gets bigger and bigger). Similarly $y \to 0$ means 'y tends to 0' (gets smaller and smaller in magnitude).

$y = a^x$ for $0 < a < 1$

- All the graphs go through **1** at $\boldsymbol{x = 0}$ since $\boldsymbol{a^0 = 1}$ for any a.
- $0 < a < 1$ — so $\boldsymbol{y}$ **decreases as** $\boldsymbol{x}$ **increases**.
- The **smaller** a is, the **faster** the graphs decrease (so the curve is **steeper**).

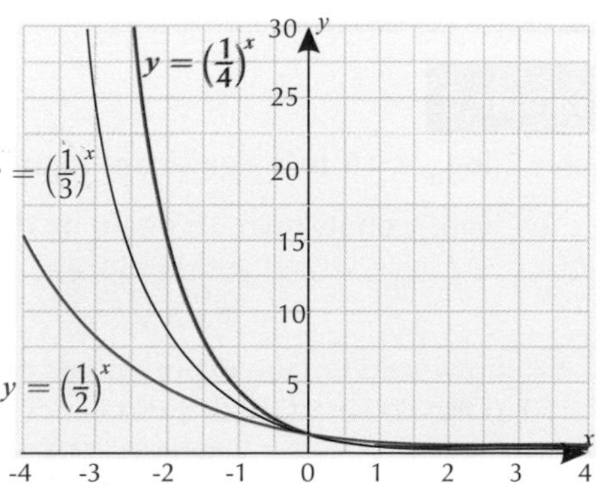

- As x **increases**, y **decreases** at a **smaller and smaller rate** — y will approach zero, but never actually get there.
- This means as $\boldsymbol{x \to \infty}$, $\boldsymbol{y \to 0}$ and as $\boldsymbol{x \to -\infty}$, $\boldsymbol{y \to \infty}$.

Tip: These graphs have the same shapes as the ones above but reflected in the y-axis. This makes sense since $\left(\frac{1}{a}\right)^x$ is the same as a^{-x} — remember your graph transformations from pages 5-12.

Exponentials and logs

Solving equations

Exponential functions are always in the form $a^x = b$. If you remember, in the first part of this chapter we said that:

$$a^x = b \quad \text{... is the same as...} \quad \log_a b = x$$

This means that exponentials and logs are the **inverses** of each other — so you can use logs to **get rid** of exponentials and vice versa. This is useful for solving equations. It also means that:

$$a^{\log_a x} = x = \log_a a^x$$

You can use this to get rid of logs easily when solving equations.

Tip: Laws of logs help prove this — i.e. $\log_a a^x = x\log_a a = x$.

Example 1

Solve $2^{4x} = 3$ to 3 significant figures.

- To solve the equation, you want ***x* on its own**.
- To do this you can **take logs** of both sides:

$$\log 2^{4x} = \log 3$$

- Now use one of the **laws of logs**: $\log x^k = k \log x$:

$$4x \log 2 = \log 3$$

- You can now **divide** both sides by 4 log 2 to get x on its own:

$$x = \frac{\log 3}{4 \log 2}$$

- But $\frac{\log 3}{4 \log 2}$ is just a number you can find using a **calculator**:

$$x = 0.396 \text{ (to 3 s.f.)}$$

Tip: Here, a log of base 10 has been used. There's more about this in the example on the next page.

Tip: Don't make the mistake of writing: $\frac{\log 3}{\log 2} = \log\left(\frac{3}{2}\right)$ as you can't cancel terms like this.

Example 2

Solve $7 \log_{10} x = 5$ to 3 significant figures.

- You want ***x* on its own**, so begin by **dividing** both sides by 7:

$$\log_{10} x = \frac{5}{7}$$

- You now need to **take exponentials** of both sides by doing '10 to the power of' both sides (since the log is to base 10):

$$10^{\log_{10} x} = 10^{\frac{5}{7}}$$

- Logs and exponentials are **inverse** functions, so they **cancel out**:

$$x = 10^{\frac{5}{7}}$$

- Again, $10^{\frac{5}{7}}$ is just a number you can find using a **calculator**:

$$x = 5.18 \text{ (to 3 s.f.)}$$

Tip: If you're taking exponentials, make sure you use the same base as the log (here it's 10).

Tip: You could get from $\log_{10} x = \frac{5}{7}$ to $x = 10^{\frac{5}{7}}$ just by changing from log notation to index notation — see page 50.

Example 3

Use logarithms to solve the following for x, giving the answers to 3 s.f.

a) $10^{3x} = 4000$

- There's an 'unknown' in the power, so **take logs of both sides**.
- In theory, it doesn't matter what **base** you use, but your calculator has a '$\log_{10}$' button, so base 10 is usually a good idea. But whatever base you use, use the **same** one for **both sides**.
- So taking logs to base 10 of both sides of the above equation gives:

$$\log 10^{3x} = \log 4000$$

- On the previous page you saw that $\log_a a^x = x$, so $\log_{10} 10^{3x} = 3x$, so you can simplify the left-hand side:

$$3x = \log 4000, \text{ so } x = 1.20 \text{ (to 3 s.f.)}$$

Tip: If you'd used a different base here you would have had to do $\frac{\log_a 4000}{3 \log_a 10}$ to find x.

b) $7^x = 55$

- Again, **take logs** of both sides, and use the log rules:

$$\log_{10} 7^x = \log_{10} 55$$
$$x \log_{10} 7 = \log_{10} 55$$

- So: $$x = \frac{\log_{10} 55}{\log_{10} 7} = 2.06 \text{ (to 3 s.f.)}$$

c) $\log_2 x = 5$

- To get rid of a log, you **take exponentials** — so you do 2 (the base) to the power of each side.

$$2^{\log_2 x} = 2^5$$

- Think of 'taking logs' and 'taking exponentials' as opposite processes — one cancels the other out. So you get:

$$x = 2^5 = 32$$

Tip: Remember, when taking exponentials you must always use the same base as the logarithm — here the base is 2.

In the exam, you might be asked to solve an equation where you have to use a **combination** of the methods covered in this chapter. It can be tricky to work out what's needed, but just remember that you're trying to get ***x* on its own** — and think about which laws will help you do that.

The next page has some examples.

Example 4

Solve $6^{x-2} = 3^x$, giving your answer to 3 s.f.

- Start by taking **logs** of both sides (you can use any base, so use 10).

$$\log 6^{x-2} = \log 3^x$$

- Now use $\boldsymbol{\log x^k = k \log x}$ on both sides:

$$(x - 2) \log 6 = x \log 3$$

- **Multiply out** the brackets and **collect** all the x terms on one side:

$$x \log 6 - 2 \log 6 = x \log 3 \Rightarrow x \log 6 - x \log 3 = 2 \log 6$$
$$\Rightarrow x (\log 6 - \log 3) = 2 \log 6$$

- Use $\boldsymbol{\log_a x - \log_a y = \log_a \left(\frac{x}{y}\right)}$ on the bracket:

$$x (\log 2) = 2 \log 6 \Rightarrow x = \frac{2 \log 6}{\log 2} = 5.17 \text{ (3 s.f.)}$$

Tip: Have a look back at page 52 if you can't remember the log laws.

Example 5

Solve the equation $\log_3(2 - 3x) - 2 \log_3 x = 2$.

- First, combine the log terms into one term (you can do this because they both have the same base):

$$\log_3 \frac{2 - 3x}{x^2} = 2$$

Remember that $2\log x = \log x^2$.

- Then take exponentials of both sides using base 3:

$$3^{\log_3 \frac{2-3x}{x^2}} = 3^2 \Rightarrow \frac{2 - 3x}{x^2} = 9$$

The exponential ($3^{\cdots}$) and the log ($\log_3$...) cancel each other.

- Finally, rearrange the equation and solve for x:

$$2 - 3x = 9x^2 \Rightarrow 0 = 9x^2 + 3x - 2$$
$$\Rightarrow 0 = (3x - 1)(3x + 2)$$

- So: $x = \frac{1}{3}$

Tip: Ignore the negative solution $\left(x = -\frac{2}{3}\right)$ because you can't have a log of a negative number — see p.50.

Exponential growth and decay

Logs can be used to solve **real-life** problems involving **exponential growth** and **decay**.

- Exponential **growth** is when the rate of growth **increases** faster and faster as the amount gets bigger.
- Exponential **decay** is just **negative** exponential growth. The **rate** of decay gets slower and slower as the amount gets smaller.

For example, if you have money in a bank account that earns interest at a certain percentage per year, the balance will **grow exponentially** over time (if you don't take any money out). So the **more money** you have in the account, the **more interest** you get.

Tip: Don't worry, you haven't accidentally wandered into A-Level Economics. We've just used a real-life example to make this topic fun and engaging. Ahem.

Here is an example of **exponential decay**:

Example

The radioactivity of a substance decays by 20% over a year.
The initial level of radioactivity is 400 Bq (becquerels).
Find the time taken for the radioactivity to fall to 200 Bq (the half-life).

- Write a **formula** for the radioactivity:

  $R = 400 \times 0.8^T$ where R is the **level of radioactivity** at time T years.

- We need $R = 200$, so: $200 = 400 \times 0.8^T \Rightarrow 0.8^T = \frac{200}{400} = 0.5$

- Take logs of both sides, and then use the laws of logs:

  $T \log 0.8 = \log 0.5$

  $T = \frac{\log 0.5}{\log 0.8} = 3.106$ years (4 s.f.)

Tip: A becquerel (Bq) is just a unit which measures radioactivity.

Tip: 0.8 is used as every year the radioactivity decreases by 0.2 (or 20%) and so it is 0.8 (or 80%) of what it was the previous year.

Exercise 2.1

Answers to this exercise should be given correct to 3 s.f.

Q1 Solve each of these equations for x:

a) $2^x = 3$ b) $4^x = 16$ c) $7^x = 2$

d) $1.8^x = 0.4$ e) $0.7^x = 3$ f) $0.5^x = 0.2$

g) $2^{3x-1} = 5$ h) $10^{3-x} = 8$ i) $0.4^{5x-4} = 2$

Q2 Find the value of x for each case:

a) $\log 5x = 3$ b) $\log_2 (x + 3) = 4$ c) $\log_3 (5 - 2x) = 2.5$

Q3 Solve each of these equations for x:

a) $4^{x+1} = 3^{2x}$ b) $2^{5-x} = 4^{x+3}$ c) $3^{2x-1} = 6^{3-x}$

Q4 Find the value(s) of x which satisfy each of the following equations:

a) $\log 2x = \log (x + 1) - 1$ b) $\log_2 2x = 3 - \log_2 (9 - 2x)$

c) $\log_6 x = 1 - \log_6 (x + 1)$ d) $\log_2 (2x + 1) = 3 + 2 \log_2 x$

Q5 Solve the equations $2^{x+y} = 8$ and $\log_2 x - \log_2 y = 1$ simultaneously.

Q6 Solve the equations $9^{x-2} = 3^y$ and $\log_3 2x = 1 + \log_3 y$ simultaneously.

Q7 Find the solutions of each of the following equations:

a) $2^{2x} - 5(2^x) + 4 = 0$ b) $4^{2x} - 17(4^x) + 16 = 0$

c) $3^{2x+2} - 82(3^x) + 9 = 0$ d) $2^{2x+3} - 9(2^x) + 1 = 0$

Q7 Hint: First rewrite each equation as a quadratic equation.

Q8 Howard bought several cases of wine as an investment. He paid £500 and expects the value to increase by 8% a year. He wants to sell when the wine exceeds £1500 in value. How many full years will this take?

Review Exercise — Chapter 3

Q1 Write the following using log notation:

a) $4^2 = 16$ b) $216^{\frac{1}{3}} = 6$ c) $3^{-4} = \frac{1}{81}$

Q2 Write down the values of the following:

a) $\log_3 27$ b) $\log_3 (1 \div 27)$ c) $\log_3 18 - \log_3 2$

Q3 Simplify the following, leaving your answers in terms of logs:

a) $\log 3 + 2 \log 5$ b) $\frac{1}{2} \log 36 - \log 3$ c) $\log 2 - \frac{1}{4} \log 16$

Q4 Simplify $\log_b (x^2 - 1) - \log_b (x - 1)$.

Q5 Find the value of the following, giving your answers to 3 s.f.:

a) $\log_7 12$ b) $\log_5 8$ c) $\log_{16} 125$

Q6 If $\log_a y = \log_a 5 + \log_a 3 + 1$, find an expression for y in terms of a.

Q7 Prove that $\dfrac{2 + \log_a 4}{\log_a 2a} = 2$.

Q8 a) Copy and complete the table for the function $y = 4^x$:

x	−3	−2	−1	0	1	2	3
y							

b) Plot a graph of $y = 4^x$ for $-3 \leq x \leq 3$.

c) Use the graph to solve the equation $4^x = 20$.

d) Solve the equation $4^x = 20$ algebraically, giving your answer to 3 s.f.

Q9 Solve the following, giving your answer to 3 s.f.:

a) $10^x = 240$ b) $\log_{10} x = 5.3$

c) $10^{2x+1} = 1500$ d) $4^{(x-1)} = 200$

Q10 Find the exact solutions of $2(10^{2x}) - 7(10^x) + 5 = 0$.

Q11 Find the smallest integer P such that $1.5^P > 1\,000\,000$.

Q12 Scientists are monitoring the population of curly-toed spiders at a secret location. It appears to be dropping at the rate of 25% a year. When the population has dropped below 200, the species will be in danger of extinction. At the moment the population is fairly healthy at 2000. How many whole years will it be before the spiders are in danger of extinction?

Exam-Style Questions — Chapter 3

1 a) Solve the equation

$$2^x = 9$$

giving your answer to 2 decimal places. *(3 marks)*

b) Hence, or otherwise, solve the equation

$$2^{2x} - 13(2^x) + 36 = 0$$

giving each solution to an appropriate degree of accuracy. *(5 marks)*

2 a) Solve the equation

$$\log_3 x = -\frac{1}{2}$$

leaving your answer as an exact value. *(3 marks)*

b) Find x, where

$$2 \log_3 x = -4$$

leaving your answer as an exact value. *(2 marks)*

3 a) Find x, if

$$6^{(3x + 2)} = 9$$

giving your answer to 3 significant figures. *(3 marks)*

b) Find y, if

$$3^{(y^2 - 4)} = 7^{(y + 2)}$$

giving your answers to 3 significant figures where appropriate. *(5 marks)*

4 a) Write the following expressions in the form $\log_a n$, where n is an integer:

(i) $\log_a 20 - 2\log_a 2$

(3 marks)

(ii) $\frac{1}{2}\log_a 16 + \frac{1}{3}\log_a 27$

(3 marks)

b) Find the value of:

(i) $\log_2 64$

(1 mark)

(ii) $2\log_3 9$

(2 marks)

c) Calculate the value of the following, giving your answer to 4 d.p.

(i) $\log_6 25$

(1 mark)

(ii) $\log_3 10 + \log_3 2$

(2 marks)

5 a) Solve the equation

$$\log_7 (y + 3) + \log_7 (2y + 1) = 1$$

where $y > 0$.

(5 marks)

b) Given that

$$3\log_5 t - \log_5 u = 1$$

show that $u = \frac{t^3}{5}$.

(4 marks)

6 For the positive integers p and q,

$$\log_4 p - \log_4 q = \frac{1}{2}$$

a) Show that $p = 2q$.

(3 marks)

b) The values of p and q are such that $\log_2 p + \log_2 q = 7$.

Use this information to find the values of p and q.

(5 marks)

Chapter 4 Sequences and Series

1. Sequences

A sequence is a list of numbers that follow a certain pattern — e.g. 2, 4, 6, 8..., –5, 2, –5, 2, –5, ... or 1, 4, 9, 16... There are two main ways of describing sequences — from an nth term formula and from a recurrence relation.

Learning Objectives:

- Be able to use an nth term formula to generate terms in a sequence, or find the position of a term with a given value.
- Be able to write recurrence relations and use them to generate sequences.

n^{th} term

The idea behind the nth term is that you can use a formula to generate any term in a sequence from its position, n, in the sequence.

Example 1

A sequence has the nth term $4n + 1$.

a) Find the 10th term in the sequence.

Just substitute 10 for n in the nth term expression: $4(10) + 1 = 41$

The 10th term is **41**.

b) A term in the sequence is 33. Find the position of this term.

- The position of the term is n where $4n + 1 = 33$.
- So $n = (33 - 1) \div 4 = 8$

33 is the **8th** term of the sequence.

Tip: This sequence is an example of the 'common difference' type — the first few terms are 5, 9, 13, 17, ..., which have a common difference of 4. These are actually known as arithmetic sequences — there's more about them on p.71-72.

Example 2

A sequence has the nth term $n^2 - 2$.

a) Find the first 3 terms in the sequence.

Just substitute $n = 1, 2, 3$ in the nth term expression:

$(1)^2 - 2 = -1$

$(2)^2 - 2 = 2$

$(3)^2 - 2 = 7$

So the first 3 terms in the sequence are **–1, 2, 7.**

b) Is 35 a term in the sequence?

For questions like this, you need to form and solve an equation in n and see if you get a positive whole number:

$$n^2 - 2 = 35 \Rightarrow n^2 = 37 \Rightarrow n = \sqrt{37}$$

$\sqrt{37}$ is not a positive integer, so 35 is **not** in the sequence.

Tip: If your value for n had been a positive integer, then that number would have been a term in the sequence. E.g. 34 is in the sequence, because solving $n^2 - 2 = 34$ gives $n = 6$, so 34 is the 6th term in the sequence.

Exercise 1.1

Q1 A sequence has n^{th} term $3n - 5$. Find the 20th term.

Q2 Find the 4th term of the sequence with n^{th} term $n(n + 2)$.

Q3 Find the first 5 terms of the sequence with n^{th} term $(n - 1)(n + 1)$.

Q4 The kth term of a sequence is 29.
The nth term of this sequence is $4n - 3$. Find the value of k.

Q5 A sequence has n^{th} term $= an^2 + b$, where a and b are constants.
If the 2nd term is 15, and the 5th term is 99, find a and b.

Q6 A sequence starts 9, 20, 37... . Its nth term $= en^2 + fn + 4$, where e and f are constants. Find the values of e and f.

Q7 The nth term of the sequence is given by $(n - 1)^2$. A term in the sequence is 49. Find the position of this term.

Q8 How many terms of the sequence with n^{th} term $15 - 2n$ are positive?

Q8 Hint: Start by using the nth term formula to find the first few terms of the sequence — you'll soon see what the question is getting at.

Recurrence relations

Before we get going with this section, there's some **notation** to learn:

a_k just means the **k^{th} term** of the sequence
— so a_4 is the 4th term, and a_{k+1} is the term after a_k.

Tip: The notation using subscripts is used to identify sequences all the time, so you need to get used to it. Any letter can be used, e.g. $x_n = (n - 1)(n + 1)$. It just avoids having to repeat "with n^{th} term...".

You've just seen how you can define a sequence by using a general formula for the nth term. Well, a **recurrence relation** is another way to describe a sequence. Don't be put off by the fancy name — recurrence relations are pretty easy really. The key thing to remember is:

Recurrence relations tell you how to work out a term in a sequence from the previous term.

So, using the new notation, what this is saying is that a recurrence relation describes how to work out a_{k+1} from a_k.

Tip: You can also think of this as meaning that a_{k+1} is a function of a_k — i.e. to find a_{k+1}, you do something to a_k. You might see this written as $a_{k+1} = f(a_k)$.

E.g. if each term in the sequence is **2 more** than the previous term:

$$a_{k+1} = a_k + 2$$

So, if $k = 5$, this says that $a_6 = a_5 + 2$, that is, the 6th term is equal to the 5th term + 2.

This recurrence relation will be true for loads of sequences, e.g. 1, 3, 5, 7..., and 4, 6, 8, 10... So to describe a **particular sequence** you also have to give one term. E.g. the sequence 1, 3, 5, 7... is described by:

Tip: $a_{k+1} = a_k + 2,\ a_2 = 3$ also describes the sequence 1, 3, 5, 7,...

$$a_{k+1} = a_k + 2,\ a_1 = 1$$

a_1 stands for the 1st term.

Example 1

Find the recurrence relation of the sequence 5, 8, 11, 14, 17, ...

- Each term in this sequence equals the one before it, plus 3.
- The recurrence relation is written like this:

$$a_{k+1} = a_k + 3$$

- **BUT**, as you saw on the previous page $a_{k+1} = a_k + 3$ on its own isn't enough to describe 5, 8, 11, 14, 17, ... For example, the sequence 87, 90, 93, 96, 99, ... also has each term being 3 more than the one before.
- The description needs to be more specific, so you've got to give **one term** in the sequence, as well as the recurrence relation.
- Putting all of this together gives 5, 8, 11, 14, 17, ... as:

$$a_{k+1} = a_k + 3, \quad a_1 = 5$$

Tip: You almost always give the first value, a_1.

Example 2

A sequence is given by the recurrence relation $a_{k+1} = a_k - 4$, $a_1 = 20$. Find the first five terms of this sequence.

- You're given the first term (a_1) — it's 20.
- Now you need to find the second term (a_2). If $a_1 = a_k$, then $a_2 = a_{k+1}$.

$a_2 = a_1 - 4$
$a_2 = 20 - 4$
$a_2 = 16$ ← This is 4 less than the first term.

- Repeat this to find the third, fourth and fifth terms.

$a_3 = a_2 - 4$
$a_3 = 16 - 4$
$a_3 = 12$

$a_4 = a_3 - 4$
$a_4 = 12 - 4$
$a_4 = 8$

$a_5 = a_4 - 4$
$a_5 = 8 - 4$
$a_5 = 4$

The first five terms of the sequence are **20, 16, 12, 8, 4**.

Tip: When you've got the hang of recurrence relations, you'll be able to see straight away that $a_{k+1} = a_k - 4$ just means the sequence decreases by 4 each time.

Example 3

The sequence with n^{th} term u_n is defined by the recurrence relation:

$$u_{n+1} = 3u_n + k$$

where k is a constant. The first term of the sequence is given by $u_1 = 2$.

a) Find u_3 in terms of k.

You're given the first term, u_1, so use this to generate the second term, u_2, in terms of k, then use the second term to generate the third term, u_3.

$u_{n+1} = 3u_n + k$

$u_2 = 3u_1 + k$

$u_2 = 3(2) + k$ ← Substitute in the value for u_1.

$u_2 = 6 + k$

$u_3 = 3u_2 + k$

$u_3 = 3(6 + k) + k$ ← Substitute in the expression for u_2 that you found above.

$u_3 = 18 + 4k$

b) Given that $u_4 = 28$, find k.

- Form an expression for u_4 using the definition of the sequence:

  $u_4 = 3u_3 + k$

  $u_4 = 3(18 + 4k) + k$ ← Substitute in the expression for u_3 from part a).

  $u_4 = 54 + 13k$

- The question tells you that $u_4 = 28$, so form an equation and solve to find k.

  $28 = 54 + 13k$

  $13k = -26$

  $k = -2$

Tip: This is the downside of recurrence relations — you have to go through each term to work out the one you're after. It'd take ages to find, say, the 100th term.

Example 4 on the next page is a bit harder, as there's an n^2 in there. But the method works in exactly the same way — you just end up with a slightly more complicated formula for the recurrence relation.

Example 4

A sequence has the general term $x_n = n^2$.
Write down a recurrence relation which generates the sequence.

- Start by finding the first few terms of the sequence (i.e. $n = 1, 2, 3, 4...$)

  $x_1 = 1^2 = \mathbf{1}$ $\quad x_2 = 2^2 = \mathbf{4}$ $\quad x_3 = 3^2 = \mathbf{9}$ $\quad x_4 = 4^2 = \mathbf{16}$

  So the first four terms are: 1, 4, 9, 16

- You're now at the same point as you were at the start of Example 1. You use the same method to form the recurrence relation, but it's a little trickier as n in the general term is squared.

- Look at the difference between each term:

$k =$	1		2		3		4
$x_k =$	1		4		9		16
		+3		+5		+7	
		$(2\times1) + 1$		$(2\times2) + 1$		$(2\times3) + 1$	

- To get from term x_k to the next term, x_{k+1}, you take the value of term x_k, and add $2k + 1$ to it. E.g. 3rd term = 2nd term + 2(2) + 1.

  So the recurrence relation is: $\mathbf{x_{k+1} = x_k + 2k + 1}$

- To generate the sequence you need to give **one term** in the sequence, and there's no reason not to stick to convention and use the first term:

  $\mathbf{x_{k+1} = x_k + 2k + 1, x_1 = 1}$ ← Try substituting in different k values to check your recurrence relation does generate the sequence.

Tip: It's sometimes helpful to draw some little diagrams where n^2 is involved. E.g. these diagrams let you see that it's $2k + 1$ added each time.

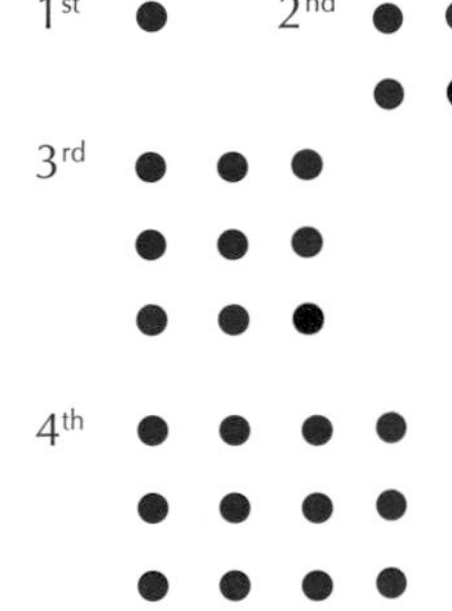

Some sequences are only defined for a **certain number** of terms.

A sequence defined for $1 \le k \le 20$ is given by the recurrence relation $a_{k+1} = a_k + 3$, $a_1 = 1$. The sequence is 1, 4, 7, 10, ..., 58 and will contain 20 terms. **This is a finite sequence.**

Tip: It's the $1 \le k \le 20$ bit that tells you it's finite — the sequence will stop when $k = 20$.

Other sequences **don't** have a specified number of terms, and could go on **forever**.

The sequence given by $u_{k+1} = u_k + 2$, $u_1 = 5$, will be 5, 7, 9, 11, 13, ... and won't have a final term. **This is an infinite sequence.**

Others are **periodic**, and just revisit the same values over and over again.

The sequence given by $u_k = u_{k-3}$, $u_1 = 1$, $u_2 = 4$, $u_3 = 2$, will be 1, 4, 2, 1, 4, 2, 1, 4, 2, ...
This is a periodic sequence with period 3.

Tip: Period 3 means that the sequence repeats every 3 terms — i.e. $u_1 = u_4$, $u_2 = u_5$ etc.

Exercise 1.2

Q1 A sequence is defined for $n \geq 1$ by $u_{n+1} = 3u_n$ and $u_1 = 10$. Find the first 5 terms of the sequence.

Q2 A sequence is given by the recurrence relation $u_{n+1} = 2u_n - 4$ and $u_1 = -2$. Find the first 5 terms of the sequence.

Q3 a) Find the first 4 terms of the sequence in which $u_1 = 2$ and $u_{n+1} = u_n^{\,2}$ for $n \geq 1$.

b) Is this sequence finite or infinite? Explain your answer.

Q4 Write down a recurrence relation which produces the sequence 3, 6, 12, 24, 48, ...

Q5 a) Write down a recurrence relation which produces the sequence
12, 16, 20, 24, 28, ...

b) The sequence is finite and ends at 100. Find the number of terms.

c) Write down an inequality to show the range of values for which the recurrence relation for this sequence is valid.

Q6 a) Hint: You need to find an operation that goes back and forth between 4 and 7. There are two possible answers — think about one of these number facts:
$7 + 4 = 11$ or
$7 \times 4 = 28$.

Q6 a) Find a recurrence relation which generates the sequence
7, 4, 7, 4, 7, ...

b) What is the period of this sequence?

Q7 In a sequence $u_1 = 4$ and $u_{n+1} = 3u_n - 1$ for $n \geq 1$.
Find the value of k if $u_k = 95$.

Q8 In a sequence $x_1 = 9$ and $x_{n+1} = (x_n + 1) \div 2$ for $n \geq 1$.
Find the value of r if $x_r = \frac{5}{4}$.

Q9 Find the first 5 terms of the sequence in which $u_1 = 7$ and $u_{n+1} = u_n + n$ for $n \geq 1$.

Q10 The sequence with n^{th} term u_n is defined by $u_{n+1} = 4u_n + k$ and $u_1 = 3$, where k is a constant.

a) Find the fourth term of the sequence in terms of k.

b) Find the value of k given that the fifth term of the sequence is 598.

Q11 Hint: Form all the equations you can from the information, and then solve them.

Q11 In a sequence $u_1 = 6$, $u_2 = 7$ and $u_3 = 8.5$. If the recurrence relation is of the form $u_{n+1} = au_n + b$, find the values of the constants a and b.

Q12 A sequence is generated by $u_1 = 8$ and $u_{n+1} = \frac{1}{2}u_n$ for $n \geq 1$.
Find the first 5 terms and a formula for u_n in terms of n.

Convergent sequences

The terms of some sequences get **closer and closer** to a **limit** without ever reaching it — these sequences are called **convergent sequences**.

If a sequence does not approach a limit, it is called a **divergent sequence**.

If the terms of a sequence approach a limit, L, then for large values of n:

$$a_n \approx a_{n+1} \approx a_{n+2} \approx \ldots \approx L$$

So, for a convergent sequence defined by a relation $a_{k+1} = f(a_k)$:

$$L \approx f(L)$$

This means that the limit, L, of the sequence as k tends to infinity can be found by solving $\boldsymbol{L = f(L)}$.

A good way to spot convergent sequences is too look at the **difference** between pairs of **consecutive terms**. If the differences are **shrinking** as k increases, then it's likely that the sequence is convergent.

Tip: There's more about convergence later in the chapter, see p.85-86.

Tip: The terms of the sequence aren't **exactly** equal to each other (hence the ≈ symbols), but they get **so close** to being equal as k tends to infinity, that you can treat them as being so.

'As k tends to infinity' just means 'as k gets really, really big'. You might also see it written as $k \to \infty$.

Example

A sequence is defined by the relation $a_{k+1} = -\frac{1}{2}a_k + 2$

a) **Given that $a_1 = 1$, say whether the sequence looks to be convergent or is divergent.**

Find the next few terms in the sequence:

$$a_2 = -\frac{1}{2}a_1 + 2 = -\frac{1}{2}(1) + 2 = \frac{3}{2} = 1.5$$

$$a_3 = -\frac{1}{2}a_2 + 2 = -\frac{1}{2}(\frac{3}{2}) + 2 = \frac{5}{4} = 1.25$$

$$a_4 = -\frac{1}{2}a_3 + 2 = -\frac{1}{2}(\frac{5}{4}) + 2 = \frac{11}{8} = 1.375$$

The difference between consecutive terms is shrinking, so this sequence looks to be convergent.

b) **Find L, the limit of a_k as k tends to infinity.**

Here, $f(a_k) = -\frac{1}{2}a_k + 2$

Now take $L = f(L)$, which gives $L = -\frac{1}{2}L + 2$

Rearranging: $\frac{3}{2}L = 2 \Rightarrow L = \frac{4}{3}$

So, the limit of the sequence as k tends to infinity is $\frac{4}{3}$.

Tip: In C2, you don't need to know how to **prove** that an arithmetic sequence is convergent, so all you can say is that a sequence looks to be convergent. And if it looks like it's convergent, then it probably is.

Exercise 1.3

Q1 In each of the following, $a_1 = 1$. Work out a_2, a_3, and a_4 and state whether the sequence looks to be convergent or divergent.

a) $a_{n+1} = a_n + 2$

b) $a_{n+1} = 0.5a_n$

c) $a_{n+1} = \frac{1}{3}a_n - 2$

d) $a_{n+1} = 2a_n + 1$

e) $2a_{n+1} = 3a_n + 4$

f) $3a_{n+1} = 2a_n - 3$

Q2 For each convergent series in Question 1, find L, the limit of a_n as n tends to infinity.

Q3 The nth term of a sequence is u_n.
A sequence is defined by $u_{n+1} = ku_n + 3$

a) Given that $u_1 = 2$ and $u_2 = 4$, find:

(i) k (ii) u_3 (iii) u_4

b) If, instead, $u_1 = 2$ and $u_2 = 7$ find:

(i) k (ii) u_3 (iii) u_4

c) Say whether each of a) and b) is divergent or looks to be convergent.

d) Where appropriate for the sequences in a) and b), find the limit of u_n as n tends to infinity.

Q4 The nth term of a sequence is u_n.
The sequence is defined by $u_{n+1} = au_n + b$ where a and b are constants.

The first three terms of the sequence are $u_1 = 4$, $u_2 = 5$ and $u_3 = 5\frac{3}{4}$.

a) Find the values of a and b.

The limit of u_n as n tends to infinity is L.

b) Write down an equation for L.

c) Solve the equation to find the value of L.

Q5 The nth term of a sequence is u_n.
The sequence is defined by $u_{n+1} = \frac{3}{4}u_n + 1$.

a) Given that $u_1 = 4$ calculate u_2 and u_3.

b) Write down the value of u_{20}.

c) What is the limit of u_n as n tends to infinity?

Q6 The nth term of a sequence is u_n.
The sequence is defined by $u_{n+1} = au_n + 3$ where a is a constant.
The limit of u_n as n tends to infinity, is $L = 6$.

a) Calculate the value of a.

b) Taking $u_1 = 8$ find the smallest value of n for which $u_n < 6.1$

c) If instead, $u_1 = 3$, find the smallest value of n for which $u_n > 5.999$

2. Arithmetic Sequences & Series

Sequences and series are very similar and quite easy to confuse. A sequence is a just list of terms that follow a pattern. You'll often want to add these terms together — when you do this, it becomes a series.

Learning Objectives:

- Be able to recognise arithmetic sequences and series.
- Be able to use the nth term formula to solve arithmetic series problems.
- Be able to find the sum of the first n terms of an arithmetic series.
- Use sigma (Σ) notation to refer to the sum of a series.
- Be able to find the sum of the first n natural numbers.

Arithmetic sequences

Right, you've got basic sequences tucked under your belt — now it's time to look at a particular type of sequence in greater detail.

When the terms of a sequence progress by **adding** a **fixed amount** each time, this is called an **arithmetic** sequence.

Here are some examples of arithmetic sequences:
5, 7, 9, 11... (add 2 each time); 20, 17, 14, 11... (add –3 each time).

The formula for u_n, the nth term of an arithmetic sequence, is:

$$u_n = a + (n - 1)d$$

where:
a is the **first term** of the sequence.
d is the amount you add each time — the **common difference**.
n is the **position** of any term in the sequence.

This box shows you how the formula is derived:

Term	n		
1st	1	a	
2nd	2	$(a) + d$	
3rd	3	$(a + d) + d$	$= a + 2d$
4th	4	$(a + 2d) + d$	$= a + 3d$
⋮	⋮	⋮	⋮
n^{th}	n		$a + (n - 1)d$

Which is the formula to find the nth term.

Tip: Arithmetic sequences are often referred to as arithmetic progressions — it's exactly the same thing.

Tip: Each term is made up of the previous one, plus d. It's a sort of recurrence relation.

Tip: The formula for the nth term of an arithmetic sequence is in the formula booklet you will get in the exam.

Example 1

Find the 20th term of the arithmetic sequence 2, 5, 8, 11, ... and find the formula for the nth term.

- The nth term of a sequence is $a + (n - 1)d$.
- For this sequence, $a = 2$ and $d = 3$.
- Plug the numbers into the nth term formula:

$$20^{th} \text{ term} = 2 + (19 \times 3) = 59$$

So the 20th term = **59**

- The general term is the nth term, i.e. $a + (n - 1)d$.
Just substitute in the a and d values and simplify:

$$n^{th} \text{ term} = 2 + (n - 1)3 = 3n - 1$$

The nth term = $\mathbf{3n - 1}$

Tip: You should always check your n^{th} term formula is correct by sticking in some values for n and seeing if it produces the terms of the sequence.

- Finally, check the formula works with a couple of values of n:
  $n = 1$ gives $3(1) - 1 = 2$ ✓
  $n = 2$ gives $3(2) - 1 = 5$ ✓

Example 2

Find the nth term of the sequence –213, –198, –183, –168, ...

- The **first term**, a, is –213.
- Each term is 15 more than the one before it. So d is 15.
- Now just put these values into the formula:

$$n^{th} \text{ term} = a + (n-1)d$$
$$= -213 + 15(n-1)$$
$$= 15n - 228$$

- Check it works:
  $n = 1$ gives $15(1) - 228 = -213$ ✓
  $n = 2$ gives $15(2) - 228 = -198$ ✓

You only actually need to know **two terms** of an arithmetic sequence (and their positions) — then you can work out any other term.

Example 3

The 2nd term of an arithmetic sequence is 21, and the 9th term is –7. Find the 23rd term of this sequence.

Tip: If a sequence is decreasing, then the common difference, d, will be negative.

- Set up an equation for each of the known terms:
  2nd term = 21, so $a + (2-1)d = 21$
  $a + d = 21$
  9th term = –7, so $a + (9-1)d = -7$
  $a + 8d = -7$
- You've now got two **simultaneous equations** — so solve them to find a and d:
  $a + d = 21$ — ①
  $a + 8d = -7$ — ②
  ① – ②: $-7d = 28 \Rightarrow$ $\boldsymbol{d = -4}$
  ①: $a + d = 21 \Rightarrow a - 4 = 21 \Rightarrow$ $\boldsymbol{a = 25}$

Tip: The common difference and the first term have also been found along the way here (questions sometimes ask you to find these).

- Write the nth term formula... n^{th} term $= a + (n-1)d$
  $= 25 + (n-1) \times -4$
  $= -4n + 29$
- ... and use it to find the 23rd term ($n = 23$): 23rd term $= -4 \times 23 + 29$
  23rd term = **–63**

Exercise 2.1

Q1 An arithmetic progression has first term 7 and common difference 5. Find its 10th term.

Q2 Find the nth term for each of the following sequences:

a) 6, 9, 12, 15, ...

b) 4, 9, 14, 19, ...

c) 12, 8, 4, 0, ...

d) 1.5, 3.5, 5.5, 7.5 ...

Q3 Morag starts a new job. In the first week she is paid £60, but this rises by £3 per week, so she earns £63 in the second week and £66 in the third week. How much does she earn in her 12th week?

Q4 Mario opens a sandwich shop. On the first day he sells 40 sandwiches. As people hear about the shop, sales increase and on the second day he sells 45 sandwiches. Daily sales rise in an arithmetic sequence. On which day will he sell 80 sandwiches?

Q3-4 Hint: Sequence questions are often set in real-life contexts. But the maths behind them is just the same.

Q5 In an arithmetic sequence, the fourth term is 19 and the tenth term is 43. Find the first term and common difference.

Q6 The 7th term of an arithmetic progression is 34.
Given that the progression has common difference 2, find:

a) the first term of the progression,

b) the 15th term of the progression.

Q7 An arithmetic progression has common difference 6.
The sixth term of the progression is 88.
Find an expression for the nth term of the progression.

Q8 In an arithmetic progression, $u_7 = 8$ and $u_{11} = 10$. Find u_3.

Q9 In an arithmetic sequence, $u_3 = 15$ and $u_7 = 27$.
Find the value of k if $u_k = 66$.

Q10 A retro cassette-walkman product is launched into the market. In the first month after launch, the product takes £300 000 of revenue. It takes £270 000 in the second month and £240 000 in the third. If this pattern continues, when would you expect monthly sales to fall below £50 000?

Arithmetic series

Here is an arithmetic sequence. It's an infinite sequence — it goes on forever.

5, 8, 11, 14, 17, 20, ...

Now suppose you wanted to find the sum of the first 5 terms of this sequence. You'd write this by replacing the commas with '+' signs like this:

5 + 8 + 11 + 14 + 17

This is now an **arithmetic series**. It's a finite series with 5 terms. And if you actually added up the numbers you'd find that the **sum** for this series is 55.

So sequences become series when you add up their terms to find sums.

Sum of the first *n* terms

It would very quickly stop being fun if you had to find the sum of a 100 term series manually. Instead, you can use one of these **two formulas**.

S_n represents the **sum of the first *n* terms**

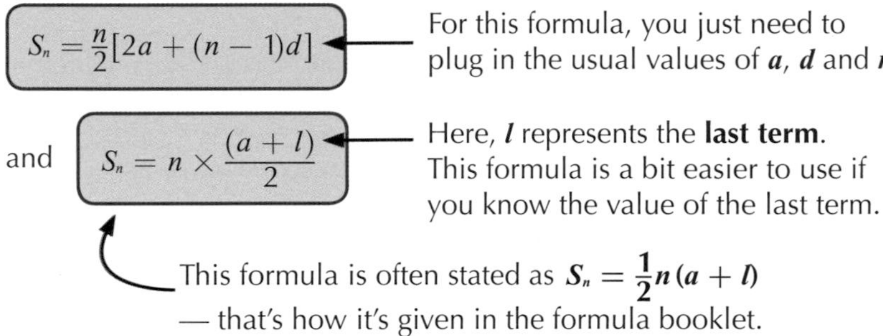

$S_n = \frac{n}{2}[2a + (n - 1)d]$
For this formula, you just need to plug in the usual values of ***a***, ***d*** and ***n***
and
$S_n = n \times \frac{(a + l)}{2}$
Here, ***l*** represents the **last term**. This formula is a bit easier to use if you know the value of the last term.
This formula is often stated as $S_n = \frac{1}{2}n(a + l)$ — that's how it's given in the formula booklet.

Tip: You can work out a, d and the nth term for a series, just as you would for a sequence. So in the 5-term series above, $a = 5$, $d = 3$ and n^{th} term $= 3n + 2$ (for $1 \le n \le 5$). Also, because the series is finite, you can state its last term, which is 17.

Both of these formulas are in the formula booklet, so you don't need to learn them. However, there's a nice little proof for them which is worth knowing:

For any series, you can express S_n as:
$S_n = a + (a + d) + (a + 2d) + ... + (a + (n - 3)d) + (a + (n - 2)d) + (a + (n - 1)d)$

Now, if you reverse the order of the terms you can write it as:
$S_n = (a + (n - 1)d) + (a + (n - 2)d) + (a + (n - 3)d) + ... + (a + 2d) + (a + d) + a$

Adding the two expressions for S_n gives:
$2S_n = (2a + (n - 1)d) + (2a + (n - 1)d) + (2a + (n - 1)d) + ... + (2a + (n - 1)d)$

So we've now got the term "$(2a + (n - 1)d)$" repeated n times, which is:

$2S_n = n \times (2a + (n - 1)d) \Rightarrow S_n = \frac{n}{2}[2a + (n - 1)d]$

So we've derived the first formula. Now to get the second, just replace "$a + (n - 1)d$" with l:

$S_n = \frac{n}{2}[a + a + (n - 1)d]$, so $S_n = \frac{n}{2}[a + l]$

Now it's time to try out the sum formulas in some worked examples.

Example 1

Find the sum of the series with first term 3, last term 87 and common difference 4.

- You're told the last term, so use the S_n formula with l in: $S_n = n \times \frac{(a+l)}{2}$
- You know a (3) and l (87), but you don't know n yet.
- Find n by putting what you do know into the 'n^{th} term' formula:

$$a + (n-1)d = 87$$
$$3 + (n-1)4 = 87$$
$$4n - 1 = 87$$
$$n = 22$$

- You're now all set to plug the values for a, l and n into the S_n formula:

$$S_n = n \times \frac{(a+l)}{2}$$

$n = 22$ means that there are 22 terms in the series.

$$S_{22} = 22 \times \frac{(3+87)}{2}$$
$$= 22 \times 45$$
$$= 990$$

The sum of the series is **990**.

Example 2

This question is about the sequence –5, –2, 1, 4, 7...

a) Is 67 a term in the sequence? If it is, give its position.

First, find the formula for the nth term of the sequence:

$$n^{\text{th}} \text{ term} = a + (n-1)d$$
$$= -5 + (n-1)3 \qquad a = -5 \text{ and } d = 3$$
$$= 3n - 8$$

Put 67 into the formula and see if this gives a whole number for n:

$$67 = 3n - 8$$
$$3n = 75 \Rightarrow n = 25$$

67 **is** a term in the sequence. It's the **25th** term.

b) Find the sum of the first 20 terms.

We know $a = -5$, $d = 3$ and $n = 20$, so plug these values into the formula $S_n = \frac{n}{2}[2a + (n-1)d]$:

$$S_{20} = \frac{20}{2}[2(-5) + (20-1)3]$$
$$S_{20} = 10[-10 + 19 \times 3]$$
$$S_{20} = 470$$

The sum of the first 20 terms is **470**.

Tip: This question could just have easily been about the series –5 + –2 + 1 + 4 + 7 + ... — the working would have been exactly the same.

Example 3

Find the possible numbers of terms in the arithmetic series starting 21 + 18 + 15... if the sum of the series is 75.

- You're told the first term, a, is 21 and the sum of the series, S_n, is 75. You can see that the common difference, d, is –3. What you need to work out is n, the number of terms in the series.
- With a bit of rearranging, you can use the S_n formula for this:

$$S_n = \frac{n}{2}[2a + (n - 1)d]$$

$$S_n = \frac{n}{2}[2(21) + (n - 1) \times -3]$$

$$75 = \frac{n}{2}[42 - 3n + 3]$$

$$75 = \frac{45n}{2} - \frac{3n^2}{2}$$

$$-3n^2 + 45n - 150 = 0$$

Divide through by –3 to simplify the quadratic

$$n^2 - 15n + 50 = 0$$

$$(n - 5)(n - 10) = 0$$

$$n = 5 \text{ or } n = 10$$

There are **5** or **10** terms in the series.

Tip: There are two answers to this one. It's because the series goes into negative numbers, so the sum of 75 is reached twice. Look at the first 10 terms of the series written out in full and you'll see what I mean: 21 + 18 + 15 + 12 + 9 + 6 + 3 + 0 + (–3) + (–6).

Example 4

Genetically modified super-chickens lay eggs for 7 days. The number of eggs they lay each day will always form an arithmetic sequence.

A super-chicken lays 19 times as many eggs on the seventh day as it did on the first day, and lays 350 eggs in total over the week.

How many extra eggs does it lay each day compared to the previous?

- You've been asked to find the common difference, d, of the series. You know that S_n is 350, and that there are 7 numbers in the series (so n = 7). Call the first term a, and the last term $19a$.
- Plug these values into the formula: $S_n = n \times \frac{(a + l)}{2}$

$$350 = 7 \times \frac{(a + 19a)}{2}$$

$$100 = 20a$$

$$a = 5$$

- The last term, l, is $19a$, so $l = 95$.
- You're now just one step from finding the common difference, d.

$l = a + (n - 1)d$

$95 = 5 + (7 - 1)d$

$d = 15$

15 more eggs are laid each day than the day before.

Tip: You might just come across an exam question with numbers in context. Whether the context is super-chickens, money or something else, start by seeing what you know out of a, d, n, l and S_n.

Sigma notation

So far, the letter S has been used for the sum. The Greeks did a lot of work on this — their capital letter for S is Σ or **sigma**. This is used today, together with the general term, to mean the sum of the series.

For example, the following means 'the sum of the series with n^{th} term $2n + 3$'.

$$\sum_{n=1}^{15}(2n+3)$$

Starting with $n = 1$... ...and ending with $n = 15$

Example 5

Find $\sum_{n=1}^{15}(2n+3)$.

- The first term ($n = 1$) is 5, the second term ($n = 2$) is 7, the third is 9, ... and the last term ($n = 15$) is 33. So in other words, you need to find $5 + 7 + 9 + ... + 33$. This gives $a = 5$, $d = 2$, $n = 15$ and $l = 33$.
- You know all of a, d, n and l, so you can use either formula:

$$S_n = n\frac{(a+l)}{2}$$
$$S_{15} = 15\frac{(5+33)}{2}$$
$$S_{15} = 15 \times 19$$
$$S_{15} = 285$$

It makes no difference which formula you use.

$$S_n = \frac{n}{2}[2a + (n-1)d]$$
$$S_{15} = \frac{15}{2}[2 \times 5 + 14 \times 2]$$
$$S_{15} = \frac{15}{2}[10 + 28]$$
$$S_{15} = 285$$

Exercise 2.2

Q1 An arithmetic series has first term 8 and common difference 3. Find the 10th term and the sum of the first 10 terms.

Q2 In an arithmetic series $u_2 = 16$ and $u_5 = 10$. Find a, d and S_8.

Q3 In an arithmetic series $a = 12$ and $d = 6$. Find u_{100} and S_{100}.

Q4 Find $\sum_{n=1}^{12}(5n-2)$.

Q5 Find $\sum_{n=1}^{9}(20-2n)$.

Q6 "Cornflake Collector" magazine sells 6000 copies in its first month of publication, 8000 in its second month and 10 000 in its third month. If this pattern continues, how many copies will it sell in the first year of publication?

Q7 In an arithmetic series $a = 3$ and $d = 2$. Find n if $S_n = 960$.

Q8 An arithmetic series has first term 14 and common difference 8. Find the number of terms required for their sum to exceed 176.

Q9 Given that $\sum_{n=1}^{k}(5n+2) = 553$ show that the value of k is 14.

Q10 An arithmetic sequence begins $x + 11$, $4x + 4$, $9x + 5$, ... Find the sum of the first 11 terms.

Q10 Hint: You're eventually going to need to find a and d (or l) so you can use them in the sum formula, but start off by writing down what you know, and don't be put off by the x's.

Sum of the first n natural numbers

You probably know that the **natural numbers** are the positive whole numbers, i.e. 1, 2, 3, 4...

They form a very simple arithmetic progression with $a = 1$ and $d = 1$. So you could find the sum to any number of terms using one of the sum formulas from the previous pages. But there's actually a separate formula that's normally used for doing this.

The sum of the first n natural numbers is: $S_n = \frac{1}{2}n(n + 1)$

This formula can be easily derived from the previous sum formulas just by plugging in values, like this:

The sum of the first n natural numbers looks like this:

$$S_n = 1 + 2 + 3 + \ldots + (n - 2) + (n - 1) + n$$

So $a = 1$, $l = n$ and also $n = n$.

$$S_n = n \times \frac{(a + l)}{2} \longrightarrow S_n = \frac{1}{2}n(n + 1)$$

You can also derive the formula from first principles — the proof is almost identical to the one for a general arithmetic series on p.74.

- $S_n = 1 + 2 + 3 + \ldots + (n - 2) + (n - 1) + n$ ①
- Rewrite ① with the terms reversed:
  $S_n = n + (n - 1) + (n - 2) + \ldots + 3 + 2 + 1$ ②
- ①+② gives:

$$2S_n = (n + 1) + (n + 1) + (n + 1) + \ldots + (n + 1) + (n + 1) + (n + 1)$$

$$\Rightarrow 2S_n = n(n + 1)$$

$$\Rightarrow \mathbf{S_n = \frac{1}{2}n(n + 1)}$$

Tip: It's unlikely that you'd be asked to prove any of these sum formulas, but stranger things have happened. So it's worth making sure you know these steps.

Example 1

Find the sum of the first 100 natural numbers.

$$S_n = \frac{1}{2}n(n + 1)$$

$$S_{100} = \frac{1}{2} \times 100 \times 101$$

$$S_{100} = 5050$$

Sum of the first 100 natural numbers = **5050**

Comment: Easy peasy.

Example 2

The sum of the first k natural numbers is 861. Find the value of k.

- Form an equation in k:

$$\frac{1}{2}k(k+1) = 861$$

- Expand the brackets and rearrange:

$$k^2 + k = 1722$$
$$k^2 + k - 1722 = 0$$

- So we have a quadratic in k to solve.
  We're looking for a whole number for k, so it should factorise.

$$k^2 + k - 1722 = 0$$
$$(k \qquad)(k \qquad) = 0$$

- It looks tricky to factorise, but notice that '$b = 1$', so we're just looking for two numbers that are 1 apart and multiply to 1722.

$$(k + 42)(k - 41) = 0$$
$$k = -42 \text{ or } k = 41$$

- We can ignore the negative solution here, so the answer is $k = 41$.

Tip: In this question we have k numbers added together, so an answer of $k = -42$ wouldn't make any sense.

Exercise 2.3

Q1 Find the sum of the first: a) 10, b) 2000 natural numbers.

Q2 Find $\sum_{n=1}^{32} n$.

Q3 Find $\sum_{n=1}^{10} n$ and $\sum_{n=1}^{20} n$. Hence find $\sum_{n=11}^{20} n$.

Q3 Hint: This uses a handy little trick for finding series sums that don't start from $n = 1$.

Q4 Frazer draws one dot in the first square of his calendar for July, two dots in the second square, and so on up to 31 dots in the last day of the month. How many dots does he draw in total?

Q5 The sum of the first n natural numbers is 66. Find n.

Q6 Find k if $\sum_{n=1}^{k} n = 120$.

Q7 Find the sum of the series 16 + 17 + 18 + ... + 35.

Q8 How many natural numbers are needed for the sum to exceed 1 000 000?

Q9 Laura puts 1p in her jar one day, 2p in the next day, 3p in on the third day, etc. How many days will it take her to collect over £10?

3. Geometric Sequences & Series

Learning Objectives:

- Be able to recognise geometric sequences and series.
- Know and be able to use the formula for the general term of a geometric sequence or series.
- Know and be able to use the formula for the sum of the first n terms of a geometric sequence or series.
- Be able to recognise convergent geometric series and find their sum to infinity.

You've just seen how to find the general term and the sum of a number of terms for arithmetic sequences and series.
Now you'll do the same thing for geometric sequences and series.

Geometric sequences

In the last section you came across **arithmetic** sequences, where you get from one term to the next by **adding** a fixed amount each time.

They have a **first term** (a), and the amount you add to get from one term to the next is called the **common difference** (d).

With **geometric sequences**, rather than adding, you get from one term to the next by **multiplying** by a **constant** called the **common ratio** (r).

- This is a **geometric sequence** where you find each term by **multiplying** the previous term by 2:

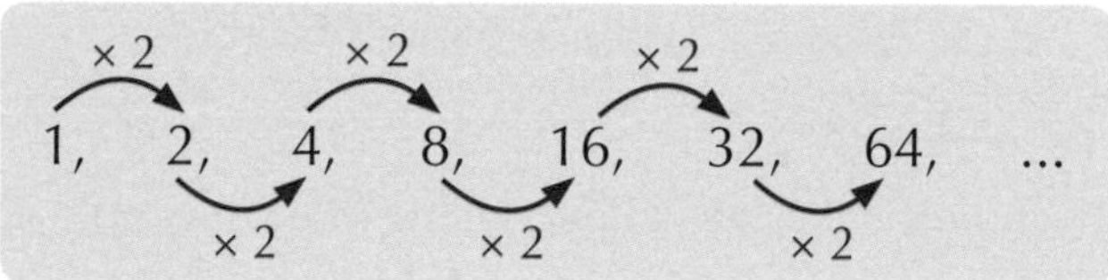

- If the common ratio is **negative**, the signs of the sequence will **alternate**. For this geometric sequence the common ratio is –3. → 2, –6, 18, –54, 162, –486, ...
- The common ratio might **not** be a **whole number**. Here, it's $\frac{3}{4}$. → $16, 12, 9, \frac{27}{4}, \frac{81}{16}, \frac{243}{64}, \ldots$

Tip: Geometric sequences are also called **geometric progressions**.

You get each term by multiplying the first term by the common ratio some number of times. In other words, each term is the **first term** multiplied by **some power** of the **common ratio**.

This is how you describe geometric sequences using **algebra**:

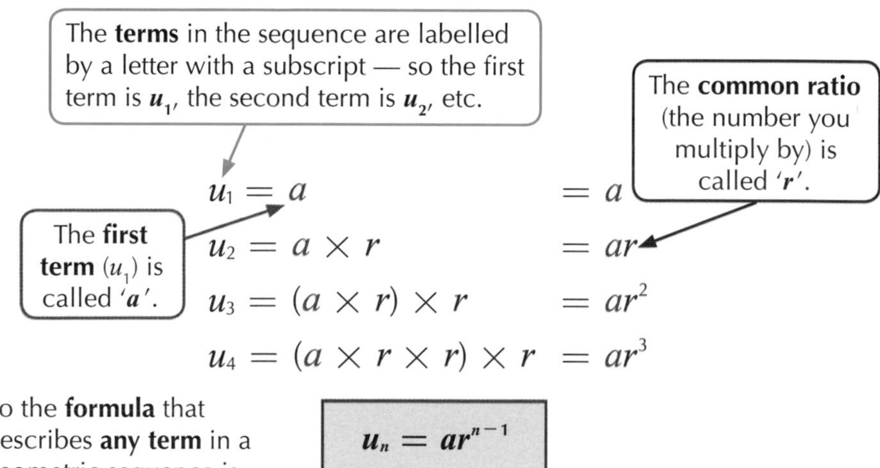

The **terms** in the sequence are labelled by a letter with a subscript — so the first term is u_1, the second term is u_2, etc.
The **common ratio** (the number you multiply by) is called 'r'.
The **first term** (u_1) is called 'a'.
$u_1 = a = a$
$u_2 = a \times r = ar$
$u_3 = (a \times r) \times r = ar^2$
$u_4 = (a \times r \times r) \times r = ar^3$

Tip: In the first sequence at the top of the page (1, 2, 4, 8, ...) $a = 1$ and $r = 2$.

Tip: The term u_n is called the 'n^{th} term', or '**general term**' of the sequence. This formula for the general term is in the formula booklet.

So the **formula** that describes **any term** in a geometric sequence is:

$$u_n = ar^{n-1}$$

If you know the values of a and r, you can substitute them into the **general formula** to find an expression that describes the whole sequence:

Example

A chessboard has a 1p piece on the first square, 2p on the second square, 4p on the third, 8p on the fourth and so on until the board is full.
Find a formula for the amount of money on each square.

- This is a **geometric sequence**: $u_1 = 1$, $u_2 = 2$, $u_3 = 4$, $u_4 = 8$...
- You get each term in the sequence by **multiplying** the previous one by **2**.
- So $\boldsymbol{a}$ **= 1** (because you start with 1p on the first square) and $\boldsymbol{r}$ **= 2**.
- Then the **formula** for the amount of money on each square is:

$$u_n = ar^{n-1} = 1 \times (2^{n-1}) = 2^{n-1}$$

$$u_n = 2^{n-1}$$

Tip: The trick with questions like this is to recognise that you're being asked about a geometric sequence.

You can also use the formula to find the **first term** a, the **common ratio** r or a **particular term** in the sequence, given other information about the sequence:

Examples

a) Find the 5th term in the geometric sequence 1, 3, 9, ...

- First find the common ratio r. Each term is the previous term multiplied by r, so you find the common ratio by dividing consecutive terms:

$$\text{second term} = \text{first term} \times r \;\Rightarrow\; r = \frac{\text{second term}}{\text{first term}} = \frac{3}{1} = 3$$

- Then find the 5th term. The 3rd term is 9, so:

4th term = 3rd term × r = 9 × 3 = 27
5th term = 4th term × r = 27 × 3 = 81

Tip: You can choose any two consecutive terms — e.g. dividing the third term by the second will also give you r.

Tip: Working up from the last term you know is a good method for finding a couple more terms in the sequence, but when you're asked for a higher term you're better off using the method in example b).

b) A geometric sequence has first term 2 and common ratio 1.2.
Find the 15th term in the sequence to 3 significant figures.

$a = 2$ and $r = 1.2$, and the formula for the nth term is $u_n = ar^{n-1}$

So $u_n = ar^{n-1} = 2 \times (1.2)^{n-1}$

Then the 15th term is $u_{15} = 2 \times (1.2)^{14} = 2 \times 12.839... = 25.7$ to 3 s.f.

c) A geometric sequence has a first term 25 and 10th term 80.
Calculate the common ratio. Give your answer to 3 significant figures.

$a = 25$, so the nth term is given by $u_n = ar^{n-1} = 25r^{n-1}$.

The 10th term is $80 = u_{10} = 25r^9$

$$80 = 25r^9 \;\Rightarrow\; r^9 = \frac{80}{25} \;\Rightarrow\; r = \sqrt[9]{\frac{80}{25}} = 1.137... = 1.14 \text{ to 3 s.f.}$$

Tip: Make sure you know how to find the nth root on your calculator — and remember, $\sqrt[n]{x}$ is the same as $x^{\frac{1}{n}}$.

d) The 8th term of a geometric sequence is 4374 and the common ratio is 3.
What is the first term?

The common ratio $r = 3$, so the nth term is $u_n = ar^{n-1} = a(3)^{n-1}$.

Then the 8th term is $4374 = a(3)^7 = 2187a \;\Rightarrow\; a = \frac{4374}{2187} = 2$

Exercise 3.1

Q1 A geometric progression has first term 12 and common ratio 2. Find the tenth term in the progression.

Q2 Find the seventh term in the geometric progression 2, 3, 4.5, 6.75 ...

Q3 The sixth and seventh terms of a geometric sequence are 2187 and 6561 respectively. What is the first term?

Q4 A geometric sequence is 24, 12, 6, ... What is the 9th term?

Q5 The 14th term of a geometric progression is 9216. The first term is 1.125. Calculate the common ratio.

Q6 Hint: Write yourself an equation or inequality and then solve it using logs. Have a flick through Chapter 3 if you need a reminder of how to use logs.

Q6 The first and second terms of a geometric progression are 1 and 1.1 respectively. How many terms in this sequence are less than 4?

Q7 A geometric progression has a common ratio of 0.6. If the first term is 5, what is the difference between the 10th term and the 15th term? Give your answer to 5 d.p.

Q8 A geometric sequence has a first term of 25 000 and a common ratio of 0.8. Which term is the first to be below 1000?

Q9 A geometric sequence is 5, –5, 5, –5, 5, ... Give the common ratio.

Q10 The first three terms of a geometric progression are $\frac{1}{4}$, $\frac{3}{16}$ and $\frac{9}{64}$.

a) Calculate the common ratio.

b) Find the 8th term. Give your answer as a fraction.

Q11 The 7th term of a geometric sequence is 196.608 and the common ratio is 0.8. What is the first term?

Q12 A geometric progression has third term 36 and sixth term 972.

a) Calculate the common ration of the progression.

b) Find the first term of the progression.

Q13 Hint: The modulus of a number is just its size ignoring the sign, so the modulus of –1 is 1. A number with modulus less than 1 is between –1 and 1.

Q13 3, –2.4, 1.92,... is a geometric progression.

a) What is the common ratio?

b) How many terms are there in the sequence before you reach a term with modulus less than 1?

Geometric series

Geometric series work just like geometric sequences (they have a **first term** and a **common ratio**), but they're written as a **sum of terms** rather than a list:

geometric sequence:	geometric series:
3, 6, 12, 24, 48, ...	3 + 6 + 12 + 24 + 48 + ...

Sometimes you'll need to find the **sum** of the **first few terms** of a geometric series:

- The sum of the **first *n* terms** is called S_n.
- S_n can be written in terms of the first term ***a*** and the common ratio ***r***:
  $$S_n = u_1 + u_2 + u_3 + u_4 + ... + u_n = a + ar + ar^2 + ar^3 + ... + ar^{n-1}$$
- There's a nice **formula** for finding S_n that doesn't involve loads of adding. It's worth learning the **proof** of the formula — luckily it's fairly straightforward:

For any geometric sequence:
$$S_n = a + ar + ar^2 + ar^3 + ... + ar^{n-2} + ar^{n-1} \quad ①$$
Multiplying this by r gives:
$$rS_n = ar + ar^2 + ar^3 + ... + ar^{n-2} + ar^{n-1} + ar^n \quad ②$$
Subtract equation ② from equation ①: $S_n - rS_n = a - ar^n$

Factorise both sides: $(1 - r)S_n = a(1 - r^n)$

Then divide through by $(1 - r)$: $S_n = \frac{a(1 - r^n)}{1 - r}$

So the sum of the first n terms of a geometric series is:

$$S_n = \frac{a(1 - r^n)}{1 - r}$$

This formula is given in the formula booklet (but the proof isn't).

Tip: Remember — a sequence becomes a series when you add the terms to find the sum.

Tip: Geometric series can be infinite sums (i.e. they can go on forever). We're just adding up bits of them for now, but summing an infinite series is covered on page 87.

Tip: You could also subtract equation ① from equation ② to get:
$$S_n = \frac{a(r^n - 1)}{r - 1}$$
Both versions are correct.

Examples

a) A geometric series has first term 3.5 and common ratio 5. Find the sum of the first 6 terms.

You're told that $a = 3.5$ and $r = 5$, and you're looking for the sum of the first 6 terms, so just stick these values into the formula for S_6:

$$S_6 = \frac{a(1 - r^6)}{1 - r} = \frac{3.5(1 - 5^6)}{1 - 5} = 13\,671$$

b) The first two terms in a geometric series are 20, 22. To 2 decimal places, the sum of the first *k* terms of the series is 271.59. Find *k*.

$a = 20$, $r = \frac{\text{second term}}{\text{first term}} = \frac{22}{20} = 1.1$, so put these into the sum formula:

$$S_k = \frac{a(1 - r^k)}{1 - r} = \frac{20(1 - (1.1)^k)}{1 - 1.1} = -200(1 - (1.1)^k)$$

$$\text{So } 271.59 = -200(1-(1.1)^k) \Rightarrow -\frac{271.59}{200} - 1 = -(1.1)^k$$
$$\Rightarrow -2.35795 = -(1.1)^k$$
$$\Rightarrow 2.35795 = 1.1^k$$
$$\Rightarrow \log(2.35795) = k\log(1.1)$$
$$\Rightarrow k = \frac{\log(2.35795)}{\log(1.1)} = 9$$

Tip: Look back at p.52 for a reminder of how to use the laws of logs.

Tip: You're looking for a number of terms so the answer must be a positive integer.

Sigma notation

You saw on page 77 that the **sum** of the first n **terms** of a series (S_n) can also be written using **sigma (Σ) notation**.
For geometric series, sigma notation looks like this:

$$S_n = u_1 + u_2 + u_3 + \ldots + u_n = a + ar + ar^2 + \ldots + ar^{n-1} = \sum_{k=0}^{n-1} ar^k$$

So, using the formula from the previous page, the sum of the first n terms can be written:

$$\sum_{k=0}^{n-1} ar^k = \frac{a(1-r^n)}{1-r}$$

Tip: Remember, Σ just means sum (it's the Greek letter for S). In this case, it's the sum of ar^k from $k = 0$ to $k = n - 1$. Be careful with the limits — it's $n - 1$ on top of the Σ, but the sum is S_n.

Tip: The sum of the first n terms can also be expressed as $\sum_{k=1}^{n} ar^{k-1} = \frac{a(1-r^n)}{1-r}$.

Example

$a + ar + ar^2 + \ldots$ is a geometric series, and $\sum_{k=0}^{4} ar^k = 85.2672$.
Given that $r = -1.8$, find the first term a.

You've got the sum of the first 5 terms:

$$85.2672 = \sum_{k=0}^{4} ar^k = S_5 = \frac{a(1-r^5)}{1-r}$$

So plug the value of r into the formula:

$$85.2672 = \frac{a(1-r^5)}{1-r} = \frac{a(1-(-1.8)^5)}{1-(-1.8)} = a\frac{19.89568}{2.8} = 7.1056a$$
$$\Rightarrow a = \frac{85.2672}{7.1056} = 12$$

Exercise 3.2

Q1 The first term of a geometric sequence is 8 and the common ratio is 1.2. Find the sum of the first 15 terms.

Q2 A geometric series has first term $a = 25$ and common ratio $r = 0.7$. Find $\sum_{k=0}^{9} 25(0.7)^k$.

Q3 The sum of the first n terms of a geometric series is 196 605. The common ratio of the series is 2 and the first term is 3. Find n.

Q4 A geometric progression starts with 4, 5, 6.25. The first x terms add up to 103.2 to 4 significant figures. Find x.

Q5 The 3rd term of a geometric series is 6 and the 8th term is 192. Find:

a) the common ratio b) the first term

c) the sum of the first 15 terms

Q6 $k + 10, k, 2k - 21, ...$ is a geometric progression, k is a positive constant.

a) Show that $k^2 - k - 210 = 0$.

b) Hence show that $k = 15$.

c) Find the common ratio of this series.

d) Find the sum of the first 10 terms.

Q6 a) Hint: The ratio of the first term to the second is the same as the ratio of the second term to the third.

Q7 The first three terms of a geometric series are $1, x, x^2$. The sum of these terms is 3 and each term has a different value.

a) Find x. b) Calculate the sum of the first 7 terms.

Q8 $a, ar, ar^2, ar^3, ...$ is a geometric progression. Given that $a = 7.2$ and $r = 0.38$, find $\sum_{k=0}^{9} ar^k$.

Q9 The sum of the first eight terms of a geometric series is 1.2. Find the first term of the series, given that the common ratio is $-\frac{1}{3}$.

Q10 $a, -2a, 4a, -8a, ...$ is a geometric sequence. Given that $\sum_{k=0}^{12} a(-2)^k = -5735.1$, find a.

Convergent geometric series

Convergent sequences

Some geometric sequences **tend towards zero** — in other words, they get closer and closer to zero (but they never actually reach it). For example:

$$1, \frac{1}{2}, \frac{1}{4}, \frac{1}{8}, \frac{1}{16}, ... \to 0$$

Tip: Look back at page 69 for more on convergent sequences.

Tip: The arrow here means 'tends to'.

- Sequences like this are called **convergent** — the terms **converge** (get closer and closer) to a **limit** (the number they get close to).
- Geometric sequences either **converge to zero** or **don't converge** at all.
- A sequence that doesn't converge is called **divergent**.
- A geometric sequence $a, ar, ar^2, ar^3, ...$ will converge to **zero** if each term is **closer** to zero than the one before.
- This happens when $-1 < r < 1$. You can write this as $|r| < 1$, where $|r|$ is the modulus of r (the size of r ignoring its sign), so:

$$a, ar, ar^2, ar^3, ... \to 0 \text{ when } |r| < 1$$

Tip: You ignore the sign of r because you can still have a convergent sequence when r is negative. In that case the terms will alternate between > 0 and < 0, but they'll still be getting closer and closer to zero.

Convergent series

- When you **sum** a geometric sequence that converges to zero you get a **convergent series.**
- Because each term in the geometric sequence is getting closer and closer to zero, you're **adding smaller and smaller** amounts each time. So the sum gets **closer and closer** to a certain number, but never reaches it — this is the **limit** of the series.

For example, the **sum** of the **convergent sequence** $1, \frac{1}{2}, \frac{1}{4}, \frac{1}{8}, \frac{1}{16}, \ldots$ gets closer and closer to 2:

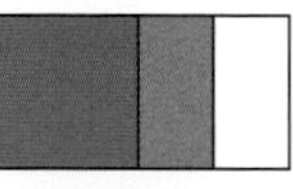

$S_1 = 1$

The more terms you add, the closer you get to the **limit** of the **series**.

$S_2 = 1 + \frac{1}{2} = 1\frac{1}{2} = 1.5$

Tip: This is the sum of the sequence from the previous page.

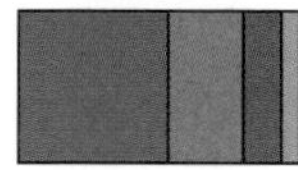

$S_3 = 1 + \frac{1}{2} + \frac{1}{4} = 1\frac{3}{4} = 1.75$

$S_4 = 1 + \frac{1}{2} + \frac{1}{4} + \frac{1}{8} = 1\frac{7}{8} = 1.875$

$S_5 = 1 + \frac{1}{2} + \frac{1}{4} + \frac{1}{8} + \frac{1}{16} = 1\frac{15}{16} = 1.9375$

Because the terms are getting **closer to 0**, the sum will never reach 2.

As you **add more terms**, the sum is **tending to 2**.

$$\mathbf{1 + \frac{1}{2} + \frac{1}{4} + \frac{1}{8} + \frac{1}{16} + \ldots = 2}$$

- So when the **sequence** $a, ar, ar^2, ar^3, \ldots$ **converges** to zero, the **series** $a + ar + ar^2 + ar^3 + \ldots$ **converges** to a **limit.**
- Like sequences, series converge when $|r| < 1$.

Tip: Not all sequences that tend to zero produce a convergent series — this rule is only true for geometric progressions.
For example, the series $1 + \frac{1}{2} + \frac{1}{3} + \frac{1}{4} + \frac{1}{5} + \ldots$ diverges.

Geometric series
$a + ar + ar^2 + ar^3 + \ldots$
with $|r| < 1$ are **convergent**

Geometric series
$a + ar + ar^2 + ar^3 + \ldots$
with $|r| \geq 1$ are **divergent**

Examples

Determine whether or not each sequence below is convergent.

a) 1, 2, 4, 8, 16, ... **b) 81, –27, 9, –3, 1, ...**

a) $r = \frac{2^{nd} \text{ term}}{1^{st} \text{ term}} = \frac{2}{1} = 2$, $|r| = |2| = 2 > 1$, so the series is not convergent

b) $r = \frac{2^{nd} \text{ term}}{1^{st} \text{ term}} = \frac{-27}{81} = -\frac{1}{3}$, $|r| = \left|-\frac{1}{3}\right| = \frac{1}{3} < 1$, the series is convergent

Tip: You can usually spot straight away if a geometric series is convergent — the terms will be getting closer and closer to zero. But you still need to check $|r| < 1$ to prove it.

Summing to infinity

When a series is **convergent** you can find its **sum to infinity**.

- The sum to infinity is called S_∞ — it's the **limit** of S_n as $n \to \infty$.
- This just means that the sum of the first n terms of the series (S_n) gets closer and closer to S_∞ the more terms you add (the bigger n gets).
- In other words, it's the **number** that the **series converges to**.

Example

A geometric series has first term 2 and common ratio $\frac{1}{2}$. Find the sum to infinity of the series.

$u_1 = 2 \longrightarrow S_1 = 2$

$u_2 = 2 \times \frac{1}{2} = 1 \longrightarrow S_2 = 2 + 1 = 3$

$u_3 = 1 \times \frac{1}{2} = \frac{1}{2} \longrightarrow S_3 = 2 + 1 + \frac{1}{2} = 3\frac{1}{2}$

$u_4 = \frac{1}{2} \times \frac{1}{2} = \frac{1}{4} \longrightarrow S_4 = 2 + 1 + \frac{1}{2} + \frac{1}{4} = 3\frac{3}{4}$

$u_5 = \frac{1}{4} \times \frac{1}{2} = \frac{1}{8} \longrightarrow S_5 = 2 + 1 + \frac{1}{2} + \frac{1}{4} + \frac{1}{8} = 3\frac{7}{8}$

These values are getting closer (**converging**) to 4. So the sum to infinity is 4.

These values are getting **smaller** each time.

You can show this **graphically**. The line on the graph is getting **closer and closer** to 4, but it'll never actually get there.

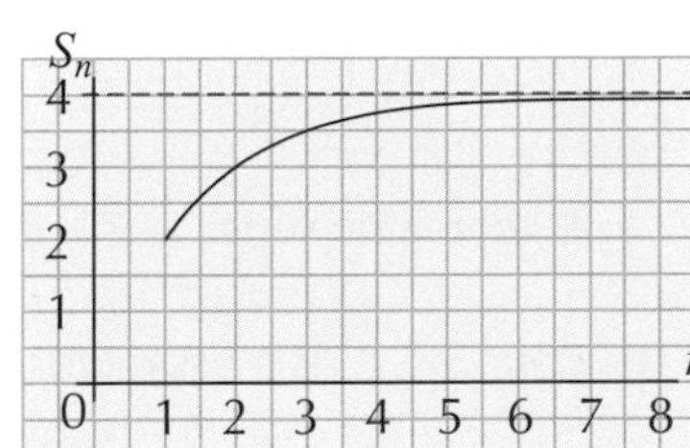

Tip: Luckily you don't have to find a list of sums like this to get the sum to infinity — there's a nifty formula for working it out further down the page. This example is just to show you what's going on when a series converges.

There's a **formula** you use to work out the **sum to infinity** of a geometric series. It comes from the formula for the sum of the first n terms (see p.83):

- The sum of the **first n terms** of a geometric series is $S_n = \dfrac{a(1 - r^n)}{1 - r}$
- If $|r| < 1$ and n is very, very big, then r^n will be very, very **small**, i.e. $r^n \to 0$ as $n \to \infty$.
- This means $(1 - r^n)$ will get really **close to 1**, so $(1 - r^n) \to 1$ as $n \to \infty$.
- Putting this back into the sum formula gives $S_n \to \dfrac{a \times 1}{1 - r} = \dfrac{a}{1 - r}$ as $n \to \infty$.
- So:

$$S_\infty = \frac{a}{1 - r}$$

This formula is given in the formula booklet.

Tip: Remember, $|r| < 1$ just means $-1 < r < 1$.

Examples

a) **A geometric series has first term 2 and common ratio $\frac{1}{2}$. Find the sum to infinity of the series.**

$|r| = \left|\frac{1}{2}\right| = \frac{1}{2} < 1$, so the series converges and you can find its sum to infinity using the formula for S_∞:

$$S_\infty = \frac{a}{1 - r} = \frac{2}{1 - \frac{1}{2}} = \frac{2}{\frac{1}{2}} = 4$$

Tip: This is the same as the example above, but this time the sum to infinity is worked out using the formula.

b) Find the sum to infinity of the series 8 + 2 + 0.5 + 0.125 + ...

First find a and r as before: $a = 8$, $r = \frac{2^{nd}\text{ term}}{1^{st}\text{ term}} = \frac{2}{8} = 0.25$

Again, $|r| < 1$.

Now find the sum to infinity: $S_\infty = \frac{a}{1-r} = \frac{8}{1-0.25} = \frac{32}{3} = 10\frac{2}{3}$

Divergent series **don't** have a **sum to infinity**.

Because the terms aren't tending to zero, the size of the sum will just keep increasing as you add more terms, so there is **no limit** to the sum.

Exercise 3.3

Q1 Hint: If $r = 1$, the sequence is just the same term repeated, so it diverges. If $r = -1$, the sequence alternates between two terms forever.

Q1 State which of these sequences will converge and which will not.

a) $1, 1.1, 1.21, 1.331, \ldots$

b) $0.8, 0.8^2, 0.8^3, \ldots$

c) $1, \frac{1}{4}, \frac{1}{16}, \frac{1}{64}, \ldots$

d) $3, \frac{9}{2}, \frac{27}{4}, \ldots$

e) $1, -\frac{1}{2}, \frac{1}{4}, -\frac{1}{8}, \frac{1}{16}, \ldots$

f) $5, 5, 5, 5, 5, \ldots$

Q2 A geometric series is $9 + 8.1 + 7.29 + \ldots$ Calculate the sum to infinity.

Q3 $a, ar, ar^2, \ldots$ is a geometric sequence. Given that $S_\infty = 2a$, find r.

Q4 The sum to infinity of a geometric progression is 13.5 and the first 3 terms add up to 13.

a) Find the common ratio r

b) Find the first term a.

Q5 $a + ar + ar^2 + \ldots$ is a geometric series. $ra = 3$ and $S_\infty = 12$. Find r and a.

Q6 The sum to infinity of a geometric series is 10 and the first term is 6.

a) Find the common ratio.

b) What is the 5th term?

Q7 The 2nd term of a geometric progression is –48 and the 5th term is 0.75. Find:

a) the common ratio

b) the first term

c) the sum to infinity

Q8 Hint: Find a mathematical statement to express the first sentence.

Q8 The sum of the terms after the 10th term of a convergent geometric series is less than 1% of the sum to infinity.
The first term is positive. Show that the common ratio $|r| < 0.631$.

4. Sequences & Series Problems

You should by now have a handy 'toolbox' of formulas that can be used for arithmetic and geometric progressions. Now it's time to put those formulas to use and solve problems involving sequences and series.

Learning Objective:

- Be able to apply the formulas that can be used with arithmetic and geometric sequences and series to solve problems.

Sequences & series problems

First, a reminder of the formulas you've seen already:

Arithmetic Progressions

$$u_n = a + (n-1)d$$

$$S_n = \frac{n}{2}[2a + (n-1)d] = n \times \frac{(a+l)}{2}$$

Geometric Progressions

$$u_n = ar^{n-1}$$

$$S_n = \frac{a(1-r^n)}{1-r}$$

$$S_\infty = \frac{a}{1-r}$$

Tip: Remember — all these formulas are in the formula booklet, so you don't need to learn them.

Some problems will require you to use a **combination** of these formulas to find one or more missing values.

To do this, you'll often have to form a set of **simultaneous equations**.
For a geometric progression, you might need to solve a **quadratic equation** to find a solution to these simultaneous equations.

Example 1

The sum of the first five terms of an arithmetic progression is 5, and the sixth term is 13. Find the eighth term in the progression.

- The question gives you a particular term and a sum of terms, so use the formulas:

$$u_n = a + (n-1)d \qquad S_n = \frac{n}{2}[2a + (n-1)d]$$

- Plugging in the values given in the question gives:

$$u_6 = a + (6-1)d = 13 \quad \text{and} \quad S_5 = 5 = \frac{5}{2}[2a + (5-1)d]$$

- Which simplify to:

$a + 5d = 13$ ...call this ① $\qquad a + 2d = 1$ ...call this ②

- Solve the simultaneous equations:

① – ② $\Rightarrow 3d = 12 \Rightarrow d = 4$

Substituting $d = 4$ in ② $\Rightarrow a + 2(4) = 1$
$a = 1 - 8 = -7$

- Finally, use $a + (n-1)d$ to find the 8th term:

$$u_8 = a + (n-1)d = -7 + (7 \times 4) = 21$$

Tip: Look at what you're told in the question, and what you're being asked to find, and use the corresponding formulas.

Example 2

The sum to infinity of a geometric series is –32. The second term of the progression is –8. Find the common ratio of the progression.

- Use the formula for the nth term of a geometric progression: $u_n = ar^{n-1}$ and the sum to infinity of a geometric series: $S_\infty = \frac{a}{1-r}$
- Plugging in the information from the question gives:

$u_2 = ar = -8$ ...call this ①

$S_\infty = -32 = \frac{a}{1-r}$ ...call this ②

- Rearrange ① into the form $a = -\frac{8}{r}$ in order to eliminate a from ②:

$$-32 = \frac{\left(\frac{-8}{r}\right)}{1-r}$$

$$-32(1-r) = \frac{(-8)}{r}$$

$$-32r + 32r^2 = -8$$

$$4r^2 - 4r + 1 = 0$$

$$(2r-1)^2 = 0$$

$$2r = 1$$

$$\Rightarrow r = \frac{1}{2}$$

Tip: If you were trying to find a, then you would rearrange to eliminate r instead.

Tip: This quadratic only has one root. If you get a quadratic with two roots, pick the one for which $|r| < 1$, as a series with a sum to infinity must be convergent.

Exercise 4.1

Q1 The sum of the first 4 terms of an arithmetic progression is 24 and the 5th term is 11. Find:

a) the common difference of the progression,

b) the first term,

c) the 7th term.

Q2 5 terms form an arithmetic progression adding up to 155. The last term is 47.

a) Calculate the five terms.

b) If the progression continues, which is the first term to exceed 200?

Q3 The 5th, 6th, and 7th terms of an arithmetic progression add up to 111 and the 10th term is 57.

a) Find the first term and the common difference.

b) What is the 15th term?

Q4 In an arithmetic progression the 1st, 2nd and 7th terms add up to zero. Show that the 10th term is 10 times larger than the 4th term.

Q5 In an arithmetic progression the 8th term is twice the 4th term.

a) Show that the common difference is the same value as the first term.

b) If the 30th term is 60, show that the progression is the set of positive even numbers.

c) Find the sum of the terms from the 6th to the 30th inclusive.

Q6 The sum to infinity of a geometric progression is 16 and the second term of the sequence is 4.

a) Find the common ratio.

b) What is the first term?

c) Which is the first term that is below 0.01?

Q7 The sum to infinity of a geometric progression is 40.5 and the first four terms add up to 40. Find the first four terms, given that they are all positive.

Q8 The sum to infinity of a geometric progression with non-zero terms is four times the value of the first term. Find the common ratio.

Q9 The sum to infinity of a geometric progression is 1562.5 and the sum of the first three terms is 1225.

a) Calculate the common ratio.

b) The nth term of the series is u_n.

Work out $\sum_{n=4}^{\infty} u_n$.

Q10 The eighth, fourth and second terms of an arithmetic progression form the first three terms of a geometric series.

The arithmetic progression has first term A and common difference d, and the geometric progression has first term G and common ratio r.

a) Given that $d \neq 0$, find the value of r.

b) Given that $A = 2$, find the sum to infinity of the geometric progression.

Q10 Hint: Remember that the common ratio of a geometric progression can be found by dividing any term of the progression by the previous term.

5. Binomial Expansions

Learning Objectives:

- Be able to use Pascal's triangle to find the coefficients of a binomial expansion.
- Be able to find binomial coefficients using factorials and using the notation $\binom{n}{r}$ or ${}^nC_r$.
- Be able to use the formula to expand binomials of the form $(1 + x)^n$.
- Be able to use the formula to expand binomials of the form $(1 + ax)^n$.

Binomials are just polynomials that only have two terms (the 'bi' and 'poly' bits come from the Greek words for 'two' and 'many'). Binomial expansions are all about multiplying out brackets with two terms. This section has a few methods you can use on different types of expansions.

Pascal's triangle

- A **binomial expansion** is what you get when you **multiply out the brackets** of a polynomial with two terms, like $(1 + x)^5$ or $(2 - 3x)^8$.
- It would take ages to multiply out a bracket like this by hand if the power was really big — fortunately binomial expansions **follow a pattern**:

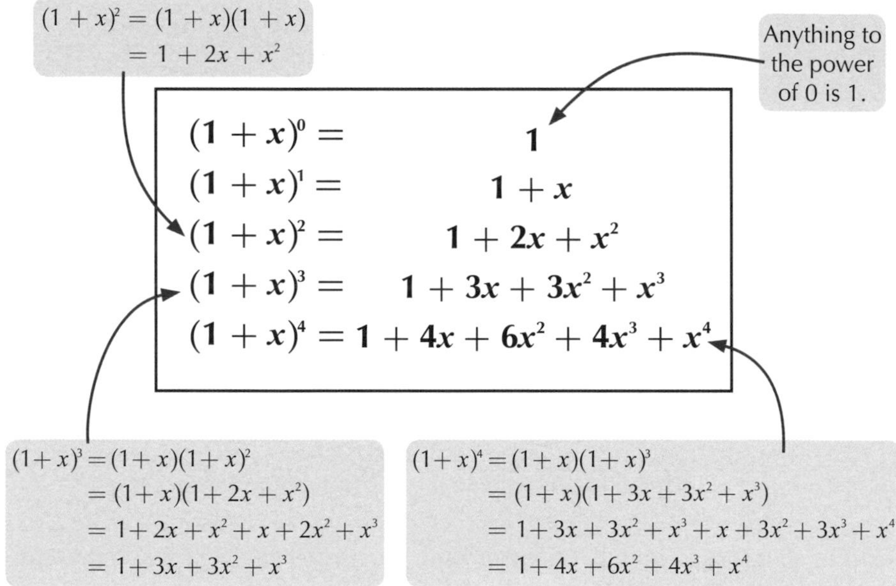

$(1 + x)^2 = (1 + x)(1 + x)$
$= 1 + 2x + x^2$
Anything to the power of 0 is 1.
$(1 + x)^0 = 1$
$(1 + x)^1 = 1 + x$
$(1 + x)^2 = 1 + 2x + x^2$
$(1 + x)^3 = 1 + 3x + 3x^2 + x^3$
$(1 + x)^4 = 1 + 4x + 6x^2 + 4x^3 + x^4$
$(1+x)^3 = (1+x)(1+x)^2$
$= (1+x)(1+2x+x^2)$
$= 1+2x+x^2+x+2x^2+x^3$
$= 1+3x+3x^2+x^3$
$(1+x)^4 = (1+x)(1+x)^3$
$= (1+x)(1+3x+3x^2+x^3)$
$= 1+3x+3x^2+x^3+x+3x^2+3x^3+x^4$
$= 1+4x+6x^2+4x^3+x^4$

Tip: When you expand a binomial you usually write it in increasing powers of x, starting with x^0 and going up to x^n.

Tip: For the moment we're just looking at $(1 + x)^n$. Binomials of the form $(a + bx)^n$, like $(2 - 3x)^8$, are covered on pages 97-100.

A Frenchman called Blaise Pascal spotted the pattern in the **coefficients** and wrote them down in a **triangle**, so it's imaginatively known as '**Pascal's Triangle**'. The pattern's easy — each number is the **sum** of the two above it:

Tip: The triangle is symmetrical, so once you've got the first half of the coefficients you don't need to work out the rest.

1
1 1
1 2 1
1 3 3 + 1
1 4 6 = 4 1

So the next line is: **1 5 10 10 5 1**

Giving: $\mathbf{(1 + x)^5 = 1 + 5x + 10x^2 + 10x^3 + 5x^4 + x^5}$.

If you're expanding a binomial with a power that's not too huge, writing out a quick **Pascal's triangle** is a good way to **find the coefficients**.

Example

Find the binomial expansion of $(1 + x)^6$.

Draw **Pascal's triangle** — you're raising the bracket to the **power of 6**, so go down to the **7th row**.

1
1 1
1 2 1
1 3 3 1
1 4 6 4 1
1 5 10 10 5 1
1 6 15 20 15 6 1

Write the answer out, getting the **coefficients** from the 7th row, and increasing the power of x from left to right:

$$(1 + x)^6 = 1 + 6x + 15x^2 + 20x^3 + 15x^4 + 6x^5 + x^6$$

Tip: Make sure you go down to the correct row — you need one more row than the power you're raising the bracket to.

Binomial expansions — $(1 + x)^n$

For expansions with **higher powers** you don't need to write out Pascal's triangle — there's a **formula** you can use instead:

$$(1 + x)^n = 1 + \frac{n}{1}x + \frac{n(n-1)}{1 \times 2}x^2 + \frac{n(n-1)(n-2)}{1 \times 2 \times 3}x^3 + ... + x^n$$

At first glance this looks a bit awful, but each term follows a pattern:

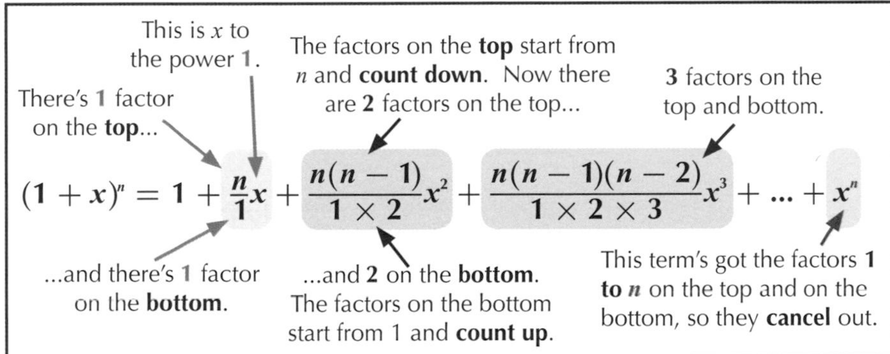

This is x to the power 1.
There's 1 factor on the top...
The factors on the top start from n and count down. Now there are 2 factors on the top...
3 factors on the top and bottom.
$(1 + x)^n = 1 + \frac{n}{1}x + \frac{n(n-1)}{1 \times 2}x^2 + \frac{n(n-1)(n-2)}{1 \times 2 \times 3}x^3 + ... + x^n$
...and there's 1 factor on the bottom.
...and 2 on the bottom. The factors on the bottom start from 1 and count up.
This term's got the factors 1 to n on the top and on the bottom, so they cancel out.

Tip: Try to remember the patterns from term to term — it should sink in if you get plenty of practice using it.

Once you get **halfway** along, the **factors** on the top and bottom start to **cancel**, and the coefficients repeat themselves (they're symmetrical):

$$(1 + x)^5 = 1 + \frac{5}{1}x + \frac{5 \times 4}{1 \times 2}x^2 + \frac{5 \times 4 \times 3}{1 \times 2 \times 3}x^3 + \frac{5 \times 4 \times 3 \times 2}{1 \times 2 \times 3 \times 4}x^4 + \frac{5 \times 4 \times 3 \times 2 \times 1}{1 \times 2 \times 3 \times 4 \times 5}x^5$$

$$= 1 + \frac{5}{1}x + \frac{5 \times 4}{1 \times 2}x^2 + \frac{5 \times 4}{1 \times 2}x^3 + \frac{5}{1}x^4 + x^5$$

$$= 1 + 5x + 10x^2 + 10x^3 + 5x^4 + x^5$$

Example

a) Expand $(1 + x)^{20}$, giving the first 4 terms only.

- The binomial formula is:

$$(1 + x)^n = 1 + \frac{n}{1}x + \frac{n(n-1)}{1 \times 2}x^2 + \frac{n(n-1)(n-2)}{1 \times 2 \times 3}x^3 + ... + x^n$$

- You're looking for $(1 + x)^{20}$, so $n = 20$:

$$(1 + x)^{20} = 1 + \frac{20}{1}x + \frac{20 \times 19}{1 \times 2}x^2 + \frac{20 \times 19 \times 18}{1 \times 2 \times 3}x^3 + ... + x^{20}$$

Tip: Make sure you write down your working — if you just bung the numbers straight into your calculator, you won't be able to spot if you've made a mistake.

- The first 4 terms are:

$$(1+x)^{20} = 1 + \frac{20}{1}x + \frac{\overset{10}{\cancel{20}} \times 19}{1 \times \cancel{2}}x^2 + \frac{\overset{10}{\cancel{20}} \times 19 \times \overset{6}{\cancel{18}}}{1 \times \cancel{2} \times \cancel{3}}x^3 + \dots$$
$$= 1 + 20x + (10 \times 19)x^2 + (10 \times 19 \times 6)x^3 + \dots$$
$$= 1 + 20x + 190x^2 + 1140x^3 + \dots$$

b) What is the term in x^7 in this expansion? Give your answer in its simplest form.

- The term in x^7 has 7 factors on the top of the coefficient, and 7 factors on the bottom.
- In this expansion n is 20, so on the top you count down from 20.
- Term in $x^7 = \frac{\cancel{20} \times 19 \times \cancel{18} \times 17 \times 16 \times 15 \times \cancel{14}}{1 \times \cancel{2} \times \cancel{3} \times \cancel{4} \times \cancel{5} \times \cancel{6} \times \cancel{7}}x^7$

$$= (19 \times 17 \times 16 \times 15)x^7$$
$$= 77\,520x^7$$

There are a few bits of **notation** you need to know that will make writing out the binomial formula a bit easier.

Factorials

- The product on the **bottom** of each binomial coefficient is $\mathbf{1 \times 2 \times \dots \times r}$, where r is the **power x is raised to** in that term.

Tip: $r! = 1 \times 2 \times \dots \times r$ is said 'r factorial'.

- This product can be written as a **factorial**: $\mathbf{r! = 1 \times 2 \times \dots \times r}$.
E.g. in the binomial expansion of $(1+x)^{20}$, the coefficient of the term in x^3 is:

$$\frac{20 \times 19 \times 18}{1 \times 2 \times 3} = \frac{20 \times 19 \times 18}{3!}$$

Tip: Here you've multiplied top and bottom by 17! — this is just so you can write the factors on the top as a factorial (you need to multiply all the way down to 1 to do this).

- In fact, you can write the **whole** coefficient using **factorials**.
For example, the coefficient of x^3 above is:

$$\frac{20 \times 19 \times 18}{1 \times 2 \times 3}$$
$$= \frac{20 \times 19 \times 18 \times 17 \times \dots \times 2 \times 1}{1 \times 2 \times 3 \times 1 \times 2 \times \dots \times 17}$$
$$= \frac{20 \times 19 \times \dots \times 1}{(1 \times 2 \times 3)(1 \times 2 \times \dots \times 17)}$$
$$= \frac{20!}{3!17!}$$

- For a general binomial expansion of $(1+x)^n$, the coefficient of x^r is:

$$\frac{n \times (n-1) \times \dots \times (n-(r-1))}{1 \times 2 \times \dots \times r}$$
$$= \frac{n \times (n-1) \times \dots \times (n-(r-1)) \times (n-r) \times \dots \times 2 \times 1}{1 \times 2 \times \dots \times r \times 1 \times 2 \times \dots \times (n-r)}$$
$$= \frac{n \times (n-1) \times \dots \times 1}{(1 \times 2 \times \dots \times r)(1 \times 2 \times \dots \times (n-r))}$$
$$= \frac{n!}{r!(n-r)!}$$

Tip: The two numbers on the bottom of the factorial fraction should always add up to the number on the top.

- So the terms in a **binomial expansion** of $\mathbf{(1+x)^n}$ are of the form:

$$\frac{n(n-1)(n-2)\dots(n-(r-1))}{1 \times 2 \times 3 \times \dots \times r}x^r = \frac{\mathbf{n!}}{\mathbf{r!(n-r)!}}x^r$$

n is the power you're raising the **bracket** to,
r is the power of x in the **term** the coefficient belongs to.

^nC_r notation

There are a couple of even **shorter ways** of writing the **binomial coefficients**:

$$\boxed{\frac{n!}{r!(n-r)!}} = \boxed{\binom{n}{r}} = \boxed{{}^nC_r}$$

There's a button on your calculator for finding this.

For example, going back to the coefficient of x^3 in the expansion of $(1 + x)^{20}$:

$$\frac{20 \times 19 \times 18}{1 \times 2 \times 3}x^3 = \frac{20!}{3!17!}x^3 = \binom{20}{3}x^3 = {}^{20}C_3x^3$$

So the **binomial formula** can be written using **any** of these notations, and you need to **be familiar with all of them**:

$$(1 + x)^n = 1 + \frac{n!}{1!(n-1)!}x + \frac{n!}{2!(n-2)!}x^2 + \frac{n!}{3!(n-3)!}x^3 + ... + x^n$$

$$(1 + x)^n = 1 + \binom{n}{1}x + \binom{n}{2}x^2 + \binom{n}{3}x^3 + ... + x^n$$

$$(1 + x)^n = 1 + {}^nC_1x + {}^nC_2x^2 + {}^nC_3x^3 + ... + x^n$$

- Most **calculators** will have an '**nCr**' button for finding binomial **coefficients**. To use it you put in n, press '**nCr**', then put in r.
- This is particularly handy if you're just looking for a **specific term** in a **binomial expansion** and you don't want to write the whole thing out.

Tip: This is in the formula booklet.

Tip: The C in ^nC_r stands for 'choose' — you say these coefficients 'n choose r', e.g. $\binom{3}{2}$ is '3 choose 2'. This is because the value of ^nC_r is the number of ways you can choose r items from a set of n items.

Tip: These coefficients will always come out as a positive integer — if you get a coefficient that isn't, then you know you've made a mistake somewhere.

Tip: If you get confused with which number's which, remember $n \geq r$.

Example

Find the 6th term of the expansion of $(1 + x)^8$.

- You're raising the **bracket** to the power of 8, so $n = 8$.
- The **6th term** is the x^5 term (the first term is $1 = x^0$, the second is the $x = x^1$ term and so on), so $r = 5$.
- So put '**8 nCr 5**' into your calculator: $^8C_5 = 56$.
- The question asks for the **whole term** (not just the coefficient), so the answer is: $56x^5$

Exercise 5.1

Q1 Use Pascal's triangle to expand $(1 + x)^4$.

Q2 Use your calculator to work out the following:

a) $^6C_2$ b) $\binom{12}{5}$ c) $\frac{30!}{4!26!}$ d) $^8C_8$

Q3 Without a calculator work out the following:

a) $\frac{9!}{4!5!}$ b) $^{10}C_3$ c) $\frac{15!}{11!4!}$ d) $\binom{8}{6}$

Q4 Find the first 4 terms, in ascending powers of x, of the binomial expansion of $(1 + x)^{10}$. Give each term in its simplest form.

Q5 Write down the full expansion of $(1 + x)^6$.

Q6 Find the first 4 terms in the expansion of $(1 + x)^7$.

Q7 Find the coefficient of x^8 in the expansion of $(1 + x)^{15}$.

Binomial expansions — $(1 + ax)^n$

When the **coefficient of x** in your binomial **isn't 1** (e.g. $(1 + 2x)^6$) you have to substitute the **whole x term** (e.g. $2x$) into the **binomial formula**:

Tip: You're not given the expansion of $(1 + ax)^n$ in the formula booklet, but you can use the one for $(1 + x)^n$ and replace x with (ax).

$$(1 + ax)^n = 1 + \binom{n}{1}(ax) + \binom{n}{2}(ax)^2 + \binom{n}{3}(ax)^3 + ... + (ax)^n$$

When a is **–1** (i.e. $(1 - x)^n$) the formula looks just like the formula for $(1 + x)^n$, but the **signs** of the terms **alternate**:

$$\begin{aligned}(1 - x)^n &= (1 + (-x))^n \\ &= 1 + \tfrac{n}{1}(-x) + \frac{n(n-1)}{1 \times 2}(-x)^2 + \frac{n(n-1)(n-2)}{1 \times 2 \times 3}(-x)^3 + ... + (-x)^n \\ &= 1 - \tfrac{n}{1}x + \frac{n(n-1)}{1 \times 2}x^2 - \frac{n(n-1)(n-2)}{1 \times 2 \times 3}x^3 + ... \pm x^n\end{aligned}$$

So for **$(1 - x)^n$** you just use the usual binomial **coefficients**, but with **alternating signs**:

Tip: The sign of the last term is **plus** if n is **even** and **minus** if n is **odd**.

$$(1 - x)^n = 1 - \binom{n}{1}x + \binom{n}{2}x^2 - \binom{n}{3}x^3 + ... \pm x^n$$

Examples

a) What is the term in x^5 in the expansion of $(1 - 3x)^{12}$?

The **general** binomial formula for **$(1 - 3x)^n$** is:

$$\begin{aligned}(1 - 3x)^n &= (1 + (-3x))^n \\ &= 1 + \tfrac{n}{1}(-3x) + \frac{n(n-1)}{1 \times 2}(-3x)^2 + \frac{n(n-1)(n-2)}{1 \times 2 \times 3}(-3x)^3 + ... + (-3x)^n\end{aligned}$$

So for **n = 12** this is:

$$(1 - 3x)^{12} = 1 + \tfrac{12}{1}(-3x) + \frac{12 \times 11}{1 \times 2}(-3x)^2 + \frac{12 \times 11 \times 10}{1 \times 2 \times 3}(-3x)^3 + ... + (-3x)^{12}$$

The **term in x^5** is: $\frac{12!}{5!7!}(-3)^5x^5 = \binom{12}{5}(-3x)^5 = (792 \times -243)x^5$

$= -192456x^5$

b) Find the coefficient of x^2 in the expansion of $(1 + 6x)^4(1 - 2x)^6$.

To find the x^2 term in the combined expansion you'll need to find all the **terms up to x^2** in both expansions (because these will form the x^2 term when they're multiplied) and then **multiply** together:

- $(1 + 6x)^4 = 1 + \binom{4}{1}(6x) + \binom{4}{2}(6x)^2 + ... = 1 + 24x + 216x^2 + ...$
- $(1 - 2x)^6 = 1 + \binom{6}{1}(-2x) + \binom{6}{2}(-2x)^2 + ... = 1 - 12x + 60x^2 - ...$
  - So: $(1 + 6x)^4(1 - 2x)^6 = (1 + 24x + 216x^2 + ...)(1 - 12x + 60x^2 - ...)$
  $= 1 - 12x + 60x^2 - ... + 24x - 288x^2 + 1440x^3 - ...$
  $+ 216x^2 - 2592x^3 + 12\,960x^4 - ...$
  $= 1 + 12x - 12x^2 +$ (*terms with higher powers*) $+ ...$
  - So the coefficient of x^2 is: -12

Tip: Most of this line of working isn't needed — you only really need to pick out the terms in the brackets which will multiply to give x^2. These are just $(1 \times 60x^2)$, $(24x \times -12x)$ and $(216x^2 \times 1)$ which give $60x^2$, $-288x^2$ and $216x^2$.

Exercise 5.2

Q1 Find the full expansions of:
a) $(1 - x)^6$ b) $(1 + x)^9 - (1 - x)^9$

Q2 Find the first 3 terms in the expansion of $(1 + x)^3(1 - x)^4$.

Q3 Find the coefficient of x^3y^2 in the expansion of $(1 + x)^5(1 + y)^7$.

Q4 Find the first 4 terms of the binomial expansion $(1 - 3x)^6$.

Q5 Find the full expansion of $(1 - 2x)^5$.

Q6 Find the first 4 terms, in ascending powers of x, of the binomial expansion of $(1 + kx)^8$, where k is a non-zero constant.

Q7 Find, in their simplest form, the first 5 terms in the expansion of $\left(1 + \frac{x}{2}\right)^{12}$, in ascending powers of x.

Q1 b) Hint: You'll find some of the terms vanish when you subtract the second expansion.

Q2 Hint: You'll need to go up to x^2 in both expansions, then multiply the expansions together to find all the terms up to x^2 in the combined expansion.

Binomial expansions — $(a + b)^n$

When your binomial is of the form $(a + b)^n$ (e.g. $(2 + 3x)^7$, where $a = 2$ and $b = 3x$) you can use a slightly **different formula**:

$$(a + b)^n = a^n + \binom{n}{1}a^{n-1}b + \binom{n}{2}a^{n-2}b^2 + ... + \binom{n}{n-1}ab^{n-1} + b^n$$

Tip: The powers of a decrease (from n to 0) as the powers of b increase (from 0 to n). The sum of the powers of a and b is always n.

This formula is in the formula booklet and you don't need to know the proof, but seeing where it comes from might make things a bit clearer.

You can find it from the binomial formula you've already seen:

- First rearrange so the binomial's in a form you can work with:

$$(a+b)^n = \left(a\left(1+\frac{b}{a}\right)\right)^n = a^n\left(1+\frac{b}{a}\right)^n$$

- You expand this by putting '$\frac{b}{a}$' into the **binomial formula** for $(1 + x)^n$, just like in the previous section:

$$= a^n\left(1 + \binom{n}{1}\left(\frac{b}{a}\right) + \binom{n}{2}\left(\frac{b}{a}\right)^2 + \dots + \binom{n}{n-1}\left(\frac{b}{a}\right)^{n-1} + \left(\frac{b}{a}\right)^n\right)$$

$$= a^n\left(1 + \binom{n}{1}\frac{b}{a} + \binom{n}{2}\frac{b^2}{a^2} + \dots + \binom{n}{n-1}\frac{b^{n-1}}{a^{n-1}} + \frac{b^n}{a^n}\right)$$

- **Multiply** through by a^n:

$$= a^n + \binom{n}{1}a^{n-1}b + \binom{n}{2}a^{n-2}b^2 + \dots + \binom{n}{n-1}ab^{n-1} + b^n$$

This is a general formula that works for any a and b, including 1 and x. So given **any binomial** you can pop your values for a, b and n into this formula and you'll get the **expansion**.

Example 1

Give the first 3 terms, in ascending powers of x, of the expansion of $(4 - 5x)^7$.

- Use the **formula**:

$$(a+b)^n = a^n + \binom{n}{1}a^{n-1}b + \binom{n}{2}a^{n-2}b^2 + \dots + \binom{n}{n-1}ab^{n-1} + b^n$$

- In this case, $a = 4$, $b = -5x$ and $n = 7$.
- $(4 - 5x)^7 = (4 + (-5x))^7$

$$= 4^7 + \left(\binom{7}{1} \times 4^6 \times (-5x)\right) + \left(\binom{7}{2} \times 4^5 \times (-5x)^2\right) + \dots$$

$$= 16\,384 + (7 \times 4096 \times -5x) + (21 \times 1024 \times 25x^2) + \dots$$

$$= 16\,384 - 143\,360x + 537\,600x^2 + \dots$$

Tip: Be careful with b here — there's a minus sign that might catch you out.

Your other option with expansions of $(a + b)^n$ is to **factorise** the binomial so you get $a^n\left(1+\frac{b}{a}\right)^n$, then plug $\frac{b}{a}$ into the **original binomial formula** (as you did with $(1 + ax)^n$ expansions in the last section).

Example 2

What is the coefficient of x^4 in the expansion of $(2 + 5x)^7$?

- Factorise: $(2 + 5x) = 2\left(1 + \frac{5}{2}x\right)$, so $(2 + 5x)^7 = 2^7\left(1 + \frac{5}{2}x\right)^7$.
- So the expansion $(2 + 5x)^7$ is the same as the expansion of $\left(1 + \frac{5}{2}x\right)^7$, multiplied by 2^7.

Tip: If you do it this way, make sure you don't forget to multiply back through by a^n when you give your final answer.

- Find the coefficient of x^4 in the expansion of $\left(1 + \frac{5}{2}x\right)^7$.

The term is:

$$\binom{7}{4} \times \left(\frac{5}{2}x\right)^4 = \frac{7\times6\times5\times4}{1\times2\times3\times4} \times \frac{5^4}{2^4}x^4 = 35 \times \frac{5^4}{2^4}x^4 = \frac{21875}{16}x^4$$

So the coefficient is: $\frac{21875}{16}$

- Multiply this by 2^7 to get the coefficient of x^4 in the original binomial:

$$2^7 \times \frac{21875}{16} = 175\,000$$

You can find an **unknown** in a binomial expansion if you're given some information about the coefficients:

Example 3

a) The coefficient of x^5 in the binomial expansion of $(4 + kx)^7$ is 81 648. Find k.

- From the $(a + b)^n$ formula, the term in x^5 of this expansion is:

$$^7C_5 4^2(kx)^5 = 21 \times 16 \times k^5 \times x^5 = 336k^5x^5$$

- So the coefficient of x^5 is $336k^5$.
- $336k^5 = 81\,648 \Rightarrow k^5 = 243 \Rightarrow k = 3$

b) In the expansion of $(1 + x)^n$, the coefficient of x^5 is twice the coefficient of x^4. What is the value of n?

- The coefficient of x^5 is $\frac{n!}{5!(n-5)!}$, the coefficient of x^4 is $\frac{n!}{4!(n-4)!}$.
- The coefficient of x^5 is twice the coefficient of x^4, so:

$$\frac{n!}{5!(n-5)!} = 2 \times \frac{n!}{4!(n-4)!}$$

$$\Rightarrow \frac{1}{5!(n-5)!} = 2 \times \frac{1}{4!(n-4)!}$$ ← Cancel the n!

$$\Rightarrow \frac{1}{5 \times 4! \times (n-5)!} = 2 \times \frac{1}{4! \times (n-4) \times (n-5)!}$$

$$\Rightarrow \frac{1}{5} = 2 \times \frac{1}{(n-4)}$$ ← Cancel the 4! and the $(n-5)$!

$$\Rightarrow n - 4 = 10$$

$$\Rightarrow n = 14$$

- To check: $^{14}C_5 = 2002$, $^{14}C_4 = 1001$, i.e. $^{14}C_5 = 2 \times {}^{14}C_4$

The value of n is 14

Tip: Just as with the $(1 + x)^n$ formula, you need to be familiar with all the ways of writing the binomial coefficients.

Tip: $5! = 5 \times 4!$ and $(n-4)! = (n-4) \times (n-5)!$

Tip: It's really easy to check your answer for questions like this, so make sure you do.

Sometimes you'll come across a binomial with a **power of x** or **two functions of x** inside the brackets. Fortunately, these aren't really any more difficult to expand than the expansions you've already seen, as long as you're careful with the algebra and **use the formulas**.

Example 4

Expand $\left(1 + \frac{2}{x^2}\right)^4$**.**

> **Tip:** You can use the coefficients from Pascal's triangle or the formula for expanding $(1 + x)^n$ from page 93 to expand $(1 + x)^4$.

The trick here is to break the problem down into stages.

- First, expand $(1 + x)^4$, but write $\left(\frac{2}{x^2}\right)$ in place of every x...

$$\left(1 + \frac{2}{x^2}\right)^4 = 1 + 4\left(\frac{2}{x^2}\right) + 6\left(\frac{2}{x^2}\right)^2 + 4\left(\frac{2}{x^2}\right)^3 + \left(\frac{2}{x^2}\right)^4$$

> **Tip:** Remember: $(x^m)^n = x^{(m \times n)}$ (see p. 1)

- ...then deal with the powers of x and tidy it up:

$$= 1 + 4\left(\frac{2}{x^2}\right) + 6\left(\frac{4}{x^4}\right) + 4\left(\frac{8}{x^6}\right) + \left(\frac{16}{x^8}\right)$$

$$= 1 + \frac{8}{x^2} + \frac{24}{x^4} + \frac{32}{x^6} + \frac{16}{x^8}$$

Example 5

Expand and simplify $\left(2x + \frac{1}{x}\right)^5$**.**

- Use the formula:

$$(a + b)^n = a^n + \binom{n}{1}a^{n-1}b + \binom{n}{2}a^{n-2}b^2 + \ldots + \binom{n}{n-1}ab^{n-1} + b^n$$

- In this case, $a = 2x$, $b = \frac{1}{x}$ and $n = 5$.

$$\left(2x + \frac{1}{x}\right)^5 = (2x)^5 + \binom{5}{1}(2x)^4\left(\frac{1}{x}\right) + \binom{5}{2}(2x)^3\left(\frac{1}{x}\right)^2 + \binom{5}{3}(2x)^2\left(\frac{1}{x}\right)^3 + \binom{5}{4}(2x)\left(\frac{1}{x}\right)^4 + \left(\frac{1}{x}\right)^5$$

- Now simplify:

$$= 32x^5 + 5(16x^4)\left(\frac{1}{x}\right) + 10(8x^3)\left(\frac{1}{x^2}\right) + 10(4x^2)\left(\frac{1}{x^3}\right) + 5(2x)\left(\frac{1}{x^4}\right) + \frac{1}{x^5}$$

$$= 32x^5 + 80x^3 + 80x + \frac{40}{x} + \frac{10}{x^3} + \frac{1}{x^5}$$

Exercise 5.3

Q1 Find the first 4 terms of the binomial expansion of $(3 + x)^6$.

Q2 Find the full expansion of $(2 + x)^4$.

Q3 In the expansion of $(1 + \lambda x)^8$ the coefficient of x^5 is 57344.

a) Work out the value of λ.

b) Find the first 3 terms of the expansion.

Q4 Find the first 4 terms in the expansion of $(3 + 5x)^7$.

Q5 a) Find the first 5 terms in the expansion of $(3 + 2x)^6$.
b) Use this expansion to find the first 5 terms of $(1 + x)(3 + 2x)^6$.

Q6 The term in x^2 for the expansion of $(1 + x)^n$ is $231x^2$.
a) What is the value of n? b) What is the term in x^3?

Q7 Find the full expansion of $(1 + 4x^2)^3$.

Q8 Fully expand
a) $(x + \frac{1}{x})^4$,
b) $(x^2 - y)^5$.

Q9 Find the coefficient of x^{12} in the expansion of $(1 - 2x^3)^7$.

Q10 Expand and simplify $(3x - \frac{2}{x})^4$.

Q11 Find the constant term in the expansion of $(2x - \frac{3}{x})^8$.

Q11 Hint: Look for powers of $2x$ and $\left(\frac{3}{x}\right)$ that will cancel each other out.

Q12 Expand and simplify $(1 + 4x)^5 - (1 - 4x)^4$.

Q13 In the expansion of $(a + 3x)^8$, the coefficient of x^2 is $\frac{32}{27}$ times bigger than the coefficient of x^5. What is the value of a?

Q14 In the expansion of $(1 + 2x)^5(3 - x)^4$, what is the coefficient of x^3?

Q15 In the expansion of $(1 + x)^n$, the coefficient of x^3 is 3 times larger than the coefficient of x^2.
a) Calculate the value of n.
b) If the coefficient of x^2 is $a \times$ (the coefficient of x), what is a?

Q16 a) Find the first 3 terms, in ascending powers of x, of the binomial expansion of $(2 + \mu x)^8$, where μ is a constant.
Write each term in its simplest form.
b) If the coefficient of x^2 is 87 808, what are the possible values of μ?

Q17 Find the coefficients of the terms indicated in the expansions of the following:
a) $(x + \frac{1}{x})^6$, term in x^2,
b) $(2x + \frac{1}{x})^7$, term in $\frac{1}{x^5}$.

Q17 Hint: Work out the powers you need to raise the terms in the brackets to so that after simplifying you're left with the required power of x.

Q18 In the expansion of $(x - \frac{k}{x})^8$, the constant term is 1120.
a) Find the value of k, given that $k > 0$.
b) Find the coefficient of the term in $\frac{1}{x^2}$

Review Exercise — Chapter 4

Q1 Find the nth term for each of the following sequences:

a) 2, 6, 10, 14, ...
b) 0.2, 0.7, 1.2, 1.7, ...
c) 21, 18, 15, 12, ...
d) 76, 70, 64, 58, ...

Q2 Find the 8th term of the sequence $x_n = n^2 - 3$.

Q3 In the sequence $u_n = n^2 + 3n + 4$, $u_k = 44$. Find the value of k.

Q4 Find the first 5 terms of the sequence $u_n = (-1)^n n$.

Q5 Find a recurrence relation which generates the sequence:

a) 65 536, 256, 16, 4, 2, ...
b) 40, 38, 34, 28, 20, ...
c) 1, 1, 2, 3, 5, 8, ... (the Fibonacci sequence)

Q6 The nth term of a sequence is u_n. The sequence is defined by $u_{n+1} = -\frac{1}{4}u_n + 3$, where $u_1 = 1$. The limit of u_n as n tends to infinity is L. Find the value of L.

Q7 In a sequence $u_1 = 2$, $u_2 = 8$ and $u_3 = 26$. If the recurrence relation is of the form $u_{n+1} = au_n + b$, find the values of the constants a and b.

Q8 Find the common difference in an arithmetic sequence that starts with –2, ends with 19 and has 29 terms.

Q9 In an arithmetic series, $u_7 = 8$ and $u_{11} = 10$. Find u_3.

Q10 In an arithmetic series, $u_3 = 15$ and $u_7 = 27$. Find the value of k if $u_k = 66$.

Q11 a) Find $\sum_{n=1}^{20}(3n - 1)$
b) Find k if $\sum_{n=1}^{k} n = 630$.

Q12 Find the common ratio of the geometric progression 3125, 1875, 1125, 675, 405, ...

Q13 Write an expression for the nth term of the geometric sequence 3, –9, 27, –81, 243, ...

Q14 For the geometric progression 2, –6, 18, ..., find:

a) the 10th term,
b) the sum of the first 10 terms.

Q15 A geometric series has first term $a = 7$ and common ratio $r = 0.6$. Find $\sum_{k=0}^{5} 7(0.6)^k$ to 2 d.p.

Q16 Find the common ratio for the following geometric series. State which ones are convergent and which are divergent.

a) $1 + 2 + 4 + ...$
b) $81 + 27 + 9 + ...$
c) $1 + \frac{1}{3} + \frac{1}{9} + ...$
d) $4 + 1 + \frac{1}{4} + ...$

Q17 For the geometric progression 24, 12, 6, ..., find:

a) the common ratio, b) the seventh term,

c) the sum of the first 10 terms, d) the sum to infinity.

Q18 A geometric progression begins 2, 6, ...
Which term of the geometric progression equals 1458?

Q19 A geometric series has first term $a = 33$, common ratio $r = 0.25$. Find $\sum_{k=0}^{\infty} ar^k$ for this series.

Q20 Give, in their simplest form, the first four terms in the binomial expansion of $(1 + x)^{12}$.

Q21 What is the term in x^4 in the expansion of $(1 - 2x)^{16}$?

Q22 Find the first 4 terms of the expansion of $\left(1 + \frac{x}{3}\right)^9$ in ascending powers of x, giving each term in its simplest form.

Q23 Find the complete expansion of $(1 + 3x)^5$.

Q24 a) Find the first 5 terms, in ascending powers of x, of the expansion of $(1 + ax)^8$, where a is a non-zero constant.

Given that the coefficient of x^2 in this expansion is double the coefficient of x^3,

b) find the value of a

c) find the coefficient of x.

Q25 Find the first 3 terms of the binomial expansion of $(4 - 5x)^7$.
Give each term in its simplest form.

Q26 a) Find the first 3 terms of the binomial expansion of $(2 + kx)^{13}$, where k is a non-zero constant.

b) Given that the coefficient of x in this expansion is $\frac{1}{6}$ of the coefficient of x^2, find the value of k.

Q27 Expand $(2 + a)^4(3 - 4a)^5$ up to and including the term in a^3.

Q28 The expression $(1 - \frac{2}{x^3})^4$ can be written as $1 - \frac{a}{x^3} + \frac{b}{x^6} - \frac{c}{x^9} + \frac{d}{x^{12}}$.

Find the values of a, b, c and d.

Exam-Style Questions — Chapter 4

1 A geometric series has the first term 12 and is defined by: $u_{n+1} = 12 \times 1.3^n$.

a) Is the series convergent or divergent? *(1 mark)*

b) Find the values of the 3rd and 10th terms. *(2 marks)*

2 The first term of an arithmetic sequence is 22 and the common difference is –1.1.

a) Find the value of the 31st term. *(2 marks)*

b) If the kth term of the sequence is 0, find k. *(2 marks)*

c) The sum to n terms of the sequence is S_n.
Find the value of n at which S_n first becomes negative. *(3 marks)*

3 a) Use binomial expansion to express $(1 + 3x)^5$ in the form
$1 + ax + bx^2 + cx^3 + dx^4 + ex^5$, where a, b, c, d and e are constants. *(2 marks)*

b) Hence show that the coefficient of the x^2 term in the expansion of
$(1 + 3x)^5(1 + x)$ is 105. *(3 marks)*

4 In a geometric series, $a = 20$ and $r = \frac{3}{4}$.
Find values for the following, giving your answers to 3 significant figures where necessary:

a) S_∞ *(2 marks)*

b) u_{15} *(2 marks)*

c) The smallest value of n for which $S_n > 79.76$. *(5 marks)*

5 Two different geometric series have the same second term and sum to infinity:

$$u_2 = 5 \text{ and } S_\infty = 36.$$

a) Show that $36r^2 - 36r + 5 = 0$, where r represents the two possible ratios. *(4 marks)*

b) Hence find the values of r, and the corresponding first terms,
for both geometric series. *(4 marks)*

6 Find the coefficients of x, x^2, x^3 and x^4 in the binomial expansion of $(4 + 3x)^{10}$. *(4 marks)*

7 a) Find, to 2 decimal places, the sum of the first 8 terms of the geometric series

$$2 + 5 + 12.5 + 31.25 + \ldots$$

(3 marks)

b) State the condition for an infinite geometric series to be convergent. *(1 mark)*

c) Find the sum to infinity of the geometric series that has first term 8 and common ratio $-\frac{3}{4}$, giving your answer to 2 decimal places. *(2 marks)*

8 u_n is the nth term of the sequence defined by $u_{n+1} = au_n + b$, where a and b are constants. The first three terms of the sequence are $u_1 = 10$, $u_2 = -1$ and $u_3 = \frac{6}{5}$. Find:

a) a and b. *(5 marks)*

b) the value of u_5. *(2 marks)*

c) L, the limit of u_n as n tends to infinity. *(2 marks)*

9 A sequence is defined by the recurrence relation: $h_{n+1} = 2h_n + 2$ when $n \geq 1$.

a) Given that $h_1 = 5$, find the values of h_2, h_3, and h_4. *(3 marks)*

b) Calculate the value of $\sum_{r=3}^{6} h_r$. *(3 marks)*

10 $a + ar + ar^2 + ar^3 + \ldots$ is a geometric series.
The second term of the series is –2 and the sum to infinity of the series is –9.

a) Show that $9r^2 - 9r + 2 = 0$. *(3 marks)*

b) Find the possible values of r. *(2 marks)*

c) Hence find the possible values of a. *(2 marks)*

Given that r takes its smallest possible value,

d) find the 7th term in the series to 4 decimal places, *(2 marks)*

e) find the sum of the first 5 terms to 2 decimal places. *(2 marks)*

11 a) Find the binomial expansion of $\left(\frac{1}{2x} + \frac{x}{2}\right)^3$. Simplify your answer. *(3 marks)*

b) Hence find the coefficient of x in the expansion of $(2 + x^2)\left(\frac{1}{2x} + \frac{x}{2}\right)^3$. *(3 marks)*

Chapter 5 Differentiation

1. Differentiating x^n

Learning Objectives:
- Be able to differentiate powers of x, including negative and fractional powers.
- Be able to differentiate sums and differences of powers of x.

You've already done some differentiation back in C1. For C2, you'll have to do more of the same sort of stuff, but for a wider variety of functions — this time not all the powers of x will be positive integers. We'll start with a bit of a recap of the differentiation that was covered in C1.

When n is a positive integer

Differentiating produces an **algebraic expression** for the gradient of a curve as a **function of x** — its numerical value **changes** as you move along the curve.

In C1, you learnt about differentiating positive integer powers of x, using the following formula:

$$\text{If } y = x^n, \text{ then } \frac{dy}{dx} = nx^{n-1}$$

Example

Differentiate each of the following using the formula for powers of x.

a) $y = x^4$

For 'normal' powers, n is just the power of x. Here $n = 4$.

$$\frac{dy}{dx} = nx^{n-1} = 4x^3$$

Tip: When it says 'differentiate', it actually means 'differentiate **with respect to x**' as it's a function of x you're differentiating.

b) $y = 5x^2$

This is just a normal power with $n = 2$, but there's a constant (a number) in front of it.

$$y = 5x^2$$
$$\frac{dy}{dx} = 5(nx^{n-1}) = 5(2x^{2-1}) = 10x^1 = 10x$$

If there's a number in front of the x^n term — multiply the derivative by it. Formally:

$$\text{If } y = ax^n, \frac{dy}{dx} = anx^{n-1}$$

c) $y = 9$

There are no powers of x in this expression for y so multiply by $x^0 = 1$.

$$y = 9x^0, n = 0$$
$$\frac{dy}{dx} = 9(nx^{n-1}) = 9(0x^{-1}) = 0$$

Tip: Differentiating $y = a$ where a is just a constant (i.e. a number) always gives zero, because the line has a gradient of 0.

When n is negative or a fraction

Using the laws of indices (see p.1), you can rewrite expressions like $\sqrt{x}$ or $\frac{3}{x^2}$ using **powers of x** like $x^{\frac{1}{2}}$ or $3x^{-2}$.

This makes them much easier to **differentiate** — you can use the **formula** from p.106, as with positive integer powers.

Tip: Differentiation's much easier if you know the laws of indices really well. See p.1.

Example 1

Differentiate each of the following using the formula for powers of x.

a) $y = \sqrt{x}$

First write the square root as a fractional power of x. ⟶

$$y = x^{\frac{1}{2}} \left(n = \frac{1}{2}\right)$$
$$\frac{dy}{dx} = nx^{n-1}$$
$$= \frac{1}{2}x^{\left(-\frac{1}{2}\right)}$$
$$= \frac{1}{2\sqrt{x}}$$

b) $y = \frac{1}{x^2}$

Write the fraction as a negative power of x. ⟶

$$y = x^{-2} \ (n = -2)$$
$$\frac{dy}{dx} = nx^{n-1}$$
$$= -2x^{-3}$$
$$= -\frac{2}{x^3}$$

You could be asked to **use** your gradient function to work out the **numerical value** of the gradient at a **particular point** on the curve.

Example 2

Find the gradient of the curve $y = 6\sqrt{x}$, $x \geq 0$, at $x = 1$ and $x = 9$.

- You need the gradient of the graph of $y = 6\sqrt{x}$, so rewrite the root as a power, then differentiate:
  $y = 6x^{\frac{1}{2}} \Rightarrow \frac{dy}{dx} = 6\left(\frac{1}{2}x^{-\frac{1}{2}}\right) = 3x^{-\frac{1}{2}} = \frac{3}{\sqrt{x}}$
- Now when $x = 1$, $\frac{dy}{dx} = \frac{3}{\sqrt{1}} = \frac{3}{1} = 3$
- So the gradient of the graph at $x = 1$ is 3.
- And when $x = 9$, $\frac{dy}{dx} = \frac{3}{\sqrt{9}} = \frac{3}{3} = 1$
- So the gradient of the graph at $x = 9$ is 1.

Exercise 1.1

Q1 Differentiate to find $\frac{dy}{dx}$ for:

a) $y = x^8$ b) $y = x^{-2}$ c) $y = 2x^5$ d) $y = 3\sqrt{x}$

e) $y = 7$ f) $y = 2x^{-1}$ g) $y = \frac{2}{x^3}$ h) $y = \sqrt[4]{x}$

Q2 Hint: Remember, when $y = f(x)$, $f'(x)$ is another way to write $\frac{dy}{dx}$.

Q2 Differentiate to find $f'(x)$ for:

a) $f(x) = 4x$ b) $f(x) = x^{-4}$ c) $f(x) = 8\sqrt{x}$ d) $f(x) = 3\sqrt[3]{x}$

e) $f(x) = \frac{1}{2}x^6$ f) $f(x) = 4x^{-2}$ g) $f(x) = \frac{10}{x^2}$ h) $f(x) = \frac{2}{\sqrt{x}}$

Q3 Find the gradient of each of the following functions:

a) $y = x^3$ when $x = 3$

b) $y = x^{-1}$ when $x = 2$

c) $f(x) = 2\sqrt{x}$ at the point (9, 6)

d) $y = \frac{2}{3}x^6$ when $x = -1$

e) $f(x) = 2x^{\frac{3}{2}}$ at the point (4, 16)

f) $f(x) = \frac{4}{x^3}$ when $f(x) = -\frac{1}{2}$

Differentiating functions

You can differentiate functions with **more than one** term by differentiating each bit **separately**. Formally, this means:

$$\frac{d}{dx}(x^m + x^n) = \frac{d}{dx}(x^m) + \frac{d}{dx}(x^n)$$

You can apply this rule when m and n are **negative numbers** or **fractions** too.

Example 1

Find $\frac{d}{dx}\left(6x^2 + \frac{4}{\sqrt[3]{x}} - \frac{2}{x^2} + 1\right)$.

This notation just means the derivative with respect to x of the thing in the brackets.

Rewrite the function first to get powers of x. Then differentiate each bit separately.

$x^0 = 1$

$$6x^2 + \frac{4}{\sqrt[3]{x}} - \frac{2}{x^2} + 1 = 6x^2 + 4x^{-\frac{1}{3}} - 2x^{-2} + x^0$$

$$\frac{d}{dx}\left(6x^2 + \frac{4}{\sqrt[3]{x}} - \frac{2}{x^2} + 1\right) = 6(2x) + 4\left(-\frac{1}{3}x^{-\frac{4}{3}}\right) - 2(-2x^{-3}) + 0x^{-1}$$

$$= 12x - \frac{4}{3}x^{-\frac{4}{3}} + 4x^{-3}$$

$$= 12x - \frac{4}{3\sqrt[3]{x^4}} + \frac{4}{x^3}$$

Tip: Remember — if there's a number in front of the function, multiply the derivative by the same number.

You'll often need to **simplify** a function before you can differentiate it by multiplying out **brackets** or simplifying **fractions**. If you have a fraction to simplify, check first whether the denominator is a **factor** of the numerator, otherwise you'll need to **split it up** into terms.

Example 2

a) Differentiate $y = x(x - 2)(x - 5)$

- Multiply out all brackets and simplify to powers of x.

$$y = x(x - 2)(x - 5)$$
$$= x(x^2 - 7x + 10)$$
$$= x^3 - 7x^2 + 10x$$

- Differentiate term-by-term.

$$\frac{dy}{dx} = 3x^2 - 14x + 10$$

b) Differentiate $y = \frac{x^3 + 3x^2 - 4x}{x - 1}$.

The numerator of this fraction will factorise and then one of the factors will cancel with the denominator.

$$y = \frac{x^3 + 3x^2 - 4x}{x - 1}$$
$$= \frac{x(x^2 + 3x - 4)}{x - 1}$$
$$= \frac{x(x - 1)(x + 4)}{x - 1}$$
$$= x(x + 4)$$
$$= x^2 + 4x$$
$$\frac{dy}{dx} = 2x + 4$$

Tip: If the denominator is an expression instead of just one term, chances are the numerator will have a factor that cancels with the denominator.

c) Differentiate the function $f(x) = \frac{x^3 + 4x + 1}{2x^2}$.

- This numerator won't factorise. Instead, split the fraction up into three fractional terms and then write each term as a power of x.

$$f(x) = \frac{x^3 + 4x + 1}{2x^2}$$
$$= \frac{x^3}{2x^2} + \frac{4x}{2x^2} + \frac{1}{2x^2}$$
$$= \frac{x}{2} + \frac{2}{x} + \frac{1}{2x^2}$$
$$= \frac{1}{2}x + 2x^{-1} + \frac{1}{2}x^{-2}$$

- Differentiating....

$$f'(x) = \frac{1}{2} + 2(-x^{-2}) + \frac{1}{2}(-2x^{-3})$$
$$= \frac{1}{2} - 2x^{-2} - x^{-3}$$
$$= \frac{1}{2} - \frac{2}{x^2} - \frac{1}{x^3}$$

Tip: For any a, b, c & d:

$$\frac{a + b + c}{d} = \frac{a}{d} + \frac{b}{d} + \frac{c}{d}$$

You can split up fractions using this rule.

Exercise 1.2

Q1 Differentiate these functions:

a) $y = 3x^2 + 5x^5$

b) $y = x + \frac{1}{x}$

c) $y = 3x^2 + \sqrt{x} - 5$

d) $f(x) = -2x^5 + 4x - \frac{1}{x^2}$

e) $f(x) = \sqrt{x^3} - x$

f) $f(x) = 5x - \frac{2}{x^3} + \sqrt[3]{x}$

Q2 Find the gradient of each of the following curves:

a) $y = -x^4 + 4x^3 + 7$ when $x = 2$

b) $y = 2x^5 + \frac{1}{x}$ when $x = -2$

c) $y = x(x + 1)(x + 3)$ when $x = 4$

d) $y = (x^{-2} - 2)(x + 2)$ when $x = 1$

e) $y = \sqrt{x}(x - 1)$ at $(4, 6)$

f) $f(x) = x^2\left(\frac{2}{x} + \frac{3}{x^3}\right)$ at $(-1, -5)$

g) $f(x) = \frac{1}{x^2}(x^3 - x)$ at $x = 5$

h) $f(x) = \frac{3x^3 + 10x^2 - 2x}{x^2}$ at $(2, 15)$

Q3 a) If $f(x) = (2x - 3)(x + 6)$, find the coordinates of the point on the curve $y = f(x)$ where $f'(x) = -3$.

b) If $f(x) = (\sqrt{x} + 4)(\sqrt{x} + 8)$, find the coordinates of the point on the curve $y = f(x)$ where $f'(x) = 3$.

c) If $f(x) = \frac{x^3 - 3x^2 + 2x}{x^2}$, for $x > 0$, find the coordinates of the point on the curve $y = f(x)$ where $f'(x) = \frac{1}{2}$.

Q4 Differentiate these functions:

Q4 Hint: Where there's a fraction with an expression in the denominator, try to take the denominator out of the numerator as a factor.

a) $f(x) = \frac{x^5 - 16x^3}{x + 4}$

b) $y = \frac{1}{x}(x - 3)(x - 4)$

c) $y = \sqrt{x}(x^3 - \sqrt{x})$

d) $f(x) = \frac{3 - \sqrt{x}}{\sqrt{x}}$

e) $f(x) = \frac{x + 5\sqrt{x}}{\sqrt{x}}$

f) $f(x) = \frac{x - 3\sqrt{x} + 2}{\sqrt{x} - 1}$

2. Using Differentiation

Once you've found the derivative of a function, you can use it to find tangents, normals and stationary points of the graph of the function. You'll recognise some of this from C1, but here we'll be applying the same techniques to a wider variety of functions.

Learning Objectives:

- Be able to find tangents and normals to a curve.
- Be able to find the second derivative of a function.
- Be able to use differentiation to find all the stationary points on a curve.
- Be able to identify the nature of these stationary points.
- Be able to work out where a function is increasing or decreasing.

Finding tangents and normals

Differentiation can be used to find the gradient at a point on a curve. You can use this to find the equation for the **tangent** or **normal** at that point.

Here's what you should have covered in C1:

To find the equation of the tangent or normal to a curve at a point:

- Differentiate the function.
- Find the gradient of the curve at that point.
- Use this to deduce the gradient, m, of the tangent or normal:

$$\text{gradient of the tangent} = \text{gradient of the curve}$$

$$\text{gradient of the normal} = -\frac{1}{\text{gradient of the curve}}$$

- Write the equation of the tangent or normal in the form $y = mx + c$.
- Work out the constant value c in the equation by using the coordinates of the point (which you know lies on the tangent/normal).

Tip: Remember, a tangent is a line that just touches the curve and has the same gradient as the curve at that point.

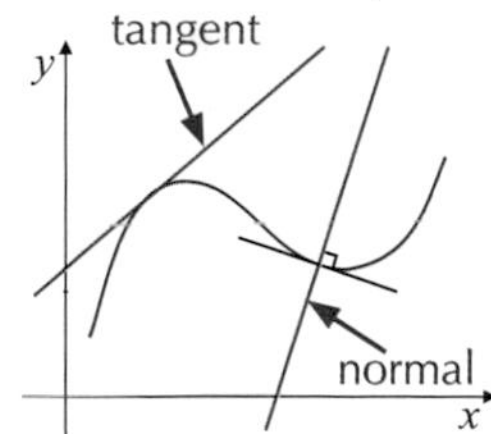

A normal is a line that is perpendicular (at right angles) to the curve at a particular point.

Example 1

Find the equation of the tangent to the curve $y = (2x + 3)(x - 5)$ at the point (–1, –6). Give your answer in the form $y = mx + c$.

- Write the curve in a form you can differentiate...

$$y = (2x + 3)(x - 5) = 2x^2 - 7x - 15$$

...and differentiate it.

$$\frac{dy}{dx} = 4x - 7$$

- Find the gradient of the curve at (–1, –6).

$$x = -1 \Rightarrow \frac{dy}{dx} = -4 - 7 = -11$$

So the gradient of the curve is –11 at (–1, –6)

- Gradient of the tangent = gradient of the curve, so $m = -11$

So the equation of the tangent is $y = -11x + c$.

- Use the point (–1, –6) to work out the value of c:

$$x = -1, y = -6 \Rightarrow -6 = 11 + c \Rightarrow c = -17$$

- So the tangent has equation $y = -11x - 17$.

Tip: Make sure you always check whether the question wants a normal or a tangent.

Example 2

Find the equation of the normal to the curve $y = \dfrac{(x+2)(x+4)}{6\sqrt{x}}$ at the point (4, 4), giving your answer in the form $ax + by + c = 0$, where a, b and c are integers.

- Simplify and differentiate.

$$y = \frac{(x+2)(x+4)}{6\sqrt{x}}$$

Denominator is one term so it'll probably need splitting up.

$$= \frac{x^2 + 6x + 8}{6x^{\frac{1}{2}}}$$

$$= \frac{x^2}{6x^{\frac{1}{2}}} + \frac{6x}{6x^{\frac{1}{2}}} + \frac{8}{6x^{\frac{1}{2}}}$$

$$= \frac{1}{6}x^{\frac{3}{2}} + x^{\frac{1}{2}} + \frac{4}{3}x^{-\frac{1}{2}}$$

$$\frac{dy}{dx} = \frac{1}{6}\left(\frac{3}{2}x^{\frac{1}{2}}\right) + \frac{1}{2}x^{-\frac{1}{2}} + \frac{4}{3}\left(-\frac{1}{2}x^{-\frac{3}{2}}\right)$$

$$= \frac{1}{4}\sqrt{x} + \frac{1}{2\sqrt{x}} - \frac{2}{3\sqrt{x^3}}$$

- Find the gradient of the curve at (4, 4).

$$x = 4 \Rightarrow \frac{dy}{dx} = \frac{1}{4}\sqrt{4} + \frac{1}{2\sqrt{4}} - \frac{2}{3\sqrt{4^3}} = \frac{1}{2} + \frac{1}{4} - \frac{1}{12} = \frac{2}{3}$$

So the gradient of the curve is $\frac{2}{3}$ at (4, 4).

- Gradient of the normal line at (4, 4) is

$$m = -\frac{1}{\text{gradient of the curve at (4, 4)}} = -\frac{3}{2}$$

- So the equation of the normal is $y = -\frac{3}{2}x + c$.

Use the point (4, 4) to work out the value of c:

$$x = 4, y = 4 \Rightarrow 4 = -\frac{3}{2}(4) + c \Rightarrow c = 10$$

Tip: Don't forget to rewrite the answer in the form the question asks for.

- So the tangent has equation $y = -\frac{3}{2}x + 10$.

Rearranging into the form $ax + by + c = 0$ gives: $3x + 2y - 20 = 0$

Exercise 2.1

Q1 Find the tangent to each of these curves at the given point, giving your answer in the form $ax + by + c = 0$, where a, b and c are integers.

a) $y = -x^3 + 3x^2 + 4$, (3, 4)

b) $y = (x - 5)(2x - 1)$, (2, –9)

c) $y = \frac{1}{x} + x + 3$, $\left(2, 5\frac{1}{2}\right)$

d) $y = 4x^2 - 3\sqrt{x}$, (1, 1)

e) $y = \frac{3}{x} + 2\sqrt{x}$, $\left(4, 4\frac{3}{4}\right)$

f) $y = \frac{1}{x} + \frac{4}{x^2}$, $\left(2, 1\frac{1}{2}\right)$

g) $y = \frac{1}{3}x^2 - 4\sqrt{x} - \frac{1}{3}$, (4, –3)

h) $y = x - \frac{2}{x} + \frac{3}{x^2}$, (–3, –2)

Q2 Find the normal to each of these curves at the given point, giving your answer in an appropriate form.

a) $y = \frac{2x^5 - 2x^4}{3x^3}$, (–2, 4)
b) $y = \frac{5x^2 - 2x + 3}{x^2}$, $(2, 4\frac{3}{4})$
c) $y = \frac{3x - x^2}{\sqrt{x}}$, (4, –2)
d) $y = \frac{1}{x} - \frac{3}{x^2} - \frac{4}{x^3} + \frac{7}{4}$, (–2, 1)
e) $y = \frac{x^3 - 5x^2 - 4x}{x\sqrt{x}}$, (4, –4)

Q3 a) Show that the curve $y = \frac{x^3 + x^2 + x + 5}{x^2}$ passes through the point $\left(-2, -\frac{1}{4}\right)$.

b) Find the equation of the tangent to the curve at this point, giving your answer in the form $ax + by + c = 0$, where a, b and c are integers.

c) Find the equation of the normal to the curve at this point, giving your answer in the form $ax + by + c = 0$, where a, b and c are integers.

Finding second order derivatives

- If you differentiate y with respect to x, you get the derivative $\frac{dy}{dx}$.
- If you then differentiate $\frac{dy}{dx}$ with respect to x, you get the **second order derivative**, denoted $\frac{d^2y}{dx^2}$.
- The **second derivative** gives the **rate of change** of the **gradient** of the curve with respect to x.
- In function notation, the **second derivative** is written **f''(x)**.

Tip: This should be familiar from C1 too.

Example 1

For the function $f(x) = \frac{x^3 - 4x + 6}{2x}$ find f'(x) and f''(x)

$$f(x) = \frac{x^3 - 4x + 6}{2x} = \frac{x^3}{2x} - \frac{4x}{2x} + \frac{6}{2x}$$
$$= \frac{x^2}{2} - 2 + \frac{3}{x}$$
$$= \frac{1}{2}x^2 - 2 + 3x^{-1}$$

$$f'(x) = \frac{1}{2}(2x^1) - 0 + 3(-x^{-2})$$ ← Differentiate for f'(x).
$$= x - 3x^{-2} = x - \frac{3}{x^2}$$

$$f''(x) = 1 - 3(-2x^{-3})$$ ← Differentiate again to get the second derivative.
$$= 1 + \frac{6}{x^3}$$

Example 2

The movement of a particle is modelled by the equation $x = t^2 + \frac{3}{t}$, for $0 < t \leq 20$, where x is the distance of the particle in metres from a fixed point after t seconds.

a) Find $\frac{dx}{dt}$, the speed of the particle after t seconds.

Differentiate x to find $\frac{dx}{dt}$:

$$x = t^2 + 3t^{-1}$$

$$\frac{dx}{dt} = 2t - 3t^{-2} = 2t - \frac{3}{t^2} \text{ ms}^{-1}$$

b) Find $\frac{d^2x}{dt^2}$, the acceleration of the particle after t seconds.

Differentiate again to find $\frac{d^2x}{dt^2}$:

$$\frac{dx}{dt} = 2t - 3t^{-2}$$

$$\frac{d^2x}{dt^2} = 2 + 6t^{-3} = 2 + \frac{6}{t^3} \text{ ms}^{-2}$$

Tip: Speed is the rate of change of distance with respect to time, and acceleration is the rate of change of speed with respect to time.

Exercise 2.2

Q1 Find $\frac{dy}{dx}$ and $\frac{d^2y}{dx^2}$ for each of these functions:

a) $y = 6x^2$ b) $y = x^6$ c) $y = \frac{1}{x}$

d) $y = \sqrt{x}$ e) $y = \frac{1}{x^2}$ f) $y = x\sqrt{x}$

Q2 Find f′(x) and f″(x) for each of these functions:

a) $f(x) = -5x^3 - 3x - 1$ b) $f(x) = 3\sqrt{x} + x\sqrt{x}$

c) $f(x) = \frac{1}{x}(3x^4 - 2x^3)$ d) $f(x) = \frac{x^2 - x\sqrt{x} + 7x}{\sqrt{x}}$

Q3 Find the value of the second derivative at the given value for x.

a) $f(x) = 9x^4 - 10x^2$, $x = -1$ b) $y = x\sqrt{x} - \frac{1}{x}$, $x = 4$

c) $f(x) = \frac{9x^2 + 3x}{3\sqrt{x}}$, $x = 1$ d) $y = (\frac{1}{x^2} + \frac{1}{x})(5 - x)$, $x = -3$

Q4 A particle moves along a path modelled by the equation $x = 4\sqrt{t^3}$, for $0 \leq t \leq 60$, where t is the time in seconds and x is the distance in metres the particle has travelled from its starting point.

a) Find the speed of the particle after t seconds.

b) What is the speed of the particle in ms^{-1} at:

(i) $t = 1$ second (ii) $t = 9$ seconds

c) Find the acceleration of the particle after t seconds.

d) Find the acceleration at $t = 4$ seconds in ms^{-2}.

e) Find the speed when the acceleration is 0.5 ms^{-2}.

Q4 Hint: For part e), use the information you've been given to work out the value of t and then put the t-value into the equation for speed.

Stationary points

As you'll have seen in C1, **stationary points** occur when the **gradient** of a graph is **zero**, and there are three types of stationary point:

Maximum
When the gradient changes from positive to negative.

Minimum
When the gradient changes from negative to positive.

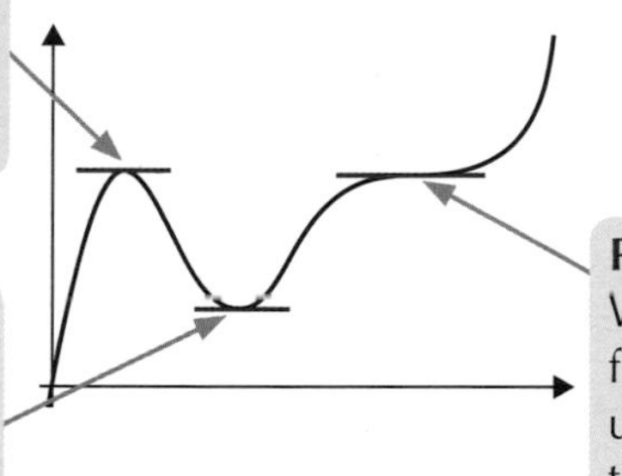

Point of inflection
When the graph briefly flattens out — these are unlikely to come up in the C2 exam.

Tip: Some stationary points are called local maximum or minimum points because the function takes on higher or lower values in other parts of the graph. The maximum and minimum points shown opposite are both local.

Because stationary points occur when the gradient is zero, you can use **differentiation** to find them:

Example

The sketch below shows the graph of $y = -3\sqrt[3]{x} + \frac{1}{4}x + 2$.
Find the coordinates of the stationary points of the graph.

- You need to find where $\frac{dy}{dx} = 0$.

  Start by writing all the terms as powers of x, then differentiate:

$$y = -3\sqrt[3]{x} + \frac{1}{4}x + 2 = -3x^{\frac{1}{3}} + \frac{1}{4}x + 2$$

$$\Rightarrow \frac{dy}{dx} = -x^{-\frac{2}{3}} + \frac{1}{4} = -\frac{1}{\sqrt[3]{x^2}} + \frac{1}{4}$$

- Then set the derivative **equal to zero** and solve for x:

$$-\frac{1}{\sqrt[3]{x^2}} + \frac{1}{4} = 0 \Rightarrow \sqrt[3]{x^2} = 4$$
$$\Rightarrow x^2 = 4^3 = 64$$
$$\Rightarrow x = \pm 8$$

- These are the x-values of the **stationary points**.
  Now find the corresponding y-values:

  $x = -8 \Rightarrow y = -3(-2) - 2 + 2 = 6$
  $x = 8 \Rightarrow y = -3(2) + 2 + 2 = -2$

- So the coordinates of the stationary points are $(-8, 6)$ and $(8, -2)$.

Tip: Don't forget this last step — once you've found x you need to also find y.

Exercise 2.3

Q1 Find the coordinates of the stationary points of the curves with the following equations:

a) $y = 2x^2 - 3x + 5$ b) $y = x^3 - 27x + 4$

c) $y = (2 - x)(3x + 1)$ d) $y = \frac{4}{x^2} + x, x \neq 0$

e) $y = \frac{1}{x^2} + 54x + 3, x \neq 0$ f) $y = \frac{8}{x} + 18x - 9, x \neq 0$

Q2 The graph of $y = \frac{3\sqrt[3]{x}}{2} - \frac{x^2}{4} + 4$ is shown on the sketch below.

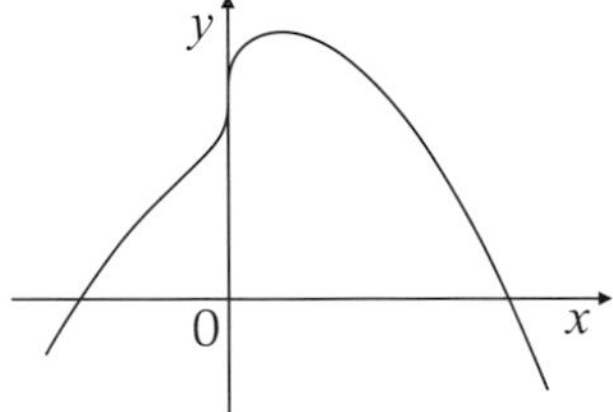

The graph has one stationary point. Find its coordinates.

Q3 Hint: 'Verify' means you can use the given coordinates in your working — you don't have to find them as the end result like in a 'show that' question.

Q3 Verify that (–3, 12) and (3, 12) are stationary points of the graph of $y = \frac{x^2}{3} + \frac{27}{x^2} + 6$.

Q4 Show that the graph of the function given by $f(x) = 3x - \frac{21}{x} - 1$ has no stationary points.

Maximum and minimum points

Tip: When a question asks you to "determine the nature of the turning points", it means you need to work out if each one is a maximum or a minimum.

The second order derivative, $\frac{d^2y}{dx^2}$ or $f''(x)$, can help you to work out whether a stationary point you've found is a **maximum** or **minimum**. (You'll already have done this for some functions in C1.)

Maximum and minimum points are also known as **turning points**.

Tip: If the second derivative is equal to zero, you can't tell what type of stationary point it is.

If $\frac{d^2y}{dx^2} < 0$, it's a maximum.

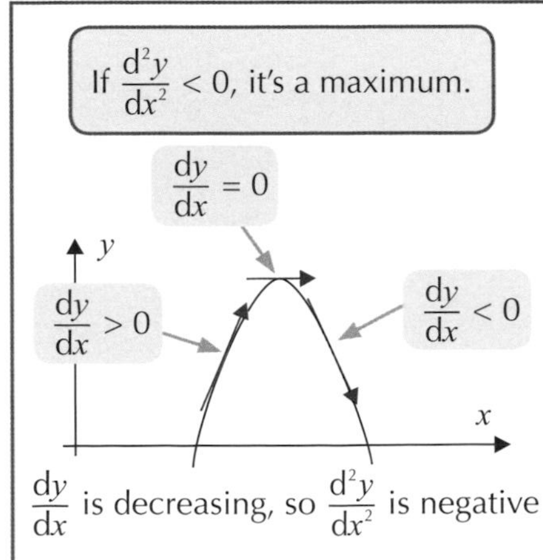

$\frac{dy}{dx}$ is decreasing, so $\frac{d^2y}{dx^2}$ is negative

If $\frac{d^2y}{dx^2} > 0$, it's a minimum.

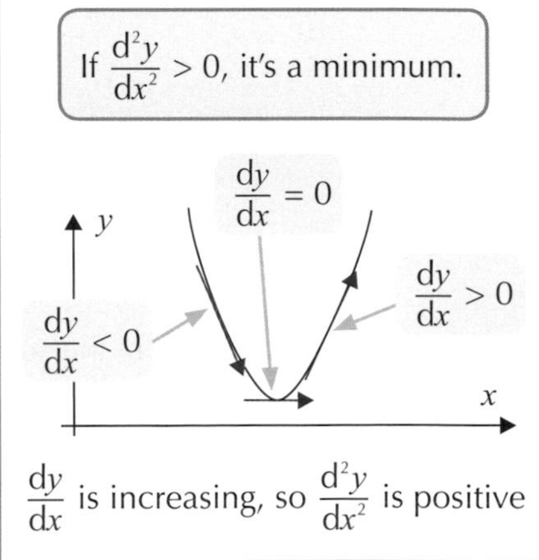

$\frac{dy}{dx}$ is increasing, so $\frac{d^2y}{dx^2}$ is positive

Example

The function $f(x) = \frac{54}{x} + x^2 + 3$ is defined for $x > 0$.
The graph of $y = f(x)$ has a stationary point at (3, 30).
Determine the nature of this stationary point.

- Start by finding the first derivative:

$$f(x) = 54x^{-1} + x^2 + 3$$
$$\Rightarrow \quad f'(x) = -54x^{-2} + 2x$$

- To determine the nature of the stationary point, **differentiate again**:

$$f''(x) = 108x^{-3} + 2 = \frac{108}{x^3} + 2$$

- Then just put in the x-value from the coordinates of the **stationary point**:

$$f''(3) = \frac{108}{3^3} + 2 = 6$$

- At $x = 3$, $f''(x)$ is **positive** — so (3, 30) is a minimum.

The graph of $y = f(x)$ near this stationary point looks like this:

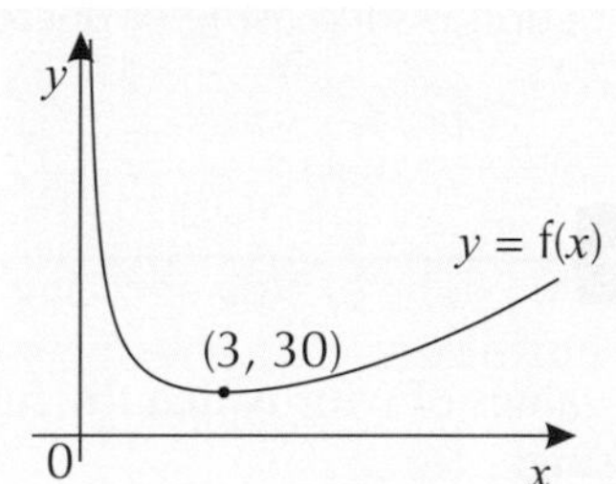

Exercise 2.4

Q1 Find the stationary points on the graphs of the following functions and say whether they're maximum or minimum turning points:

a) $y = 5 - 7x + x^2$

b) $f(x) = (x + 2)(3x - 4)$

c) $f(x) = \frac{27}{x^3} + x, \ x \neq 0$

d) $y = 15\sqrt[3]{x} - 5x - 10$

e) $f(x) = \frac{2}{x} - x^2, \ x \neq 0$

f) $y = 2\sqrt{x} - 3x$

Q2 Walter makes different sized vases. The volume of each vase is given by $V = r^2 + \frac{2000}{r}$, where r is the radius of the vase's base.

a) Find the value of r at which the volume, V, is stationary.

b) Is this a minimum or maximum point?

Q2 Hint: This question's no different to the others in this exercise — just treat V as y and r as x, and carry on as normal.

Q3 The curve given by the function $f(x) = x^2 + ax + b + \frac{c}{x}, x \neq 0$, has a local minimum with coordinates (1, 3).
If $f''(x) = 10$ at (1, 3), find a, b and c.

Increasing and decreasing functions

Here's one final recap from C1 for this chapter. You can use differentiation to find if a function is **increasing** or **decreasing** at a given point. This can help you to sketch the function and determine the nature of turning points.

A function is **increasing** when the gradient is **positive**.

y gets bigger... $\frac{dy}{dx} > 0$

...as x gets bigger

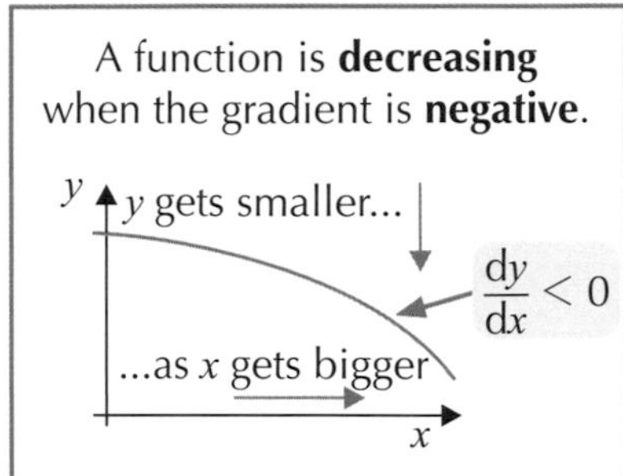

A function is decreasing when the gradient is negative.
y
y gets smaller...
dy/dx < 0
...as x gets bigger
x

You can also tell how **quickly** a function is increasing or decreasing by looking at the size of the gradient — the **bigger** the gradient (positive or negative), the **faster** the function is increasing or decreasing.

Example

Find the values of x for which the function $y = \frac{x}{4} - 5 + \frac{9}{x}$, $x \neq 0$, is increasing.

- You want to know when y is increasing — so **differentiate**.

$$y = \frac{1}{4}x - 5 + 9x^{-1}$$

$$\Rightarrow \quad \frac{dy}{dx} = \frac{1}{4} - 9x^{-2} = \frac{1}{4} - \frac{9}{x^2}$$

- It's an **increasing** function when the derivative is **greater** than zero, so write it down as an inequality and solve it.

$$\frac{dy}{dx} > 0 \Rightarrow \frac{1}{4} - \frac{9}{x^2} > 0$$

$$\Rightarrow x^2 - 36 > 0$$

$$\Rightarrow (x + 6)(x - 6) > 0$$

Tip: Solving quadratic inequalities was covered in C1.

- Solve the inequality by thinking about the graph of $y = x^2 - 36$. The coefficient of x^2 is **positive**, so the graph will be **u-shaped**. It crosses the x-axis at $\boldsymbol{x = -6}$ and $\boldsymbol{x = 6}$, so $x^2 - 36 > 0$ when $x < -6$ and when $x > 6$.

$y = x^2 - 36$

- So the function is increasing when $x < -6$ and $x > 6$.

Tip: This means the function is decreasing for $-6 < x < 6$.

- You could also look at the nature of the **stationary points** — this will tell you where the function changes between increasing and decreasing.
  $x = -6$ and $x = 6$ at the **stationary points** (as $\frac{dy}{dx} = 0$ at these points).
  $$\frac{dy}{dx} = \frac{1}{4} - 9x^{-2} \Rightarrow \frac{d^2y}{dx^2} = 18x^{-3} = \frac{18}{x^3}$$
- When $x = -6$, $\frac{d^2y}{dx^2} = -\frac{1}{12}$, which is negative, so it's a **maximum**.
  So the function is increasing as it approaches $x = -6$ and starts decreasing after $x = -6$.
- When $x = 6$, $\frac{d^2y}{dx^2} = \frac{1}{12}$, which is positive, so it's a **minimum**.
  So the function is decreasing as it approaches $x = 6$ and starts increasing after $x = 6$.
- This fits in with what you know already — that the function is increasing when $x < -6$ and when $x > 6$.

Exercise 2.5

Q1 For each of these functions, calculate the first derivative and use this to find the range of values for which the function is decreasing.

a) $y = x^2 - 6x + 1$

b) $y = 9x + \frac{1}{x} - 2,\ x \neq 0$

c) $y = 4\sqrt{x} - x,\ x \geq 0$

Q1 b) Hint: Don't forget about the $x \neq 0$ part when you write out your final answer.

Q2 Differentiate these functions and find the range of values for which each function is increasing.

a) $y = x^2 + \sqrt{x},\ x > 0$ b) $y = 4x^2 + \frac{1}{x},\ x \neq 0$

Q3 The function $f(x) = \frac{1}{2}x^2 + 7x + \frac{36}{x}$ is defined for all $x \neq 0$.

The graph of $y = f(x)$ has a turning point at $(-6, -30)$.

a) Find $f'(x)$ and use it to find the coordinates of the other turning points of the graph of $y = f(x)$.

b) Find $f''(x)$ and use it to determine the nature of each turning point of the graph of $y = f(x)$.

c) Hence find the range of values for which $f(x)$ is increasing.

Q3 a) Hint: You'll need to factorise a cubic here — you should have done this in C1.

Review Exercise — Chapter 5

Q1 Differentiate these functions with respect to x:

a) $y = 3x^3 - 5x + 10$

b) $y = x^4 + \sqrt{x}$

c) $y = \frac{7}{x^2} - \frac{3}{\sqrt{x}} + 12x^3$

Q2 Find the equations of the tangent and the normal to the curve $y = \sqrt{x^3} - 3x - 10$ at $x = 16$.

Q3 Find the equation of the tangent to the curve $y = x^3 + \frac{4}{x} + 2\sqrt{x}$ at $x = 1$.

Q4 Show that the graphs of $y = \frac{x^3}{3} - 2x^2 - 4x + \frac{86}{3}$ and $y = \sqrt{x}$ both go through the point (4, 2), and are perpendicular at that point.

Q4 Hint: You can show that two curves are perpendicular at a point in the same way you'd show that a line and a curve are perpendicular.

Q5 Consider the curve C given by the equation $y = -\frac{10}{x} - 9$, $x \neq 0$, and the line L given by the equation $y = 2x - 21$.

a) Find the coordinates of the points, A and B, where C and L intersect.

b) Find the gradient of C at points A and B.

c) Find the equations of the normals to C at A and B.
Give your answers in the form $ax + by + c = 0$, where a, b and c are integers.

Q6 Find the equations of the tangent and the normal to the curve $y = 1 + \sqrt{x^3}$ at $x = 16$.

Q7 Let $f(x) = x^2 + \frac{2}{x}$. Find $f''(x) + 2f'(x) - 4f(x)$.

Q8 A cyclist sets off from a set of traffic lights.
His movement is modelled by the equation $x = 3\sqrt{t} + \frac{1}{2}t^2$, for $0 \leq t \leq 30$,
where x is the distance travelled, in metres, from the traffic lights after t seconds.

a) Find $\frac{dx}{dt}$ and $\frac{d^2x}{dt^2}$.

b) What is the cyclist's speed after 9 seconds?

c) What is his acceleration after 25 seconds?

Q9 The function $f(x) = \frac{1}{2}x - 3 - \frac{16}{x^2}$ is defined for all $x \neq 0$.
The graph of $y = f(x)$ has one stationary point. Find its coordinates.

Q10 a) Find the stationary points of the graph of the function $y = x^3 + \frac{3}{x}$, $x \neq 0$.

b) Work out whether each stationary point is a maximum or a minimum.

Q11 Find all the stationary points of the graph of $y = 75\sqrt[3]{x} - \frac{x}{4} + 20$ and determine their nature.

Q12 Find when each of these functions is increasing and decreasing:

a) $y = \frac{1}{x^2}$, $x \neq 0$

b) $y = 6\left(\frac{1}{x} + 2\right)\left(\frac{1}{x} - 3\right)$, $x > 0$

Q13 The diagram shows a box with dimensions x cm, $2x$ cm and y cm, and volume 200 cm³.

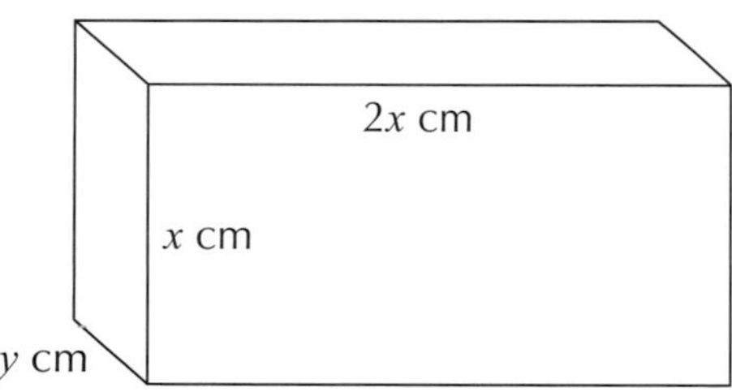

a) Show that the surface area A of the box is given by $A = 4x^2 + \frac{600}{x}$.

b) Use calculus to find the value of x that gives the minimum value of A (to 3 s.f.).

c) Hence find the minimum possible surface area of the box, correct to 3 s.f.

Q13 b) Hint: 'Use calculus' means 'use differentiation or integration' — bet you can't work out which one you need here...

Exam-Style Questions — Chapter 5

1 Differentiate with respect to x:

a) $f(x) = 2\sqrt{x} + \frac{1}{x}$ *(3 marks)*

b) $g(x) = \frac{(x+2)(x+1)}{\sqrt{x}}$ *(4 marks)*

2 Given that $y = x^7 + \frac{2}{x^3}$, find:

a) $\frac{dy}{dx}$ *(2 marks)*

b) $\frac{d^2y}{dx^2}$ *(2 marks)*

3 Find the gradient of the curve $y = \frac{1}{\sqrt{x}} + \frac{1}{x}$ at the point $\left(4, \frac{3}{4}\right)$. *(5 marks)*

4 a) Show that the expression $\frac{x^2 + 3x^{\frac{3}{2}}}{\sqrt{x}}$ can be written in the form $x^p + 3x^q$, and state the values of p and q. *(3 marks)*

b) Now let $y = 3x^3 + 5 + \frac{x^2 + 3x^{\frac{3}{2}}}{\sqrt{x}}$.
Find $\frac{dy}{dx}$, giving each coefficient in its simplest form. *(4 marks)*

5 Given that $f(x) = \frac{1}{4}x^4 + 7 + \frac{3\sqrt{x}}{x^2}$ and $x > 0$, find:

a) $f'(x)$ *(3 marks)*

b) $f''(x)$ *(3 marks)*

6 A steam train travels between Haverthwaite and Eskdale at a speed of x miles per hour and burns y units of coal per hour, where $y = 2\sqrt{x} + \frac{27}{x}$, for $x > 2$.

a) Find the speed that gives the minimum rate of coal consumption. *(5 marks)*

b) Find $\frac{d^2y}{dx^2}$, and hence verify that the speed found in part a) gives the minimum rate of coal consumption. *(2 marks)*

c) Calculate the minimum rate of coal consumption. *(1 mark)*

7 Lotte wants to build an open-top plastic fish tank for her goldfish with a capacity of 40 000 cm^3, and with sides of length x, x and y cm, as shown in **Figure 1**.

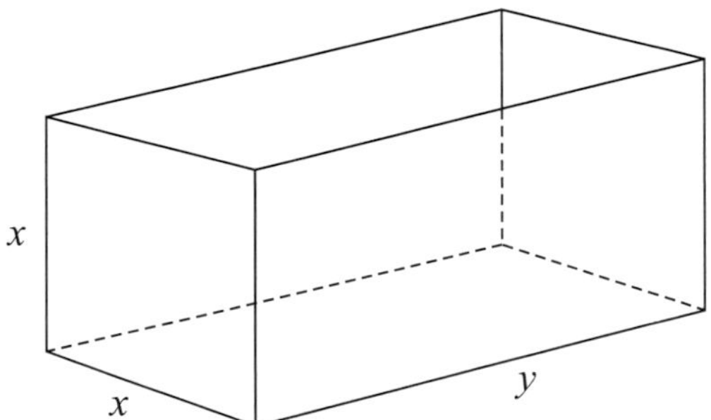

Figure 1

a) Show that the surface area of the tank in cm^2 is given by $A = 2x^2 + \frac{120\,000}{x}$ *(4 marks)*

b) Find the value of x at which A is stationary to 3 s.f., and show that this is a minimum value of A. *(6 marks)*

c) Calculate the minimum area of plastic needed to build the tank, to 3 s.f. *(2 marks)*

8 a) Determine the coordinates of the stationary points of the curve $y = 4x + 3 + \frac{1}{x}$. *(4 marks)*

b) Find whether each of these points is a maximum or minimum. *(3 marks)*

Chapter 6 Integration

1. Integration

Learning Objectives:

- Be able to integrate functions containing rational powers of x.
- Be able to find the equation of a curve, given the gradient and a point on the curve.
- Be able to evaluate definite integrals and use them to calculate the area between a curve and a line, or between two curves.

Integration is just the process of getting from $\frac{dy}{dx}$ back to y itself.

A lot of the theory in this chapter should be familiar from C1 — this first section starts with a recap of the basics of integration.

Integrating x^n

Integrating x^n where n is a positive integer

Here's what you should already know from C1:

Integration is the '**opposite**' of differentiation. When you integrate something, you're trying to find a function that returns to **what you started with** when you differentiate it. This function is called an **integral**.

The integral of a **function** f(x) with respect to x is written:

$\int$ means **the integral of**.

$$\int f(x)\,dx$$

dx means **with respect to x**.

For example, 'the integral of $2x$ with respect to x' is written $\int 2x\,dx$.
The answer could be **any function** which differentiates to give $2x$ (e.g. x^2, $x^2 + 1$, $\pi + x^2$, ...).

The formula below tells you how to integrate **any power of x** (except x^{-1}).

$$\int x^n\,dx = \frac{x^{n+1}}{n+1} + C$$

Tip: Remember, C is the constant of integration — it represents 'any number'.

In other words, to integrate a power of x,

(i) Increase the power by one — then divide by it.
(ii) Add a **constant**.

Example 1

Find $\int x^4\,dx$.

Increase the power to 5...

$$\int x^4\,dx = \frac{x^5}{5} + C$$

...divide by 5.... ...and add a constant of integration.

You can always check that you've got the right answer by differentiating it — you should end up with the thing you started with:

$$\frac{d}{dx}\left(\frac{x^5}{5} + C\right) = \frac{d}{dx}\left(\frac{x^5}{5}\right) + \frac{d}{dx}(C) = x^4 + 0 = x^4$$

Tip: Don't forget the constant of integration — missing it out is a sure way to lose easy marks in the exam.

When the function is multiplied by a **constant**, you can take the constant outside the integral. So, for some constant a:

$$\int ax^n \, dx = a\int x^n \, dx$$

Example 2

Find $\int 8x^3 \, dx$.

Take the 8 outside the integral... ...increase the power by 1 to 4...

$$\int 8x^3 \, dx = 8\int x^3 \, dx = 8\left(\frac{x^4}{4}\right) + C = 2x^4 + C$$

...divide by 4... ...and add a constant of integration.

Check your answer is correct by differentiating:

$$\frac{d}{dx}(2x^4 + C) = \frac{d}{dx}(2x^4) + \frac{d}{dx}(C) = 8x^3 + 0 = 8x^3$$

Tip: You don't need to multiply C by 8, because C represents any number so it doesn't have a specific value here.

Integrating x^n where n is negative or a fraction

You can integrate **negative integer** or **fractional** powers of x using the formula on the previous page.

Tip: You can't use the formula on p.124 to integrate $\frac{1}{x} = x^{-1}$. When you increase the power by 1, then divide by the power you get:

$$\int x^{-1} \, dx = \frac{x^0}{0}$$

This is undefined since you can't divide by 0.

Examples

Find $\int \frac{1}{x^3} \, dx$.

Increase the power by 1 to –2...

$$\int \frac{1}{x^3} \, dx = \int x^{-3} \, dx = \frac{x^{-2}}{-2} + C = -\frac{1}{2x^2} + C$$

...divide by –2... ...and add a constant of integration.

Check: $\frac{d}{dx}\left(-\frac{1}{2x^2} + C\right) = \frac{d}{dx}\left(-\frac{1}{2}x^{-2}\right) + \frac{d}{dx}(C) = x^{-3} + 0 = \frac{1}{x^3}$

Find $\int \sqrt[3]{x^4} \, dx$.

Add 1 to the power...

$$\int \sqrt[3]{x^4} \, dx = \int x^{\frac{4}{3}} \, dx = \frac{x^{\frac{7}{3}}}{\left(\frac{7}{3}\right)} + C = \frac{3\sqrt[3]{x^7}}{7} + C$$

...then divide by $\frac{7}{3}$... ...and add a constant of integration.

Check: $\frac{d}{dx}\left(\frac{3\sqrt[3]{x^7}}{7} + C\right) = \frac{d}{dx}\left(\frac{3}{7}x^{\frac{7}{3}}\right) + \frac{d}{dx}(C) = x^{\frac{4}{3}} + 0 = \sqrt[3]{x^4}$

Tip: Be careful when dividing by a fraction — dividing by $\frac{a}{b}$ is the same as multiplying by the fraction flipped upside-down, $\frac{b}{a}$.

Exercise 1.1

Q1 Find an expression for y when $\frac{dy}{dx}$ is the following:

a) x^{10} b) $7x^2$ c) 11 d) x^{-2}

e) $4x^{-4}$ f) $-6x^{-5}$ g) $x^{\frac{1}{2}}$ h) $x^{\frac{1}{3}}$

Q2 Find the following:

a) $\int x^{\frac{2}{3}}\,dx$ b) $\int 7x^{\frac{4}{3}}\,dx$ c) $\int x^{-\frac{1}{2}}\,dx$

d) $\int 2x^{-\frac{1}{3}}\,dx$ e) $\int 14x^{0.4}\,dx$ f) $\int -1.2x^{-0.6}\,dx$

g) $\int -2x^{-\frac{5}{4}}\,dx$ h) $\int -\frac{3}{2}x^{-\frac{1}{2}}\,dx$ i) $\int -\frac{4}{3}x^{-\frac{4}{3}}\,dx$

Integrating functions

Just like differentiating, if there are **lots of terms** in an expression, you can just integrate each bit **separately**, like this:

$$\int (f(x) + g(x))\,dx = \int f(x)\,dx + \int g(x)\,dx$$

Examples

Find $\int \left(3x^2 - \frac{2}{\sqrt{x}} + \frac{7}{x^2}\right) dx$.

Write as powers of x.

$$\int \left(3x^2 - \frac{2}{\sqrt{x}} + \frac{7}{x^2}\right) dx = \int (3x^2 - 2x^{-\frac{1}{2}} + 7x^{-2})\,dx$$

Integrate each term separately.

Take the constants outside the integrals.

$$= 3\int x^2\,dx - 2\int x^{-\frac{1}{2}}\,dx + 7\int x^{-2}\,dx$$

$$= \frac{3x^3}{3} - \frac{2x^{\frac{1}{2}}}{\left(\frac{1}{2}\right)} + \frac{7x^{-1}}{-1} + C$$

Just add one constant of integration.

$$= x^3 - 4\sqrt{x} - \frac{7}{x} + C$$

Tip: Remember, when you're doing lots of separate integrations, you only need one constant of integration for the whole expression — if each integral gives a constant, you can just add them up to get a new constant.

Find y if $\frac{dy}{dx} = \frac{1}{2}x^3 - 4x^{\frac{3}{2}}x$.

Integrate the derivative of y to get y.

$$y = \int \frac{dy}{dx}\,dx = \int \left(\frac{1}{2}x^3 - 4x^{\frac{3}{2}}x\right) dx$$

$$= \int \left(\frac{1}{2}x^3 - 4x^{\frac{5}{2}}\right) dx = \frac{1}{2}\int x^3\,dx - 4\int x^{\frac{5}{2}}\,dx$$

$$= \frac{1}{2}\left(\frac{x^4}{4}\right) + (-4)\left(\frac{x^{\frac{7}{2}}}{\left(\frac{7}{2}\right)}\right) + C$$

$$= \frac{x^4}{8} - \frac{8}{7}x^{\frac{7}{2}} + C$$

Tip: Some expressions will need simplifying before you integrate with the formula for powers of x.

Find $\int \left(\frac{(x-1)^2}{\sqrt{x}}\right) dx$.

Split into separate terms... ...and write as powers of x.

$$\int \left(\frac{(x-1)^2}{\sqrt{x}}\right) dx = \int \left(\frac{x^2 - 2x + 1}{x^{\frac{1}{2}}}\right) dx = \int (x^{\frac{3}{2}} - 2x^{\frac{1}{2}} + x^{-\frac{1}{2}})\, dx$$

$$= \int x^{\frac{3}{2}}\, dx - 2\int (x^{\frac{1}{2}})\, dx + \int x^{-\frac{1}{2}}\, dx$$

Do each of these bits separately.

$$= \frac{x^{\frac{5}{2}}}{\left(\frac{5}{2}\right)} - \frac{2x^{\frac{3}{2}}}{\left(\frac{3}{2}\right)} + \frac{x^{\frac{1}{2}}}{\left(\frac{1}{2}\right)} + C$$

$$= \frac{2(\sqrt{x})^5}{5} - \frac{4(\sqrt{x})^3}{3} + 2\sqrt{x} + C$$

Exercise 1.2

Q1 Find f(x) when f′(x) is given by the following:

a) $5x + 3x^{-4}$ b) $3x(3 - x)$ c) $(x + 4)^2$

d) $x\left(6x + \frac{4}{x^4}\right)$ e) $\left(x + \frac{2}{x}\right)^2$ f) $x\left(3x^{\frac{1}{2}} - \frac{2}{x^{\frac{4}{3}}}\right)$

g) $6\sqrt{x} - \frac{1}{x^2}$ h) $\frac{2}{\sqrt{x}} - 7x^2\sqrt{x}$ i) $5(\sqrt{x})^3 - \frac{3x}{\sqrt{x}}$

Q1 Hint: Remember f′(x) is just another way of saying $\frac{dy}{dx}$. When you integrate f′(x) you get f(x) and when you differentiate f(x) you get f′(x).

Q2 Find the following integrals:

a) $\int (0.55x^{0.1} - 3x^{-1.5}x)\, dx$ b) $\int \left(8x^3 - \frac{2}{\sqrt{x}} + \frac{5}{x^2}\right) dx$

c) $\int \left((\sqrt{x})^5 + \frac{1}{2\sqrt{x}}\right) dx$ d) $\int \left(\sqrt{x}\left(7x^2 - 1 - \frac{2}{x}\right)\right) dx$

e) $\int (3x - 5\sqrt{x})^2\, dx$ f) $\int \left(\frac{2x^3 - \sqrt{x}}{x}\right) dx$

g) $\int \left(\frac{10x^2 + 3x + 4}{\sqrt{x}}\right) dx$ h) $\int \left(\frac{(5x-3)^2}{\sqrt{x}}\right) dx$

i) $\int (\sqrt{x}(3 - \sqrt{x})^2)\, dx$ j) $\int (x^{\frac{1}{2}} + 1)(x^{-\frac{1}{2}} - 3)\, dx$

Q3 Given that $\frac{dy}{dx} = 1.5x^2 - \frac{4}{x^3}$, find y.

Q4 Given that $f'(x) = \frac{4}{3(x^{\frac{1}{3}})^4} + 5x^{\frac{3}{2}}$, find f($x$).

Q5 Find $\int \left(\sqrt{x}\left(\frac{3x^3}{2} - \frac{1}{x^2}\right)\right) dx$.

Q6 Find $\int \left(\frac{(\sqrt{x} + 3)(\sqrt{x} - 1)}{\sqrt{x}}\right) dx$.

Q7 Find $\int \left(\sqrt{x}\left(\sqrt{x} - \frac{1}{\sqrt{x}}\right)^2\right) dx$.

Integrating to find equations of curves

Tip: Remember, the gradient function is just the function which tells you the gradient — the derivative.

You can find the equation of a **particular curve** by integration if you know its **gradient function** and the coordinates of **one point** on the curve.

Example

The curve $y = f(x)$ goes through the point (8, –2) and $f'(x) = \frac{2}{\sqrt[3]{x^2}} - 1$. Find f(x).

Integrate f′(x) to find the function f(x).

$$f'(x) = 2x^{-\frac{2}{3}} - 1$$

$$\Rightarrow \quad f(x) = \int (2x^{-\frac{2}{3}} - 1)\,dx$$

$$= 2\left(\frac{x^{\frac{1}{3}}}{\frac{1}{3}}\right) - x + C$$

$$= 6\sqrt[3]{x} - x + C$$

Now find C using the point (8, –2):

$$f(8) = -2 \quad \Rightarrow \quad 6\sqrt[3]{8} - 8 + C = -2$$

$$\Rightarrow \quad 12 - 8 + C = -2$$

$$\Rightarrow \quad C = -6$$

So $f(x) = 6\sqrt[3]{x} - x - 6$

Exercise 1.3

Q1 For each of the following, the curve $y = f(x)$ passes through the given point. Find f(x).

a) $f'(x) = 12x^2$, (–1, –1)

b) $f'(x) = 9x^2 + 5x - 2$, (2, 25)

c) $f'(x) = \frac{5}{x^2} + 2x$, (5, 4)

d) $f'(x) = -2x(1 - x)$, (6, 104)

e) $f'(x) = x(x + \frac{3}{x^3})$, (–3, 5)

f) $f'(x) = \frac{9x^3 + 2x^{-2}}{x}$, (–1, 2)

Q2 A curve $y = f(x)$ that passes through the point (4, 9) has gradient function

$$f'(x) = \frac{3}{\sqrt{x}} + 2x$$

Find the equation of the curve.

Q3 The gradient function of a curve is given by

$$\frac{dy}{dx} = 3\sqrt{x} + \frac{1}{x^2}$$

Find the equation of the curve if it passes through the point (1, 7).

Q4 Hint: Here, just treat t the same as you've been treating x in the other questions.

Q4 Consider $\frac{dy}{dt} = (\sqrt{t} - 3)^2$.

Given that $y = 9$ when $t = 4$, find y as a function of t.

Q5 The curve $y = f(x)$ goes through the point $\left(1, \frac{1}{3}\right)$ and $f'(x) = \sqrt{x}(5x - 1)$. Find $f(x)$.

Q6 The curve $y = f(x)$ has derivative $f'(x) = x^2 + \frac{2}{x^{\frac{3}{2}}}$ and passes through the point $\left(1, -\frac{5}{3}\right)$. Find the equation of the curve.

Definite integrals

You'll probably remember from C1 that definite integrals are the ones with the **limits** next to the integral sign — they give you a definite value for an integral.

Finding a definite integral isn't really any harder than an indefinite one — there's just an **extra stage** you have to do.

- Integrate the function as normal but **don't** add a **constant of integration**.
- Once you've integrated the function, work out the **value** of the definite integral by **putting in the limits**:

If you know that the integral of $f(x)$ is $\int f(x)\,dx = g(x) + C$ then:

$$\int_a^b f(x)\,dx = [g(x)]_a^b = g(b) - g(a)$$

Subtract the value of g at the **lower** limit from the value of g at the **upper** limit.

Example

Evaluate $\int_1^4 (6\sqrt{x} + x)\,dx$.

- Find the integral in the normal way — but put the integrated function in **square brackets** and rewrite the **limits** on the right-hand side.

$$\int_1^4 (6\sqrt{x} + x)\,dx = \int_1^4 (6x^{\frac{1}{2}} + x)\,dx = \left[4x^{\frac{3}{2}} + \frac{1}{2}x^2\right]_1^4$$

- Put in the limits:

Put the upper limit into the integral...

...then subtract the value of the integral at the lower limit.

$$\left[4x^{\frac{3}{2}} + \frac{1}{2}x^2\right]_1^4 = \left[4(\sqrt{x})^3 + \frac{1}{2}x^2\right]_1^4 = \left(4(\sqrt{4})^3 + \frac{4^2}{2}\right) - \left(4(\sqrt{1})^3 + \frac{1^2}{2}\right)$$

$$= \left(4(2)^3 + \frac{16}{2}\right) - \left(4(1)^3 + \frac{1}{2}\right)$$

$$= 40 - \frac{9}{2}$$

$$= \frac{71}{2}$$

Tip: You don't need the constant of integration for definite integrals.

The area under a curve

In C1, you saw how the value of a **definite integral** represents the **area under** the graph of the function you're integrating between the two limits.

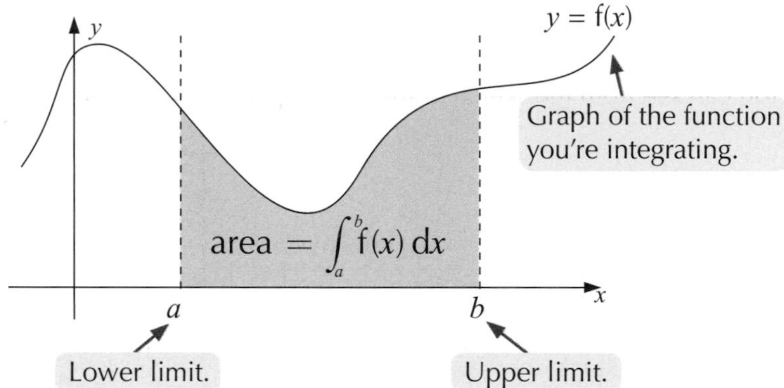

Example

Find the area bounded by the graph of $y = \frac{3}{x^2} + 2x$, the x-axis and the lines $x = 2$ and $x = 5$.

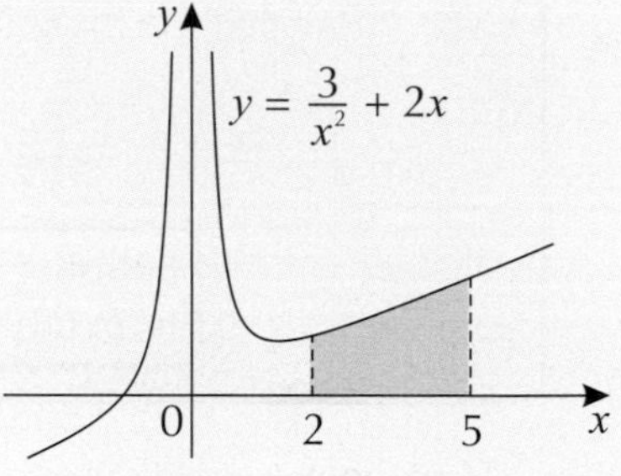

You just need to integrate the function $f(x) = \frac{3}{x^2} + 2x$ with respect to x between 2 and 5:

$$\int_2^5 (3x^{-2} + 2x)\,dx = [-3x^{-1} + x^2]_2^5$$

$$= \left(-\tfrac{3}{5} + 25\right) - \left(-\tfrac{3}{2} + 4\right)$$

$$= \frac{122}{5} - \frac{5}{2}$$

$$= \frac{219}{10}$$

If you integrate a function to find an area that lies **below** the x-axis, it'll give a **negative** value.

If you need to find an area like this, you'll need to make your answer **positive** at the end as you can't have **negative** area.

Tip: Remember that you're actually finding the area between the curve and the ***x*-axis**, not the area under the curve (the area below a curve that lies under the x-axis will be infinite).

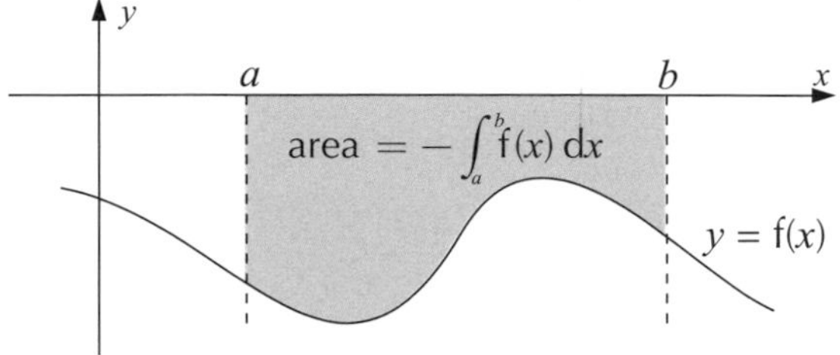

Example

Find the area between the graph of $y = \frac{x^3}{8} + \frac{1}{\sqrt{x^3}} - 10$, the x-axis and the lines $x = 2$ and $x = 4$, to 2 d.p.

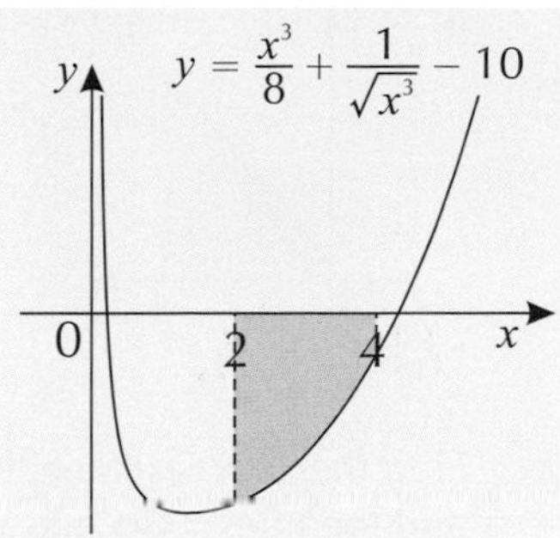

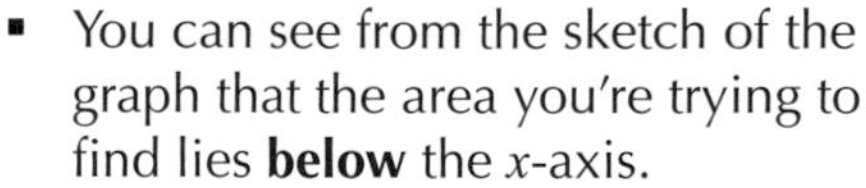

- You can see from the sketch of the graph that the area you're trying to find lies **below** the x-axis.

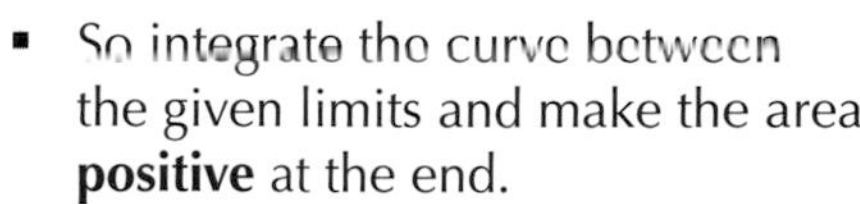

- So integrate the curve between the given limits and make the area **positive** at the end.

$$\int_2^4 \left(\frac{1}{8}x^3 + x^{-\frac{3}{2}} - 10\right) dx = \left[\frac{x^4}{32} - 2x^{-\frac{1}{2}} - 10x\right]_2^4$$

$$= \left(\frac{256}{32} - \frac{2}{2} - 40\right) - \left(\frac{16}{32} - \frac{2}{\sqrt{2}} - 20\right)$$

$$= (8 - 1 - 40) - \left(\frac{1}{2} - \sqrt{2} - 20\right)$$

$$= \sqrt{2} - \frac{27}{2} = -12.09 \text{ (to 2 d.p.)}$$

- So the area between the curve and the x-axis between $x = 2$ and $x = 4$ is 12.09 (to 2 d.p.).

Exercise 1.4

Q1 Find the value of the following, giving exact answers:

a) $\int_2^5 24x^3 \, dx$ b) $\int_{-2}^{-1} (2x^2 + 3x - 1) \, dx$

c) $\int_1^4 x^{-2} \, dx$ d) $\int_2^7 (x^{-3} + x) \, dx$

e) $\int_3^4 (6x^{-4} + x^{-2}) \, dx$ f) $\int_1^2 \left(x^2 + \frac{1}{x^2}\right) dx$

Q2 Given that $\int_1^a \frac{1}{x^2} \, dx = \frac{1}{4}$, find a.

Q3 Evaluate the following, giving exact answers:

a) $\int_0^1 \sqrt{x} \, dx$ b) $\int_8^{27} \sqrt[3]{x} \, dx$

c) $\int_0^9 (x^2 + \sqrt{x}) \, dx$ d) $\int_1^4 (3x^{-4} + \sqrt{x}) \, dx$

e) $\int_0^1 (2x + 3)(x + 2) \, dx$ f) $\int_1^4 \frac{1}{\sqrt{x}} \, dx$

Q4 Find the exact value of the following definite integrals:

a) $\int_1^4 \frac{x^2 + 2}{\sqrt{x}} \, dx$ b) $\int_0^1 (\sqrt{x} + 1)^2 \, dx$ c) $\int_4^9 \left(\frac{1}{x} + \sqrt{x}\right)^2 dx$

Q5 Calculate the exact shaded area in the following diagrams:

a) 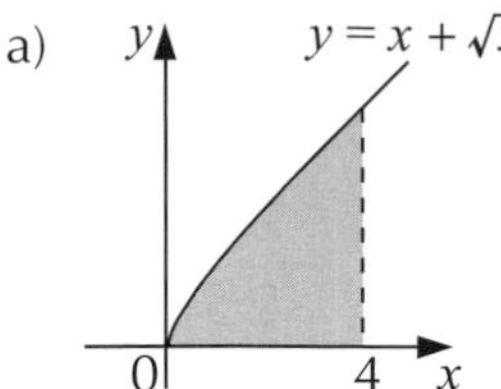

b) 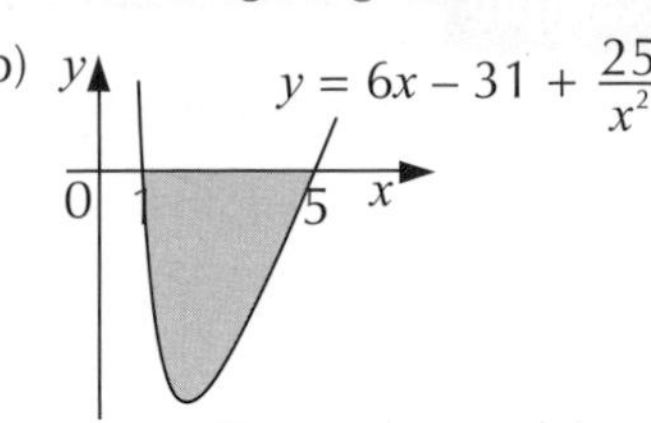

Q6 Find the exact area enclosed by the graph of $y = \frac{3}{\sqrt{x}} + 2x$, the x-axis and the lines $x = 3$ and $x = 12$.

Q7 Find the area enclosed by the graph of $y = \frac{20}{x^5}$, the x-axis and the lines $x = 1$ and $x = 2$.

Finding the area between a curve and a line

You can also use integration to find the area between a **curve** and a **line** (or even **two curves**). You'll either have to **add** or **subtract** integrals to find the area you're after.

Example 1

The diagram shows the curve $y = 3\sqrt{x} - 3$ and the line $y = -x + 15$.

Given that the curve and the line meet at (9, 6), find the area, A, enclosed by the curve, the line and the x-axis.

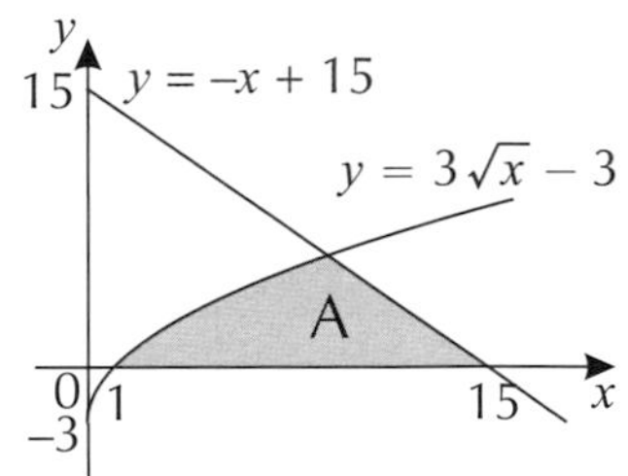

A is the area under the **red** curve between 1 and 9 (A_1) **added to** the area under the **blue** line between 9 and 15 (A_2).

$$A_1 = \int_1^9 (3x^{\frac{1}{2}} - 3)\,dx = [2x^{\frac{3}{2}} - 3x]_1^9$$
$$= (2(\sqrt{9})^3 - 3(9)) - (2(\sqrt{1})^3 - 3(1))$$
$$= (54 - 27) - (2 - 3) = 28$$

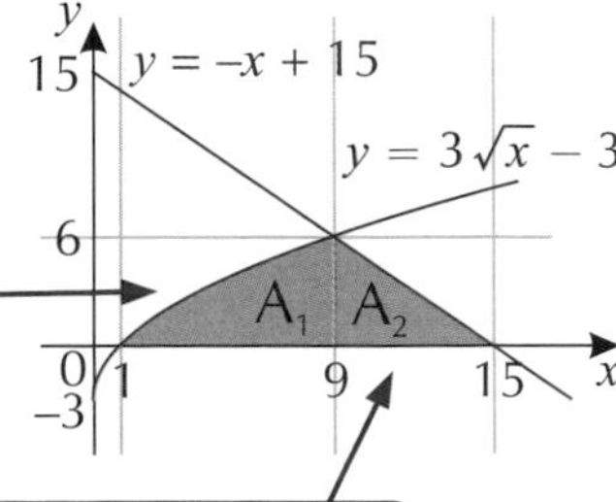

$$A_2 = \frac{1}{2}[(15 - 9) \times 6] = \frac{1}{2}[6 \times 6] = 18$$

So add A_1 and A_2 to find the total area of A:

$A = A_1 + A_2 = 28 + 18 = 46$

Tip: You could find A_2 by integrating too, but it's quicker to use the formula for the area of a triangle.

Example 2

Find the area, B, enclosed by the curves $y = 5\sqrt{x} - \sqrt{x^3}$ and $y = \dfrac{4}{\sqrt{x}}$.

y
$y = \dfrac{4}{\sqrt{x}}$
$y = 5\sqrt{x} - \sqrt{x^3}$
B
0
x

- Find out where the curves meet:

$$5\sqrt{x} - \sqrt{x^3} = \frac{4}{\sqrt{x}}$$

$$\Rightarrow\ 5x^{\frac{1}{2}} - x^{\frac{3}{2}} = \frac{4}{x^{\frac{1}{2}}}$$

$$\Rightarrow\ 5x - x^2 = 4\ \Rightarrow\ x^2 - 5x + 4 = 0$$

$$\Rightarrow\ (x-1)(x-4) = 0\ \Rightarrow\ x = 1,\ x = 4$$

They meet at $\boldsymbol{x = 1}$ and $\boldsymbol{x = 4}$.

- The area B is the area under the **blue** curve between 1 and 4 **minus** the area under the **red** curve between 1 and 4.

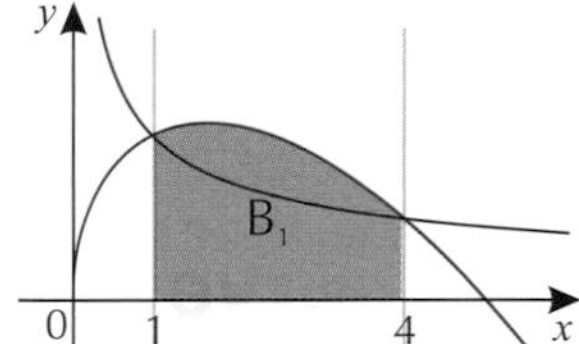

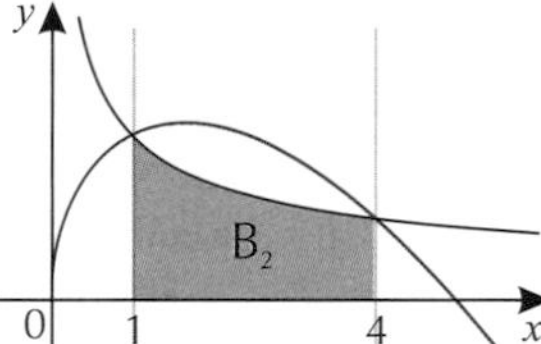

$$\begin{aligned}
B = B_1 - B_2 &= \int_1^4 (5x^{\frac{1}{2}} - x^{\frac{3}{2}})\,dx - \int_1^4 4x^{-\frac{1}{2}}\,dx \\
&= \int_1^4 (5x^{\frac{1}{2}} - x^{\frac{3}{2}} - 4x^{-\frac{1}{2}})\,dx \\
&= \left[\frac{10}{3}x^{\frac{3}{2}} - \frac{2}{5}x^{\frac{5}{2}} - 8x^{\frac{1}{2}}\right]_1^4 \\
&= \left(\frac{10}{3}(\sqrt{4})^3 - \frac{2}{5}(\sqrt{4})^5 - 8(\sqrt{4})\right) - \left(\frac{10}{3}(1) - \frac{2}{5}(1) - 8(1)\right) \\
&= \left(\frac{80}{3} - \frac{64}{5} - 16\right) - \left(\frac{10}{3} - \frac{2}{5} - 8\right) \\
&= -\frac{32}{15} - \left(-\frac{76}{15}\right) = \frac{44}{15}
\end{aligned}$$

Tip: You don't have to combine the integrals like this — if you prefer, you could find B_1 and B_2 first, then do the subtraction at the end, as in the previous example.

Exercise 1.5

Q1 Find the shaded area in each of the following diagrams:

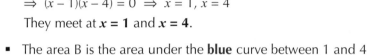

Q1 Hint: If it doesn't look like you've been given enough information, look for any hints on the graph that may tell you what line to use.

a)

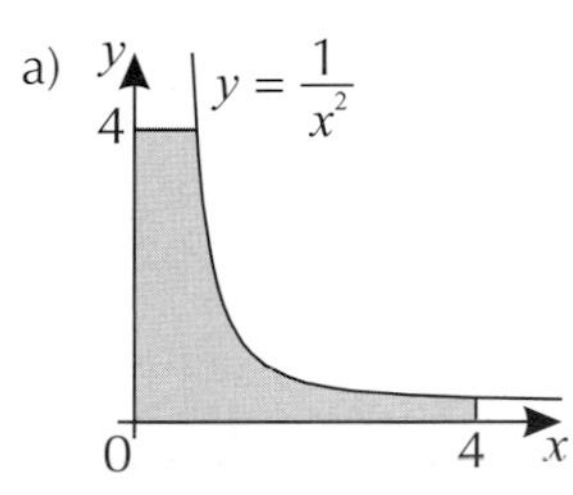

b)

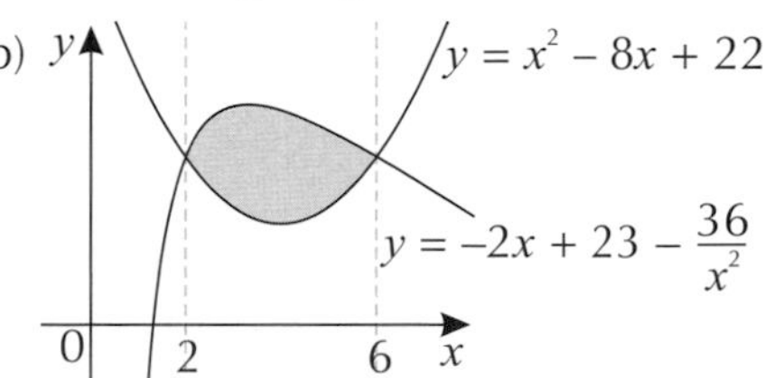

c)

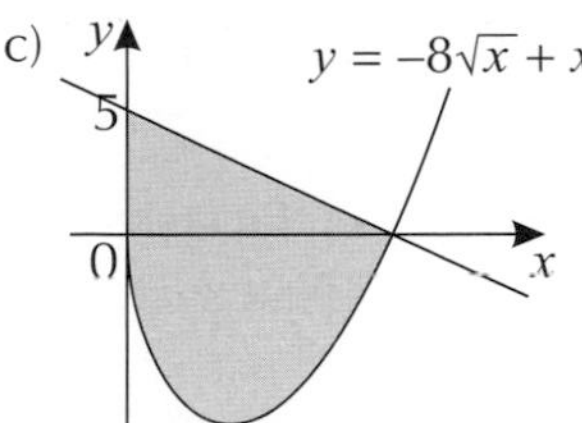

d)

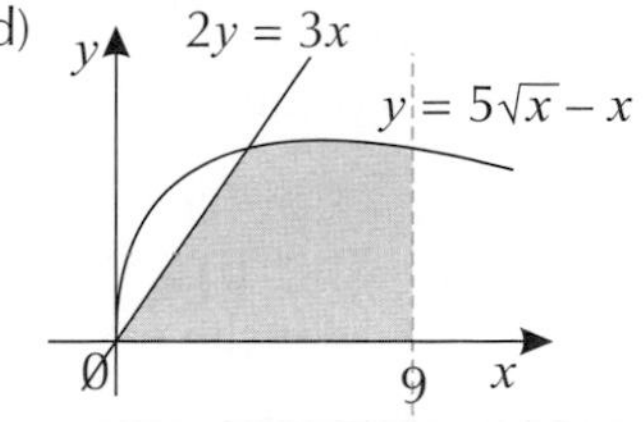

2. The Trapezium Rule

It's not always possible to integrate a function using the methods you learn at A-level, and some functions can't be integrated at all. When this happens, all is not lost — you can approximate the integral using the trapezium rule.

Learning Objective:
- Be able to use the trapezium rule to approximate the value of definite integrals.

The trapezium rule

When you find yourself with a function which is too difficult to integrate, you can **approximate** the area under the curve using lots of **trapeziums**, which gives an approximate value of the integral.

- The **area** under this curve between a and b can be approximated by the green **trapezium** shown.
- It has height $(b - a)$ and parallel sides of length $f(a)$ and $f(b)$.
- The area of the trapezium is an **approximation** of the integral $\int_a^b f(x)\,dx$.

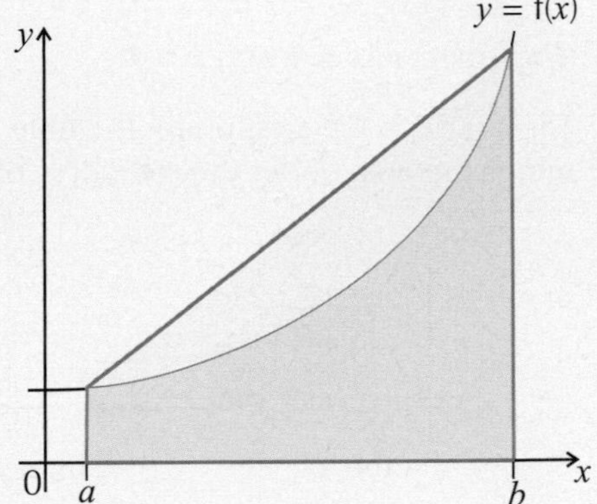

- It's not a very good approximation, but if you split the area up into **more** trapeziums, the approximation will get more and more **accurate** because the **difference** between the trapeziums and the curve will get **smaller**.

Tip: The area of a trapezium is given by the formula $\frac{h}{2}(a + b)$.

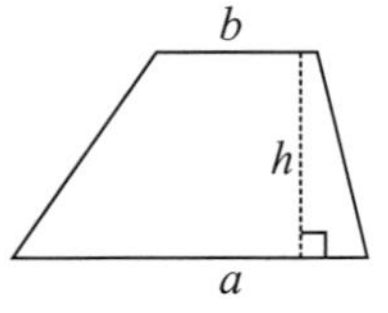

The **trapezium rule** for approximating $\int_a^b \mathbf{f(x)\,dx}$ works like this:

- n is the **number** of strips i.e. trapeziums.
- h is the **width** of each strip — it's equal to $\frac{(b-a)}{n}$.
- The **x-values** go up in steps of h, starting with $x_0 = a$.
- The **y-values** are found by putting the x-values into the equation of the curve — so $y_1 = f(x_1)$. They give the **heights** of the sides of the trapeziums.

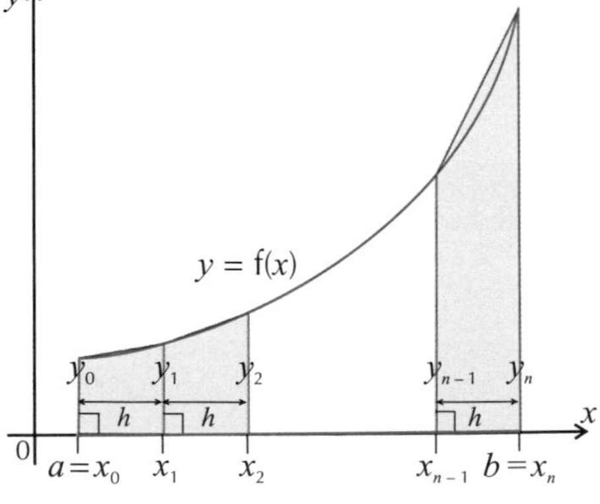

- The **area** of each trapezium is $A = \frac{h}{2}(y_{r-1} + y_r)$, for $r = 1, \ldots, n$.

Then an **approximation** for $\int_a^b f(x)\,dx$ is found by **adding** the **areas** of all the trapeziums:

$$\int_a^b f(x)\,dx \approx \frac{h}{2}(y_0 + y_1) + \frac{h}{2}(y_1 + y_2) + \ldots + \frac{h}{2}(y_{n-1} + y_n)$$
$$= \frac{h}{2}[y_0 + 2(y_1 + y_2 + \ldots + y_{n-1}) + y_n]$$

Tip: If the number of strips is n, the number of y-values is $n + 1$. The y-values are sometimes called **ordinates**.

Tip: This just says 'Add the first and last heights $(y_0 + y_n)$ and add this to twice all the other heights added up — then multiply by $\frac{h}{2}$.'

So the **trapezium rule** says:

$$\int_a^b f(x)\,dx \approx \frac{h}{2}[y_0 + 2(y_1 + y_2 + ... + y_{n-1}) + y_n]$$

This may seem like a lot of information, but it's simple if you follow this **step by step** method:

To approximate the integral $\int_a^b f(x)\,dx$:

- **Split** the interval up into a number of equal sized strips, n. You'll always be told what n is (it could be 4, 5 or even 6).
- Work out the **width** of each strip: $h = \frac{(b-a)}{n}$
- Make a **table** of x and y values:

x	$x_0 = a$	$x_1 = a + h$	$x_2 = a + 2h$	...	$x_n = b$
y	$y_0 = f(x_0)$	$y_1 = f(x_1)$	$y_2 = f(x_2)$	...	$y_n = f(x_n)$

- Put all the values into the **trapezium rule**:
$\int_a^b f(x)\,dx \approx \frac{h}{2}[y_0 + 2(y_1 + y_2 + ... + y_{n-1}) + y_n]$

Tip: The trapezium rule is in the formula booklet — always look it up. It's actually given as $\int_a^b y\,dx$, but this is the same since $y = f(x)$.

Tip: Some questions tell you the number of ordinates instead of telling you n directly. Remember, the number of ordinates is $n + 1$.

Let's have a look at an example:

Example 1

Find an approximate value for $\int_0^2 \sqrt{4 - x^2}\,dx$ using 4 strips. Give your answer to 4 s.f.

- You're told that you need **4 strips** so $n = 4$.
- Work out the **width** of each strip: $h = \frac{(b-a)}{n} = \frac{(2-0)}{4} = 0.5$
- Set up a **table** and work out the y values or heights.

x	$y = \sqrt{4 - x^2}$
$x_0 = 0$	$y_0 = \sqrt{4 - 0^2} = 2$
$x_1 = 0.5$	$y_1 = \sqrt{4 - 0.5^2} = \sqrt{3.75} = 1.936491673$
$x_2 = 1.0$	$y_2 = \sqrt{4 - 1.0^2} = \sqrt{3} = 1.732050808$
$x_3 = 1.5$	$y_3 = \sqrt{4 - 1.5^2} = \sqrt{1.75} = 1.322875656$
$x_4 = 2.0$	$y_4 = \sqrt{4 - 2.0^2} = 0$

Work out the y-values from the x-values, using the function in the integral.

The x-values increase in steps of h.

- Now put all the y-values into the formula with h and n:

$$\int_0^2 \sqrt{4 - x^2}\,dx \approx \frac{0.5}{2}[2 + 2(1.9365 + 1.7321 + 1.3229) + 0]$$
$$= 0.25[2 + (2 \times 4.9915)]$$
$$= 2.996 \text{ (4 s.f.)}$$

Tip: The x-values should go up in nice jumps — make sure that you use the right value for x when calculating y. If $x_2 = 1$ make sure you use 1 instead of 2.

Tip: If you want a more accurate approximation you just need to use more strips.

Tip: Ordinates are just y-values so don't make the mistake of writing $n = 7$ — if there are 7 y-values there are only 6 strips.

Example 2

Use the trapezium rule with 7 ordinates to find an approximation to $\int_1^{2.2} 2\log_{10}x \, dx$, giving your answer to 3 d.p.

- Remember, **7 ordinates** means **6 strips** — so $n = 6$.
- Calculate the **width** of the strips: $h = \frac{(b-a)}{n} = \frac{(2.2-1)}{6} = 0.2$
- Set up a **table** and work out the y-values using $y = 2\log_{10} x$:

x	$y = 2\log_{10} x$ (5 d.p.)
$x_0 = 1$	$y_0 = 2\log_{10} 1 = 0$
$x_1 = 1.2$	$y_1 = 2\log_{10} 1.2 = 0.15836$
$x_2 = 1.4$	$y_2 = 0.29226$
$x_3 = 1.6$	$y_3 = 0.40824$
$x_4 = 1.8$	$y_4 = 0.51055$
$x_5 = 2.0$	$y_5 = 0.60206$
$x_6 = 2.2$	$y_6 = 0.68485$

- Putting all these values in the **formula** gives:

$$\int_1^{2.2} 2\log_{10}x \, dx \approx \frac{0.2}{2}[0 + 2(0.15836 + 0.29226 + 0.40824 + 0.51055 + 0.60206) + 0.68485]$$

$$= 0.1 \times [0.68485 + (2 \times 1.97147)]$$

$$= 0.462779$$

$$= 0.463 \text{ (3 d.p.)}$$

The **approximation** that the trapezium rule gives will either be an **overestimate** (too big) or an **underestimate** (too small).

This will depend on the **shape** of the graph — draw the graph and see whether the tops of the trapeziums lie **above** the curve or stay **below** it.

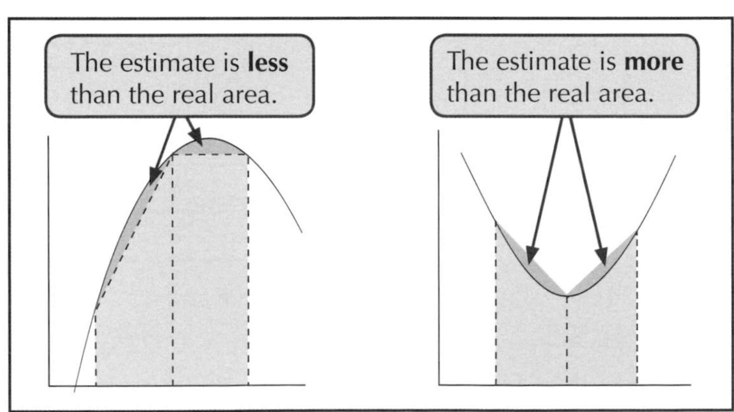
The estimate is **less** than the real area.
The estimate is **more** than the real area.

Example 3

Use the trapezium rule with 8 intervals to find an approximation to $\int_0^{\pi} \sin x \, dx$, and say whether it is an overestimate or underestimate.

- There are **8 intervals**, so $n = 8$.
- Calculate the **width** of the strips: $h = \frac{(b-a)}{n} = \frac{(\pi - 0)}{8} = \frac{\pi}{8}$
- Set up a **table** and work out the y-values. Make sure you keep your x-values in terms of π — it'll make it a lot easier:

x	$y = \sin x$ (5 d.p.)
$x_0 = 0$	$y_0 = \sin 0 = 0$
$x_1 = \frac{\pi}{8}$	$y_1 = 0.38268$
$x_2 = \frac{\pi}{4}$	$y_2 = 0.70711$
$x_3 = \frac{3\pi}{8}$	$y_3 = 0.92388$
$x_4 = \frac{\pi}{2}$	$y_4 = 1$
$x_5 = \frac{5\pi}{8}$	$y_5 = 0.92388$
$x_6 = \frac{3\pi}{4}$	$y_6 = 0.70711$
$x_7 = \frac{7\pi}{8}$	$y_7 = 0.38268$
$x_8 = \pi$	$y_8 = 0$

- So, putting all this in the **formula** gives:

$$\int_0^{\pi} \sin x \, dx \approx \frac{1}{2} \times \frac{\pi}{8}[0 + 2(0.38268 + 0.70711 + 0.92388 + 1 + 0.92388 + 0.70711 + 0.38268) + 0]$$

$$= \frac{\pi}{16} \times [2 \times 5.02734]$$

$$= 1.97 \text{ (3 s.f.)}$$

- If you sketch the graph of $y = \sin x$, you'll be able to work out if this estimate is an **overestimate** or an **underestimate**.

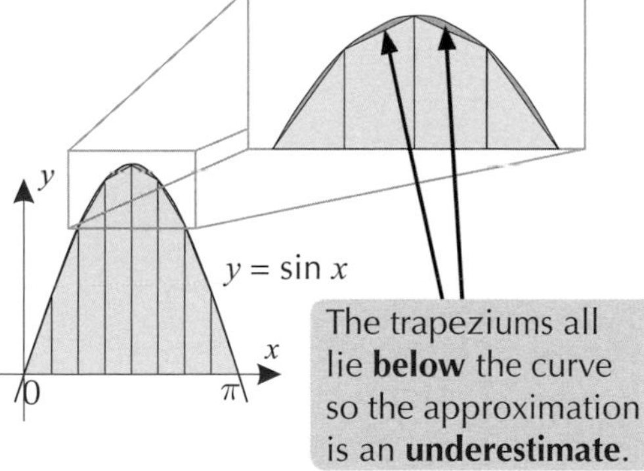
y
y = sin x
x
0
π
The trapeziums all lie below the curve so the approximation is an underestimate.

Tip: Whenever you get a question using trig functions, you have to use radians (see p.16). You'll probably be given a limit with π in, which is a good reminder.

Tip: The values of y in the table are quicker to work out if you know that the graph is symmetrical — the values will repeat.

Tip: In C3, you'll see how to integrate trig functions — this integral has the exact value 2.

Exercise 2.1

Q1 Use the trapezium rule with 4 strips to estimate the following, giving your answer to 2 d.p. Give all values in your table to 4 d.p.

a) $\int_1^3 \frac{1}{x} \, dx$

b) $\int_0^2 \sqrt{1 + 3^x} \, dx$

c) $\int_1^6 \frac{10}{8 - x} \, dx$

d) $\int_0^3 2^x \, dx$

Q2 a) Complete the table for the function $y = \sin x$, giving exact answers.

x	0	$\frac{\pi}{6}$	$\frac{\pi}{3}$	$\frac{\pi}{2}$
y				

b) Use the trapezium rule with 3 strips and the values in the table from part a) to estimate $\int_0^{\frac{\pi}{2}} \sin x \, dx$. Give your answer to 2 d.p.

Q3 Hint: See p.129-133 for more on finding definite integrals.

Q3 a) Evaluate $I = \int_{-4}^{0} (x^2 + 2x + 3) \, dx$ using integration.

b) Use the trapezium rule with 5 ordinates to estimate the value of I.

c) Comment on your answers to part a) and part b).

Q4 Hint: 'Continuous' just means there are no breaks or jumps in the curve. You need a continuous curve if you're using the trapezium rule — but you'll always be given continuous curves so you don't need to worry.

Q4 The curve $y = f(x)$ is continuous and gives the table:

x	-2	-1	0	1	2
y	10	8	7	6.5	3

Use the trapezium rule with 4 strips to estimate $\int_{-2}^{2} f(x) \, dx$.

Q5 Use the trapezium rule to estimate the following correct to 3 d.p. :

a) $\int_0^5 2^{-x} \, dx$ with 4 strips, b) $\int_0^5 2^{-x} \, dx$ with 5 strips.

c) Explain which is likely to be the more accurate estimate.

Q6 a) Use the trapezium rule to estimate $\int_1^3 (3 - (2 - x)^2) \, dx$ with 9 ordinates.

b) Sketch the graph of $y = 3 - (2 - x)^2$ for $0 \leq x \leq 4$.

c) Explain whether your approximation in part a) is an overestimate or an underestimate.

Q7 Hint: See p.21 for the cos values of some common angles.

Q7 a) Complete the table giving exact values for $y = \cos x$.

x	$-\frac{\pi}{2}$	$-\frac{\pi}{3}$	$-\frac{\pi}{6}$	0	$\frac{\pi}{6}$	$\frac{\pi}{3}$	$\frac{\pi}{2}$
y							

b) Use your answers to part a) to show that an approximation for $\int_{-\frac{\pi}{2}}^{\frac{\pi}{2}} \cos x \, dx$ is $\frac{\pi(2 + \sqrt{3})}{6}$.

c) Say whether the approximation in part b) is an overestimate or an underestimate. Explain your answer.

Review Exercise — Chapter 6

Q1 Find f(x) in each case below. Give each term in its simplest form.

a) $f'(x) = x^{-\frac{1}{2}} + 4 - 5x^3$

b) $f'(x) = 3x^2 - \dfrac{2}{x^2}$

c) $f'(x) = 6x^2 - \dfrac{1}{3\sqrt{x}}$

Q2 Find $\int \left(4x^2 + \dfrac{3}{\sqrt{x}} - 2\right) dx$.

Q3 Find $\int (3\sqrt{x} + 3)^2\, dx$.

Q4 Find y in terms of x:

a) $\dfrac{dy}{dx} = \dfrac{1}{\sqrt{x}} + \sqrt{x}$

b) $\dfrac{dy}{dx} = \dfrac{3}{x^2} + \dfrac{3}{\sqrt[3]{x}}$

Q4 Hint:
Remember that $\int \dfrac{dy}{dx}\, dx = y$

Q5 The gradient of a curve C is given by

$$\frac{dy}{dx} = \frac{(x+2)(x-2)}{\sqrt{x}}, \quad x > 0$$

a) Show that $\dfrac{dy}{dx}$ can be written in the form $Ax^{\frac{3}{2}} + Bx^{-\frac{1}{2}}$, where A and B are integers.

b) The point $\left(1, \frac{7}{5}\right)$ lies on C. Find the equation of C.

Q6 The curve C with equation $y = f(x)$ has derivative

$$f'(x) = 6x^2 - 12 - \frac{8}{x^2}, \quad x > 0$$

and passes through the point P with coordinates (–2, 5).
Find the equation of the curve C.

Q7 The curve $y = f(x)$ passes through the point P with coordinates (1, –9).
Given that

$$f'(x) = \frac{5x^2 + 1}{x^{\frac{1}{2}}} - 10, \quad x > 0,$$

find the equation of the curve.

Q8 Evaluate the following definite integrals:

a) $\int_1^2 \left(\dfrac{8}{x^5} + \dfrac{3}{\sqrt{x}}\right) dx$

b) $\int_1^6 \dfrac{3}{x^2}\, dx$

Q9 Find the shaded area in the diagram below.

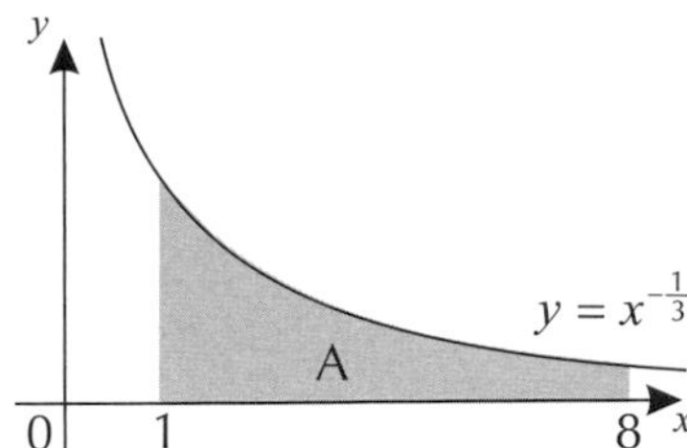

Q10 Use integration to find the shaded area in each of these graphs:

a)

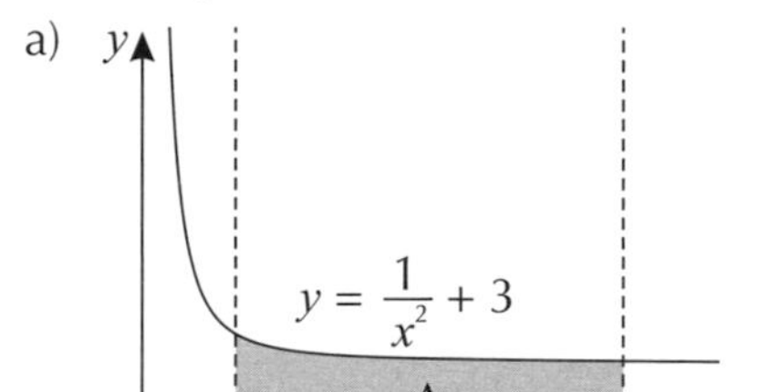

b)

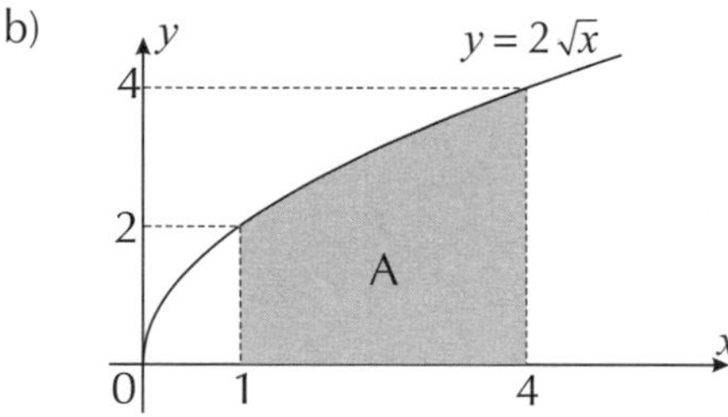

c)

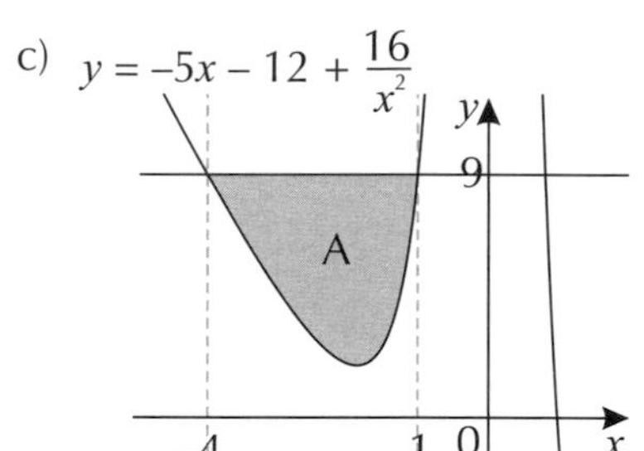

d)

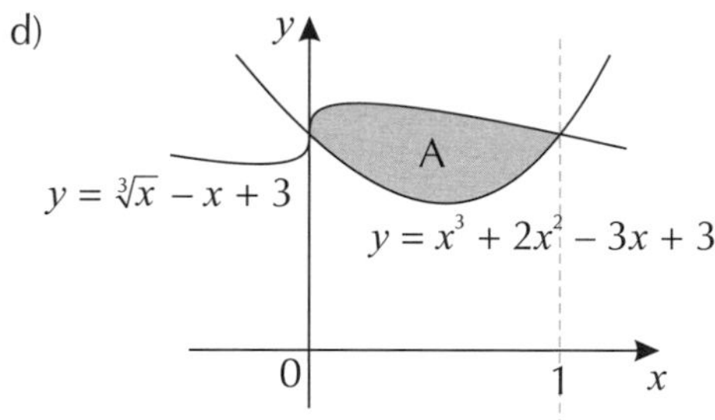

Q11 a) Complete the table for the function $y = \sqrt{1 + x}$, giving your answers to 4 d.p.

x	$x_0 = 0$	$x_1 = 0.5$	$x_2 = 1$	$x_3 = 1.5$	$x_4 = 2$
y	$y_0 =$	$y_1 =$	$y_2 =$	$y_3 =$	$y_4 =$

b) Use the trapezium rule with all the values calculated in the table to approximate the value of $\int_0^2 \sqrt{1 + x}\, dx$. Give your answer correct to 2 d.p.

Q12 Use the trapezium rule with n intervals to estimate the following to 3 s.f. Give y-values to 5 d.p. where appropriate:

a) $\int_0^3 (9 - x^2)^{\frac{1}{2}}\, dx$ with $n = 3$

b) $\int_{0.2}^{1.2} x^{x^2} dx$ with $n = 5$

c) $\int_1^3 2^{x^2}\, dx$ with $n = 4$

d) $\int_1^3 2^{x^2}\, dx$ with $n = 5$

Exam-Style Questions — Chapter 6

1 The curve C has the equation $y = f(x)$, $x > 0$. $f'(x)$ is given as $2x + 5\sqrt{x} + \frac{6}{x^2}$.
A point P on curve C has the coordinates (3, 7).

Find $f(x)$, giving your answer in its simplest form.

(6 marks)

2 The sketch below shows part of curve C, which has the equation
$y = -\frac{1}{x^2}(x + 2)(x - 3)(x - 6)$, $x \neq 0$.

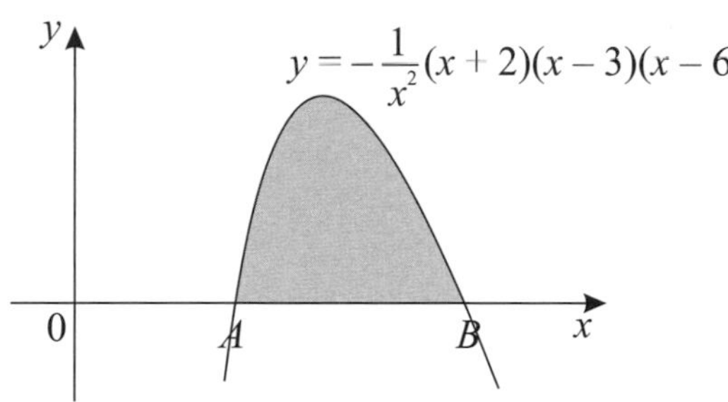

Calculate the shaded area under curve C between points A and B, where C intersects the positive x-axis.

(5 marks)

3 Curve C has equation $y = f(x)$, $x \neq 0$, where the derivative is given by $f'(x) = x^3 - \frac{2}{x^2}$.
The point P (1, 2) lies on C.

a) Find the equation for the tangent to C at the point P, giving your answer in the form $y = mx + c$, where m and c are integers.

(4 marks)

b) Find $f(x)$.

(5 marks)

4 a) Using the trapezium rule with n intervals, estimate the values of:

(i) $\int_2^8 \left(\sqrt{3x^3} + \frac{2}{\sqrt{x}}\right)dx$, $n = 3$

(4 marks)

(ii) $\int_1^5 \left(\frac{x^3 - 2}{4}\right)dx$, $n = 4$

(4 marks)

b) How could you change your application of the trapezium rule to get better approximations?

(1 mark)

5 Find the value of $\int_2^7 (2x - 6x^2 + \sqrt{x})\mathrm{d}x$. Give your answer to 4 d.p. *(5 marks)*

6 Complete the table and hence use the trapezium rule with 6 ordinates to estimate $\int_{1.5}^{4} y\,\mathrm{d}x$.
Give your answer to 3 s.f.

x	$x_0 = 1.5$	$x_1 =$	$x_2 =$	$x_3 =$	$x_4 = 3.5$	$x_5 = 4$
$y = 3x - \sqrt{2^x}$	$y_0 =$	$y_1 = 4$	$y_2 = 5.1216$	$y_3 =$	$y_4 =$	$y_5 = 8$

(5 marks)

7 A curve passes through the point P with coordinates (4, –6).
Given that

$$\frac{\mathrm{d}y}{\mathrm{d}x} = 3\sqrt{x} - \frac{5}{\sqrt{x}},\ x > 0,$$

a) find the equation of the curve in the form $y = \mathrm{f}(x)$, *(5 marks)*

b) find the equation of the normal to the curve at P, giving your answer in the form $ax + by + c = 0$, where a, b and c are integers. *(4 marks)*

8 The diagram below shows the curve C, given by $y = x - 3\sqrt{x}$ for $x \geq 0$,
and the line L, given by $4y = x - 9$. C and L intersect at point P and at the point (9, 0).

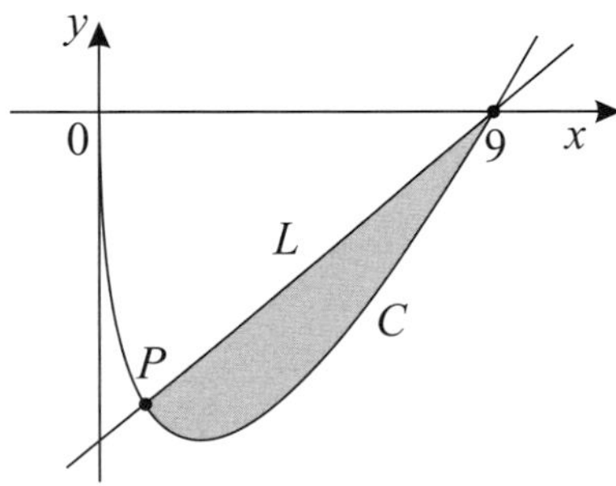

a) Show that the coordinates of point P are (1, –2). *(5 marks)*

b) Calculate $\int_1^9 (x - 3\sqrt{x})\,\mathrm{d}x$. *(3 marks)*

c) Hence find the area of the shaded region. *(2 marks)*

Answers

Chapter 1: Algebra and Functions

1. Laws of Indices

Exercise 1.1 Laws of indices

Q1 a) $2^3 \times 2^4 = 2^{3+4} = 2^7$

b) $10 \times 10^4 = 10^{1+4} = 10^5$

c) $7^2 \times 7^5 \times 7^3 = 7^{2+5+3} = 7^{10}$

d) $p^6 \times p^{-4} \times p^5 = p^{6-4+5} = p^7$

e) $y^{-1} \times y^{-2} \times y^7 = y^{-1-2+7} = y^4$

f) $5^{\frac{1}{2}} \times 5^3 \times 5^{-\frac{3}{2}} = 5^{\frac{1}{2}+3-\frac{3}{2}} = 5^2$

g) $6^5 \div 6^2 = 6^{5-2} = 6^3$

h) $x^{10} \div x^9 = x^{10-9} = x^1 = x$

i) $3^4 \div 3^{-1} = 3^{4-(-1)} = 3^{4+1} = 3^5$

j) $\frac{7^{15}}{7^5} = 7^{15-5} = 7^{10}$

k) $\frac{6^{11}}{6} = 6^{11-1} = 6^{10}$

l) $\frac{r^2}{r^6} = r^{2-6} = r^{-4}$

m) $(3^2)^3 = 3^{2\times3} = 3^6$

n) $(10^6)^{-1} = 10^{6\times(-1)} = 10^{-6}$

o) $(k^{-2})^5 = k^{(-2)\times5} = k^{-10}$

p) $(t^8)^{\frac{1}{2}} = t^{8\times\frac{1}{2}} = t^{\frac{8}{2}} = t^4$

q) $(z^4)^{-\frac{1}{8}} = z^{4\times\left(-\frac{1}{8}\right)} = z^{-\frac{4}{8}} = z^{-\frac{1}{2}}$

r) $(8^{-6})^{-\frac{1}{2}} = 8^{-6\times-\frac{1}{2}} = 8^{\frac{6}{2}} = 8^3$

s) $cd^2 \times c^3d^4 = (c \times c^3) \times (d^2 \times d^4)$
$= c^{1+3} \times d^{2+4}$
$= c^4d^6$

t) $\frac{p^5q^4}{p^4q} = (p^{5-4})(q^{4-1}) = p^1q^3 = pq^3$

u) $\frac{c^{-1}d^{-2}}{c^2d^4} = c^{-1-2}d^{-2-4} = c^{-3}d^{-6} = \frac{1}{c^3d^6}$

v) $(ab^2)^2 = (a)^2(b^2)^2 = a^2b^{2\times2} = a^2b^4$

w) $(x^2y^3z^4)^5 = (x^2)^5(y^3)^5(z^4)^5$
$= (x^{2\times5})(y^{3\times5})(z^{4\times5}) = x^{10}y^{15}z^{20}$

x) $\frac{12yz^{-\frac{1}{2}}}{4yz^{\frac{1}{2}}} = \left(\frac{12}{4}\right)\left(y^{1-1}\right)\left(z^{-\frac{1}{2}-\frac{1}{2}}\right) = 3y^0z^{-1} = \frac{3}{z}$

Q2 a) $4^{\frac{1}{2}} \times 4^{\frac{3}{2}} = 4^{\frac{1}{2}+\frac{3}{2}} = 4^2$
$4^2 = 2^q \Rightarrow 16 = 2^q \Rightarrow q = 4$

b) $1^0 = 1 = q$

c) $\left(\frac{4}{5}\right)^0 = 1 \Rightarrow q = 0$

d) $\frac{7^5 \times 7^3}{7^q} = \frac{7^{5+3}}{7^q} = \frac{7^8}{7^q} = 7^{8-q}$
$49 = 7^2$, so $\frac{7^5 \times 7^3}{7^q} = 49 \Rightarrow 7^{8-q} = 7^2$
$\Rightarrow 8 - q = 2 \Rightarrow q = 6$

e) $\frac{2^q \times 2}{2^5} = \frac{2^{q+1}}{2^5} = 2^{q+1-5} = 2^{q-4}$
$\frac{1}{2} = 2^{-1}$, so $\frac{2^q \times 2}{2^5} = \frac{1}{2} \Rightarrow 2^{q-4} = 2^{-1}$
$\Rightarrow q - 4 = -1 \Rightarrow q = 3$

f) $(3^2)^5 \div (3^q)^3 = 3^{2\times5} \div 3^{q\times3} = 3^{10} \div 3^{3q} = 3^{10-3q}$
so $(3^2)^5 \div (3^q)^3 = 3 \Rightarrow 3^{10-3q} = 3^1$
$\Rightarrow 10 - 3q = 1 \Rightarrow q = 3$

g) $(4^q)^2 \times (4^{-3})^{-\frac{1}{3}} = 4^{q\times2} \times 4^{(-3)\times\left(-\frac{1}{3}\right)}$
$= 4^{2q} \times 4^1 = 4^{2q+1}$
so $(4^q)^2 \times (4^{-3})^{-\frac{1}{3}} = 1 \Rightarrow 4^{2q+1} = 4^0$
$\Rightarrow 2q + 1 = 0 \Rightarrow q = -\frac{1}{2}$

h) $\frac{\left(2^{\frac{1}{2}}\right)^6 \times (2^{-2})^{-2}}{(2^{-1})^q} = \frac{2^{\frac{1}{2}\times6} \times 2^{(-2)\times(-2)}}{2^{(-1)\times q}}$
$= \frac{2^3 \times 2^4}{2^{-q}} = \frac{2^{3+4}}{2^{-q}} = \frac{2^7}{2^{-q}} = 2^{7-(-q)} = 2^{7+q}$
$64 = 2^6$, so $\frac{\left(2^{\frac{1}{2}}\right)^6 \times (2^{-2})^{-2}}{(2^{-1})^q} = 64 \Rightarrow 2^{7+q} = 2^6$
$\Rightarrow 7 + q = 6 \Rightarrow q = -1$

Q3 a) $\frac{1}{p} = p^{-1}$

b) $\sqrt{q} = q^{\frac{1}{2}}$

c) $\sqrt{r^3} = (r^3)^{\frac{1}{2}} = r^{3\times\frac{1}{2}} = r^{\frac{3}{2}}$

d) $\sqrt[4]{s^5} = (s^5)^{\frac{1}{4}} = s^{5\times\frac{1}{4}} = s^{\frac{5}{4}}$

e) $\frac{1}{\sqrt[3]{t}} = \frac{1}{\left(t^{\frac{1}{3}}\right)} = t^{-\frac{1}{3}}$

Q4 a) $r^{\frac{1}{2}} = \sqrt{r} = 3 \Rightarrow r = 3^2 = 9$

b) $8^{\frac{1}{3}} = \sqrt[3]{8} = 2 = r$

c) $4^r = 8 \Rightarrow (2^2)^r = 2^3 \Rightarrow 2^{2r} = 2^3 \Rightarrow 2r = 3$
$\Rightarrow r = \frac{3}{2}$

d) $27^{-\frac{1}{3}} = \frac{1}{27^{\frac{1}{3}}} = \frac{1}{\sqrt[3]{27}} = \frac{1}{3} = \frac{1}{r} \Rightarrow r = 3$

e) $r^{-\frac{3}{4}} = \frac{1}{r^{\frac{3}{4}}} = \frac{1}{8} \Rightarrow r^{\frac{3}{4}} = r^{\frac{1}{4} \times 3} = \left(r^{\frac{1}{4}}\right)^3 = (\sqrt[4]{r})^3 = 8$

$\Rightarrow \sqrt[4]{r} = \sqrt[3]{8} = 2 \Rightarrow r = 2^4 = 16$

For the final line of working, you might have written $r^3 = 8^4 = 4096$, so $r = \sqrt[3]{4096} = 16$ instead.

2. Transformations

Exercise 2.1 — Translations

Q1 a)

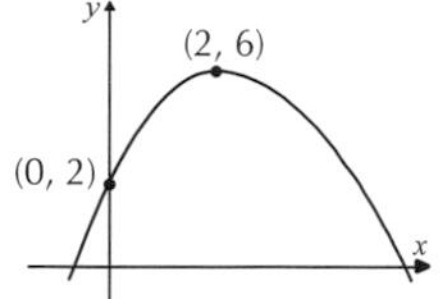

b)

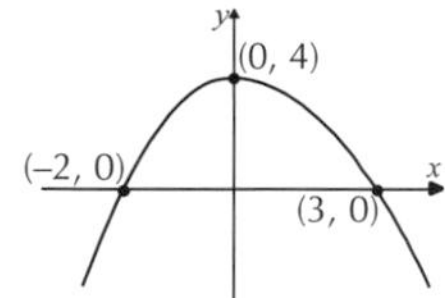

Q2 The graph of $y = g(x - 1)$ is the graph of $y = g(x)$ translated 1 unit to the right so it must be graph B.

Q3 a) The asymptotes are at $x = -3$ and $y = 0$.

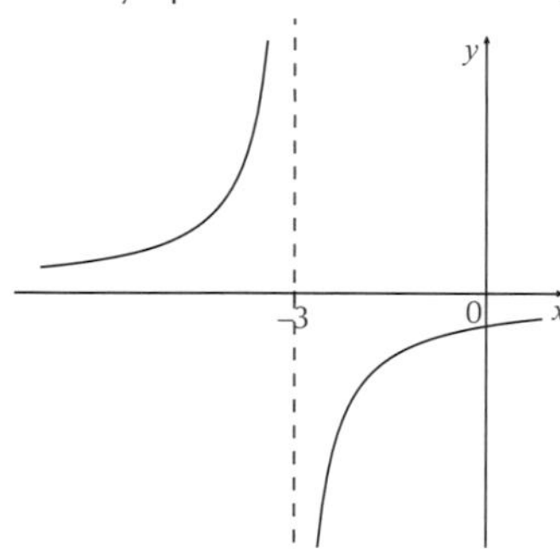

b) The asymptotes are at $x = 0$ and $y = 3$.

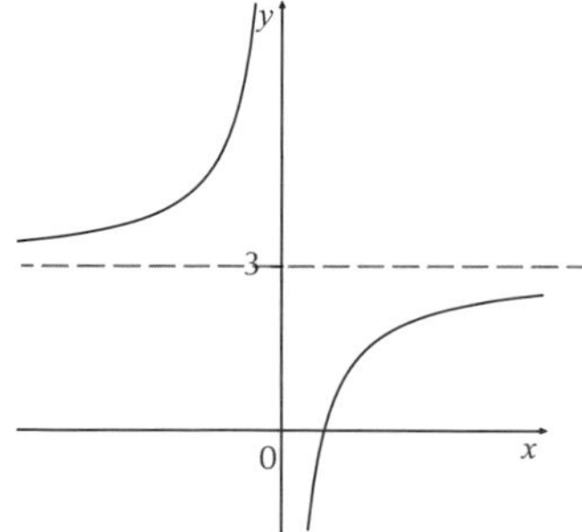

Q4 $y = (x - 2)^2(x - 6) = (x - 2)^2((x - 2) - 4)$ so it is the curve $y = x^2(x - 4)$ with x replaced by $x - 2$ so it will be translated 2 units in the positive x-direction.

Q5 a) $y = x^3 + 3x + 2 = (x^3 + 3x + 7) - 5$ so the translation will be 5 units in the negative y-direction (i.e. 5 units down).

b) $\begin{pmatrix} 0 \\ -5 \end{pmatrix}$

Q6 The equation will be $y = (x + 1)^2 - 3(x + 1) + 7$
$= x^2 + 2x + 1 - 3x - 3 + 7 = x^2 - x + 5$

Q7 a) and **b)**

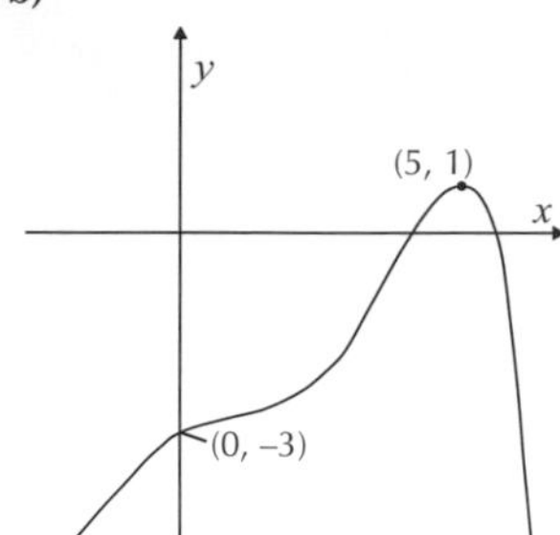

Q8 a)

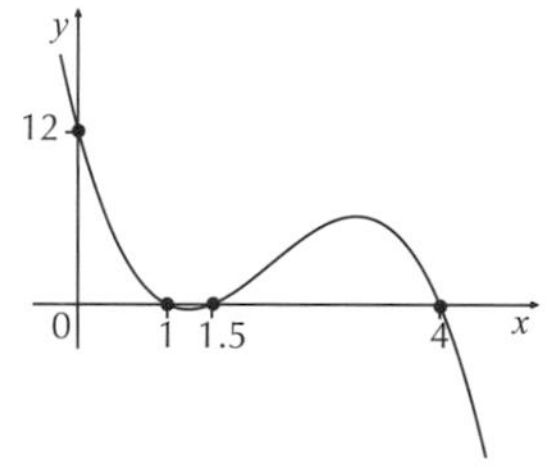

b) The graph is translated by 2 units in the positive x-direction. So, the equation of the translated graph is:
$y = ((x - 2) - 1)(2(x - 2) - 3)(4 - (x - 2))$
$= (x - 3)(2x - 4 - 3)(4 - x + 2)$
$= (x - 3)(2x - 7)(6 - x)$

c)

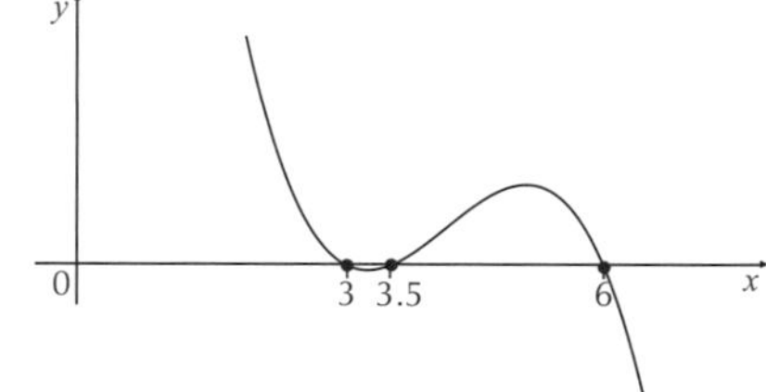

Exercise 2.2 — Stretches and reflections

Q1 a)

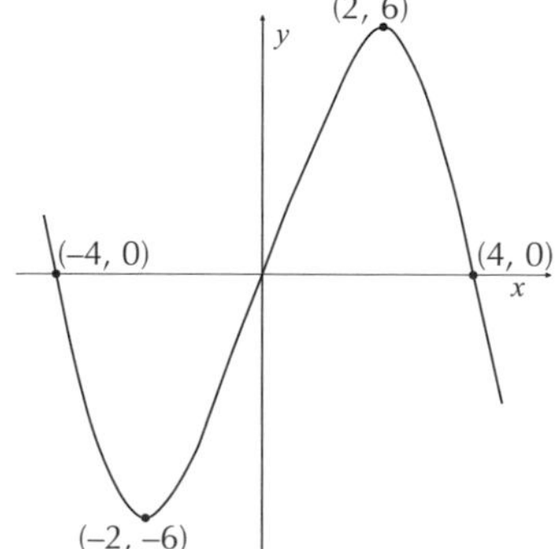

b)

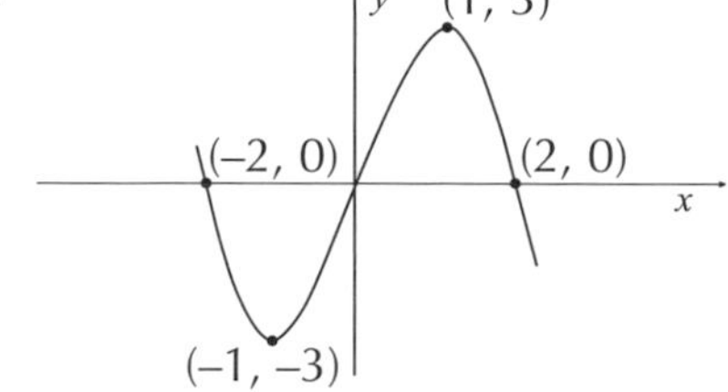

c)

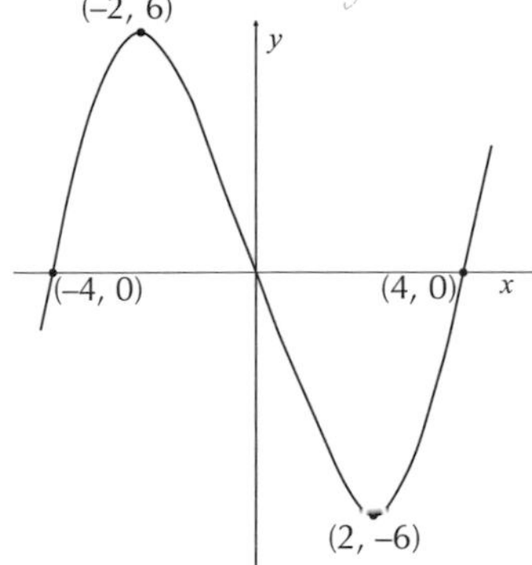

d)

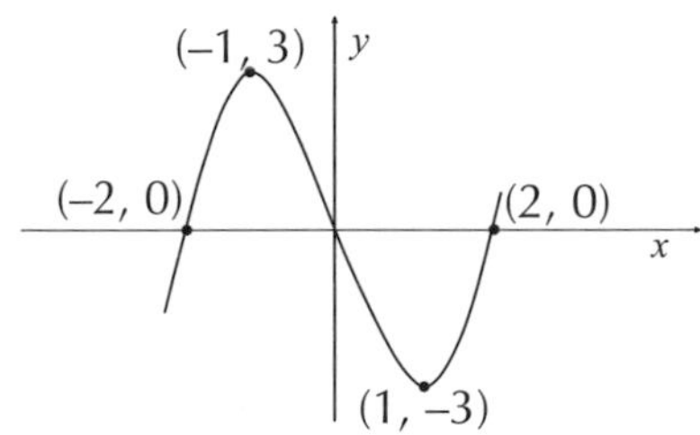

Q2 The graph has been squashed to half its width, so it's a horizontal stretch of scale factor $\frac{1}{2}$, so it must be b).

Q3 The graph has been reflected in the x-axis and stretched vertically by a factor of 3 so it must be b).

Q4 a) $f(x) = x^3 - x = x(x^2 - 1) = x(x + 1)(x - 1)$

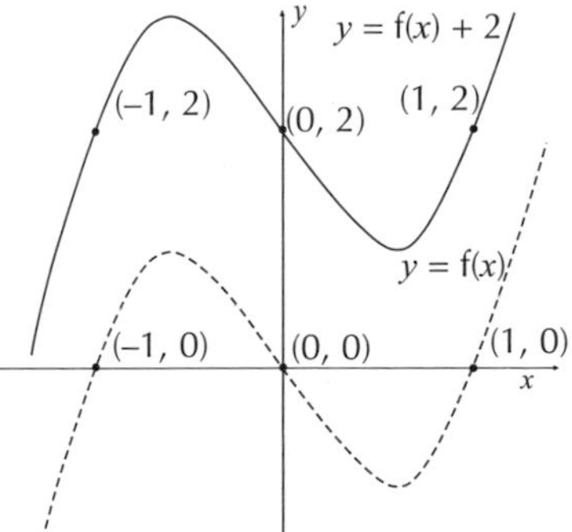

b)

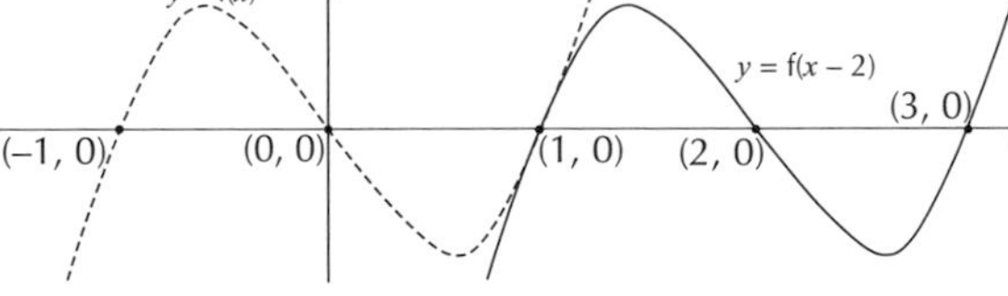

c)

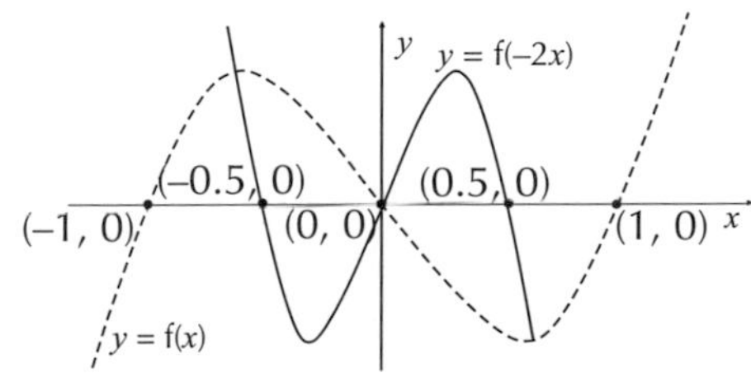

d)

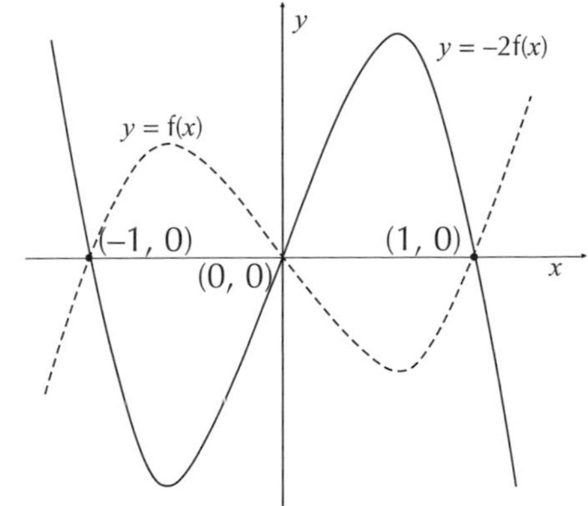

Q5 $3x^3 + 6x + 12 = 3(x^3 + 2x + 4)$ so the whole function has been multiplied by 3. This means the transformation is a stretch vertically by a scale factor of 3.

Q6 $4x^2 - 2x + 4 = (-2x)^2 + (-2x) + 4$ so x has been replaced with $-2x$. The transformation is therefore a reflection in the y-axis followed by a horizontal stretch by a scale factor of $\frac{1}{2}$.

Q7 a) Let $f(x) = 5 - 15x - 90x^2$.
$g(x) = 0.2(5 - 15x - 90x^2) = 1 - 3x - 18x^2$

b) $h(x) = g\left(\frac{1}{3}x\right) = 1 - 3\left(\frac{x}{3}\right) - 18\left(\frac{x}{3}\right)^2 = 1 - x - 2x^2$

Q8 a) $f(x) = x^2 - 6x - 7 = (x - 3)^2 - 16$, so the turning point (i.e. minimum point) is at $(3, -16)$.
Solving $(x - 3)^2 - 16 = 0$ gives $x = -1$ or 7.
So the graph is:

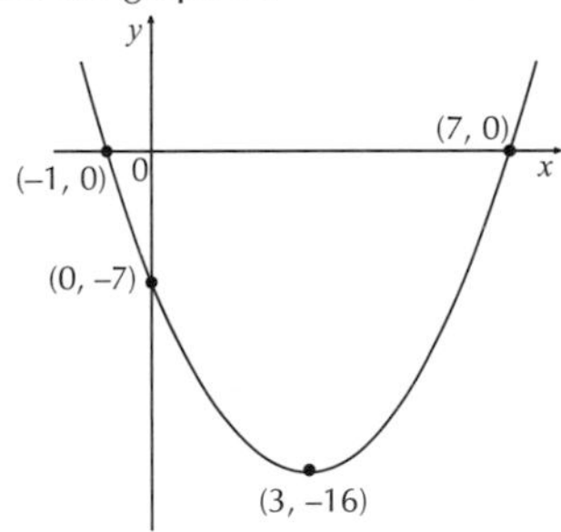

b) $y = -2f(x) = -2(x^2 - 6x - 7)$

c)

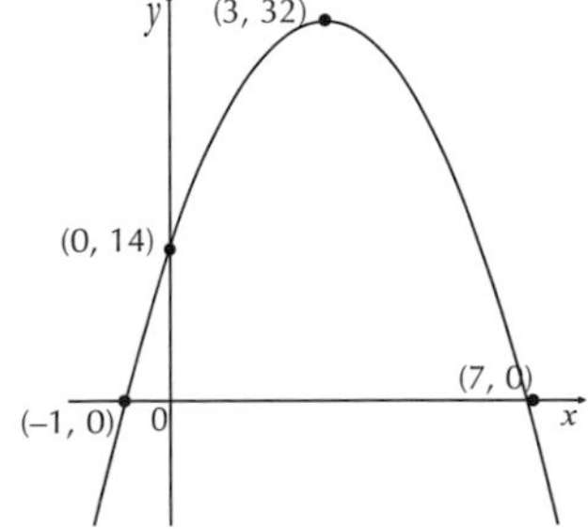

Review Exercise — Chapter 1

Q1 a) $x^{3+5} = x^8$

b) $a^{7+8} = a^{15}$

c) $x^{8-2} = x^6$

d) $a^{2\times4} = a^8$

e) $(x^{1+3})(y^{2+1})z = x^4y^3z$

f) $a^{-1}b^2c^5 = \frac{b^2c^5}{a}$

Q2 a) $\sqrt{16} = 4$

b) $(\sqrt[3]{8})^2 = 2^2 = 4$

c) $(\sqrt[4]{16})^3 = 2^3 = 8$

d) $x^0 = 1$

e) $\frac{1}{\sqrt{49}} = \frac{1}{7}$

Q3 a)

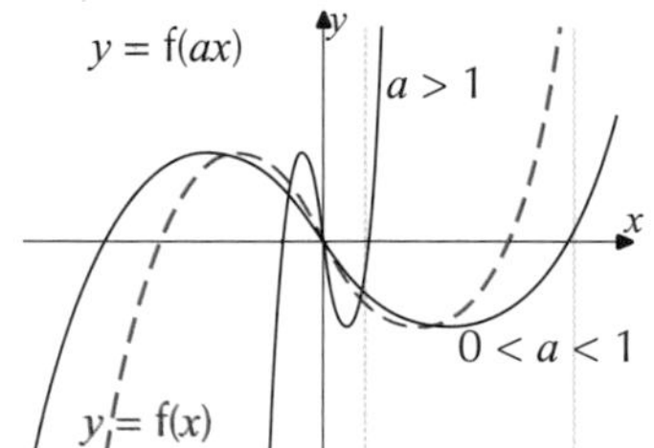

b)

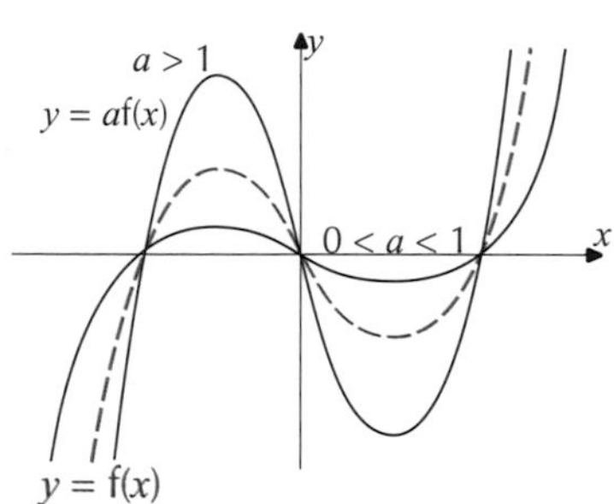

c)

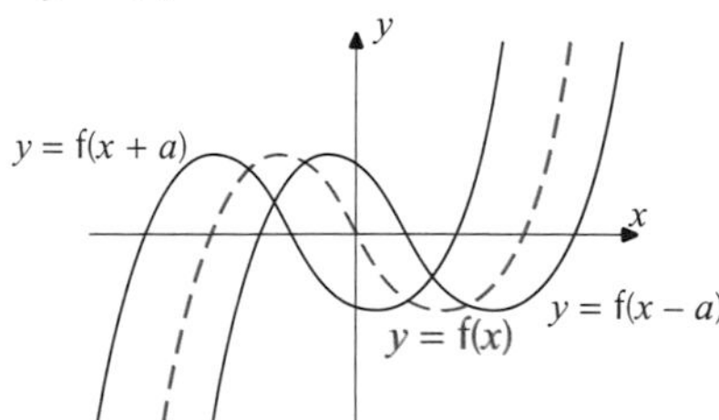

d)

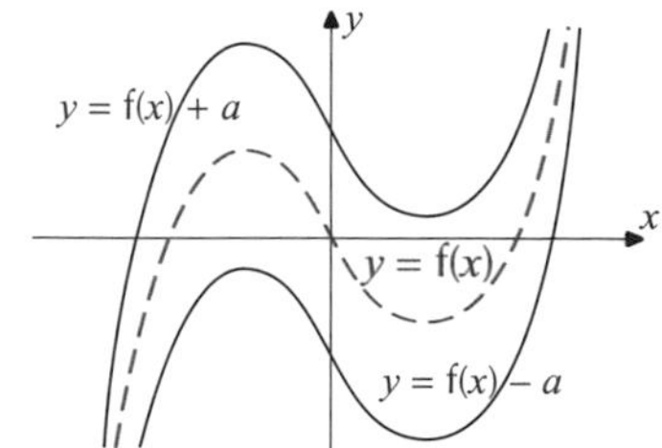

Q4 a)

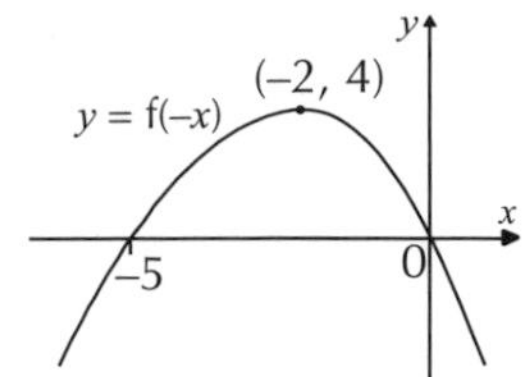

b)

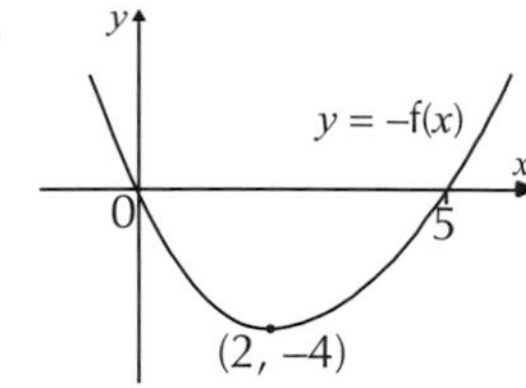

c)

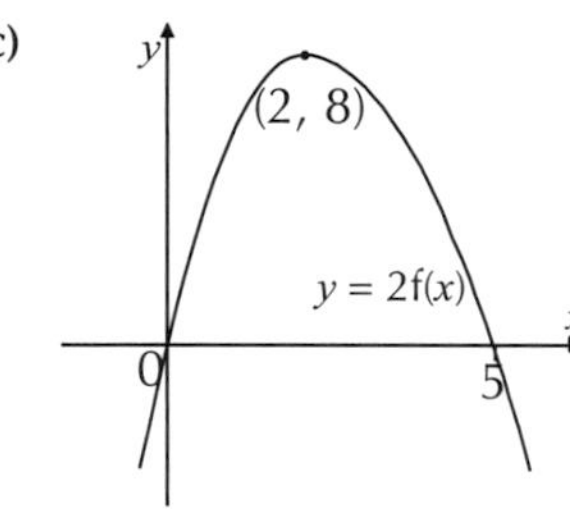

d)

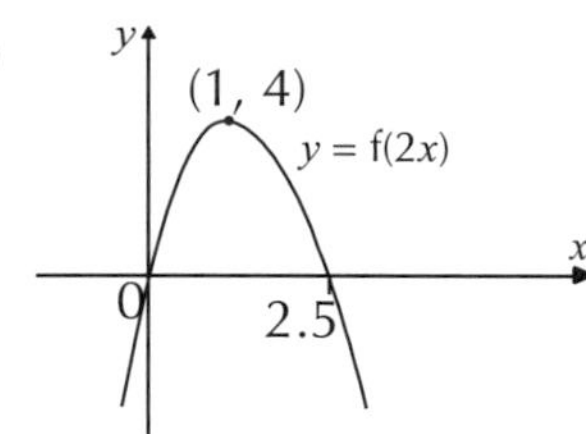

Exam-Style Questions — Chapter 1

Q1 a) $3^3 = 27 \Rightarrow a = 3$ ***[1 mark]***

b) $\sqrt[3]{27} = 27^{\frac{1}{3}} \Rightarrow b = \frac{1}{3}$ ***[1 mark]***

c) $81 = 3^4 = (\sqrt[3]{27})^4$ ***[1 mark]***

$= (27^{\frac{1}{3}})^4 = 27^{\frac{4}{3}} \Rightarrow c = \frac{4}{3}$ ***[1 mark]***

Q2 $10000\sqrt{10} = 10^4 \cdot 10^{\frac{1}{2}}$ ***[1 mark]***

$= 10^{4+\frac{1}{2}}$ ***[1 mark]***

$= 10^{\frac{9}{2}}$

so $k = \frac{9}{2}$ ***[1 mark]***

Q3 a)

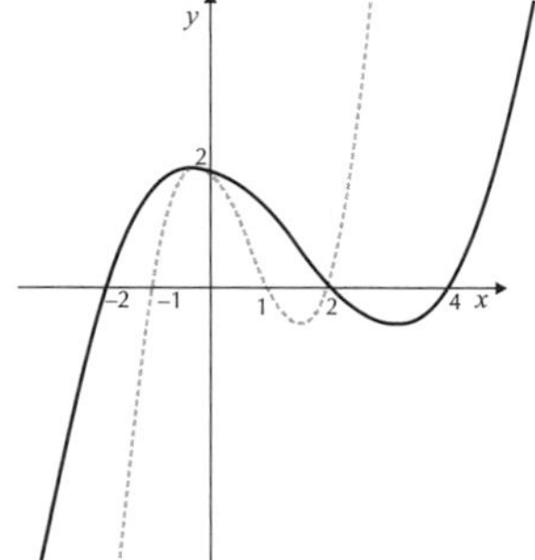

[3 marks available — 1 mark for horizontal stretch, 1 mark for x-axis intercepts at –2, 2 and 4, 1 mark for correct y-axis intercept at 2.]

b)

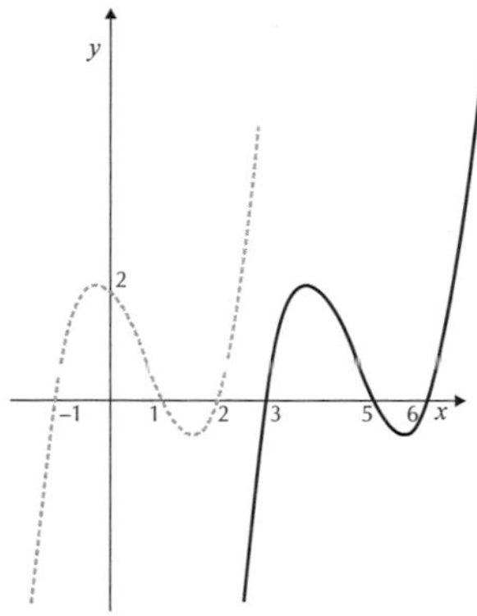

[2 marks available — 1 mark for translation in the positive x-direction, 1 mark for x-axis intercepts at 3, 5 and 6]

Q4 $\frac{x + 5x^3}{\sqrt{x}} = x^{-\frac{1}{2}}(x + 5x^3)$ ***[1 mark]***

$= x^{\frac{1}{2}} + 5x^{\frac{5}{2}}$ ***[1 mark]***

Q5 a)

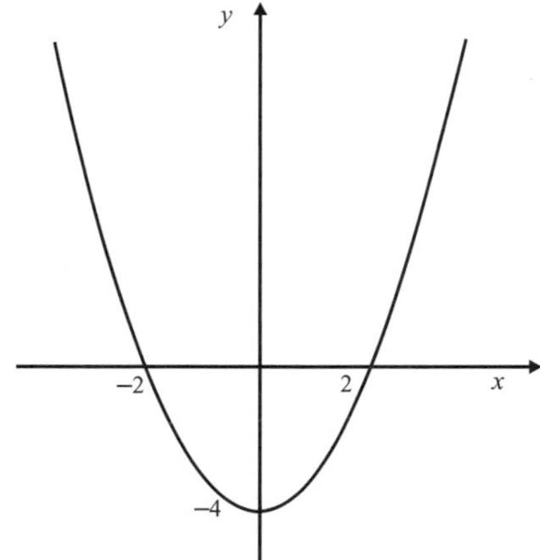

[2 marks available — 1 mark for x-axis intercepts at –2 and 2, 1 mark for correct y-axis intercept (0, –4)]

b) The curve is reflected in the x-axis ***[1 mark]***, and stretched vertically by a scale factor of 2 ***[1 mark]***.

c) $y = f(x) + 2$ ***[1 mark]***

Chapter 2 — Trigonometry

1. Arcs and Sectors

Exercise 1.1 — Radians

Q1 **a)** π **b)** $\frac{3\pi}{4}$ **c)** $\frac{3\pi}{2}$

d) $\frac{7\pi}{18}$ **e)** $\frac{5\pi}{6}$ **f)** $\frac{5\pi}{12}$

Q2 **a)** 45° **b)** 90° **c)** 60°

d) 450° **e)** 135° **f)** 420°

g) 57.3° (1 d.p.) **h)** 126° **i)** 292.5°

j) 103.1° (1 d.p.) **k)** 80° **l)** 330°

Exercise 1.2 — Arc length and sector area

Q1 $l = r\theta = 6 \times 2 = 12$ cm

$A = \frac{1}{2}r^2\theta = \frac{1}{2} \times 6^2 \times 2 = 36$ cm^2

Q2 Get the angle in radians:

$46° = \frac{46 \times \pi}{180} = 0.802...$ radians

$l = r\theta = 8 \times 0.802... = 6.4$ cm

$A = \frac{1}{2}r^2\theta = \frac{1}{2} \times 8^2 \times 0.802... = 25.7$ cm^2 (1 d.p.)

Q3 **a)** $l = r\theta = 5 \times 1.2 = 6$ cm

$A = \frac{1}{2}r^2\theta = \frac{1}{2} \times 5^2 \times 1.2 = 15$ cm^2

b) $l = r\theta = 4 \times 0.6 = 2.4$ cm

$A = \frac{1}{2}r^2\theta = \frac{1}{2} \times 4^2 \times 0.6 = 4.8$ cm^2

c) Get the angle in radians:

$80° = \frac{80 \times \pi}{180} = \frac{4\pi}{9}$ radians

$l = 9 \times \frac{4\pi}{9} = 4\pi$ cm $= 12.6$ cm

$A = \frac{1}{2} \times 9^2 \times \frac{4\pi}{9} = 18\pi$ cm$^2 = 56.5$ cm^2

d) $l = 4 \times \frac{5\pi}{12} = \frac{5\pi}{3}$ cm $= 5.24$ cm

$A = \frac{1}{2} \times 4^2 \times \frac{5\pi}{12} = \frac{10\pi}{3}$ cm$^2 = 10.5$ cm^2

Q4 Find the radius, r:

$A = \frac{1}{2}r^2\theta = \frac{1}{2} \times r^2 \times 0.9 = 16.2$ cm^2

$16.2 = 0.45r^2 \Rightarrow 36 = r^2 \Rightarrow r = 6$

$l = r\theta = 6 \times 0.9 = 5.4$ cm

Q5 Get the angle in radians:

$20° = \frac{20 \times \pi}{180} = \frac{\pi}{9}$ radians

$l = r\theta = 3 \times \frac{\pi}{9} = \frac{\pi}{3}$ cm

$A = \frac{1}{2}r^2\theta = \frac{1}{2} \times 3^2 \times \frac{\pi}{9} = \frac{\pi}{2}$ cm^2

Q6 Find the radius, r:

$l = r\theta \Rightarrow r = \frac{l}{\theta} = \frac{7}{1.4} = 5$ cm

$A = \frac{1}{2}r^2\theta = \frac{1}{2} \times 5^2 \times 1.4 = 17.5$ cm^2

2. The Sine and Cosine Rules

Exercise 2.1 — The sine and cosine rules

Q1 $a^2 = b^2 + c^2 - 2bc\cos A$

$QR^2 = 9^2 + 10^2 - (2 \times 9 \times 10 \times \cos 42°)$

$= 47.2...$

$QR = 6.87$ cm (3 s.f.)

Q2 $\frac{a}{\sin A} = \frac{b}{\sin B}$

$\Rightarrow TW = \frac{FW \times \sin F}{\sin T}$

$= \frac{15 \times \sin 39°}{\sin 82°} = 9.53$ cm (3 s.f.)

Q3 Angle $C = 180° - 48° - 65° = 67°$

Using the sine rule:

$\frac{b}{\sin B} = \frac{c}{\sin C}$

$\Rightarrow AC = \frac{AB \times \sin B}{\sin C}$

$= \frac{11 \times \sin 65°}{\sin 67°} = 10.8$ cm (3 s.f.)

Q4 Using the cosine rule:

$a^2 = b^2 + c^2 - 2bc\cos A$

$\Rightarrow \cos A = \frac{b^2 + c^2 - a^2}{2bc}$

$\Rightarrow D = \cos^{-1}\left(\frac{6^2 + 9^2 - 8^2}{2 \times 6 \times 9}\right) = 60.6°$ (3 s.f.)

Q5 Using the cosine rule:

$a^2 = b^2 + c^2 - 2bc\cos A$

$\Rightarrow (JK)^2 = 24^2 + 29^2 - (2 \times 24 \times 29 \times \cos 62°)$

$\Rightarrow JK = \sqrt{763.4...} = 27.6$ cm (3 s.f.)

Q6 Using the cosine rule:

$a^2 = b^2 + c^2 - 2bc\cos A$

$\Rightarrow (GI)^2 = 6.4^2 + 8.3^2 - (2 \times 6.4 \times 8.3 \times \cos 2.3)$

$\Rightarrow GI = \sqrt{180.6...} = 13.4$ cm (3 s.f.)

Q7 Using the cosine rule:

$a^2 = b^2 + c^2 - 2bc\cos A$

$\Rightarrow \cos A = \frac{b^2 + c^2 - a^2}{2bc}$

$\Rightarrow C = \cos^{-1}\left(\frac{14^2 + 11^2 - 23^2}{2 \times 14 \times 11}\right) = 133.5°$ (1 d.p.)

Q8 Angle $Q = \pi - 0.66 - 0.75 = 1.731...$ rad

There are π radians in a triangle (180°).

Using the sine rule:

$\frac{a}{\sin A} = \frac{b}{\sin B}$

$\Rightarrow PQ = \frac{PR \times \sin R}{\sin Q}$

$= \frac{48 \times \sin 0.75}{\sin 1.731...} = 33.1$ m (3 s.f.)

Q9 The smallest angle is between the two biggest sides, so angle F is the smallest angle.

To be safe you could just work out all 3 angles and then see which is smallest.

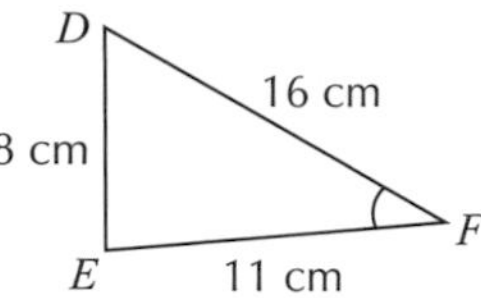

Using the cosine rule:

$a^2 = b^2 + c^2 - 2bc\cos A$

$\Rightarrow \cos F = \frac{11^2 + 16^2 - 8^2}{2 \times 11 \times 16}$

$\Rightarrow F = \cos^{-1}\left(\frac{11^2 + 16^2 - 8^2}{2 \times 11 \times 16}\right) = 27.2°$ (3 s.f.)

Q10 Area $= \frac{1}{2}ab\sin C$

$= \frac{1}{2} \times 9 \times 11 \times \sin 68°$

$= 45.9$ cm^2 (3 s.f.)

Q11 Area $= \frac{1}{2}ab\sin C$

$= \frac{1}{2} \times 12 \times 10.5 \times \sin 53°$

$= 50.3$ cm^2 (3 s.f.)

Q12 Start by finding any angle (M here).

Using the cosine rule:

$a^2 = b^2 + c^2 - 2bc\cos A$

$\Rightarrow \cos M = \frac{5^2 + 7^2 - 4.2^2}{2 \times 5 \times 7}$

$\Rightarrow M = \cos^{-1}\left(\frac{5^2 + 7^2 - 4.2^2}{2 \times 5 \times 7}\right) = 36.3...°$

Now you can find the area.

Area $= \frac{1}{2}ab\sin C$

$= \frac{1}{2} \times 5 \times 7 \times \sin 36.3...°$

$= 10.38$ cm^2 (2 d.p.)

You could have found any angle to start off then used the corresponding sides.

Q13 Start by sketching the triangle:

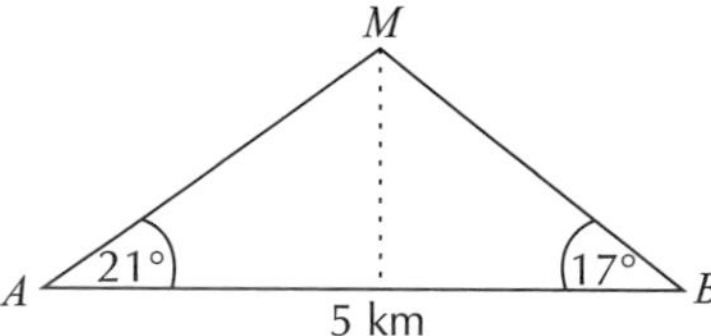

a) Angle $M = 180 - 21 - 17 = 142°$.

Using the sine rule:

$\frac{a}{\sin A} = \frac{m}{\sin M}$

$\Rightarrow a = \frac{5 \times \sin 21°}{\sin 142°} = 2.91$km (3 s.f.)

Here a is the distance BM and m is the distance AB.

b) To find the height, draw a line through the triangle from M at a right angle to AB (the dotted line shown in the diagram in part a)).

Height = sin 17° × 2.91 = 0.8509 km = 851 m (to the nearest m).

The final step just uses SOHCAHTOA — height is the opposite side and 2.91 is the hypotenuse.

Q14 a)

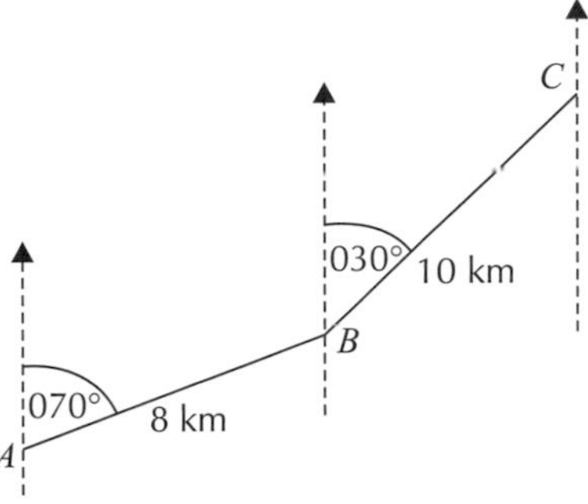

b) The angle anticlockwise from the vertical at B to A is 180° – 70° = 110° (parallel lines), so the angle ABC is 110° + 30° = 140°. Now you can use the cosine rule to find the distance AC.

$a^2 = b^2 + c^2 - 2bc\cos A$

$\Rightarrow AC = \sqrt{(BC)^2 + (AB)^2 - 2(BC)(AB)\cos B}$

$\Rightarrow AC = \sqrt{100 + 64 - 160\cos 140°}$

$= 16.928... = 16.9\text{ km (3 s.f.)}$

c) Start by finding the angle ACB using the cosine rule:

$a^2 = b^2 + c^2 - 2bc\cos A$

$\Rightarrow \cos ACB = \dfrac{10^2 + 16.928...^2 - 8^2}{2 \times 10 \times 16.928...}$

$\Rightarrow ACB = \cos^{-1}\left(\dfrac{10^2 + 16.928...^2 - 8^2}{2 \times 10 \times 16.928...}\right)$

$= 17.68...°$

The bearing required is therefore 180° + 17.68° + 30° (parallel lines) = 227.68...° = 228° (3 s.f.).

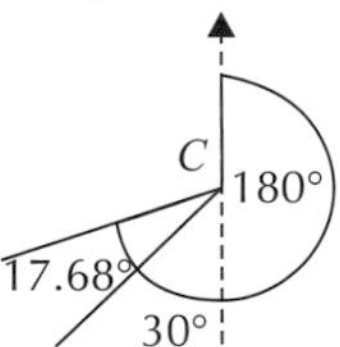

Q15 a) Using the cosine rule:

$a^2 = b^2 + c^2 - 2bc\cos A$

$\Rightarrow AC = \sqrt{9^2 + 11^2 - (2 \times 9 \times 11 \times \cos 2.58)}$

$= 19.224... = 19.2\text{ m (3 s.f.)}$

b) Find the area of each triangle individually. For the top triangle:

$\text{Area} = \frac{1}{2}ab\sin C$

$= \frac{1}{2} \times 9 \times 11 \times \sin 2.58$

$= 26.36...\text{ m}^2\text{ (3 s.f.)}$

For the bottom triangle:

$\text{Area} = \frac{1}{2}ab\sin C$

$= \frac{1}{2} \times 8 \times 19.2... \times \sin 1.38$

$= 75.50...\text{ m}^2$

So the area of the quadrilateral is 26.36... + 75.50... = 101.86... = 102 m² (3 s.f.).

Q16 Use the cosine rule to find one of the angles. Here a is 12 cm, b is 15 cm and c is 18 cm.

$a^2 = b^2 + c^2 - 2bc\cos A$

$\Rightarrow A = \cos^{-1}\left(\dfrac{b^2 + c^2 - a^2}{2bc}\right)$

$\Rightarrow A = \cos^{-1}\left(\dfrac{15^2 + 18^2 - 12^2}{2 \times 15 \times 18}\right) = 41.40...°$

Now find the area of one face:

$\text{Area} = \frac{1}{2}ab\sin C$

$= \frac{1}{2} \times 15 \times 18 \times \sin(41.40...°)$

$= 89.29...\text{ cm}^2$

So the total area needed is 4 × 89.29... = 357.17... = 357 cm² (3 s.f.).

3. Trig Identities

Exercise 3.1 — Trig identities

Q1 Use $\tan\theta \equiv \dfrac{\sin\theta}{\cos\theta}$:

$\dfrac{\sin\theta}{\tan\theta} - \cos\theta \equiv \dfrac{\sin\theta}{\left(\dfrac{\sin\theta}{\cos\theta}\right)} - \cos\theta$

$\equiv \cos\theta - \cos\theta \equiv 0$

Q2 Use $\sin^2\theta + \cos^2\theta \equiv 1$:

$\cos^2\theta \equiv 1 - \sin^2\theta \equiv (1 - \sin\theta)(1 + \sin\theta)$

Q3 Use $\sin^2 x + \cos^2 x \equiv 1$:

$\cos^2 x \equiv 1 - \sin^2 x$

$\Rightarrow \cos x = \sqrt{1 - \sin^2 x} = \sqrt{1 - \left(\frac{1}{2}\right)^2} = \sqrt{\frac{3}{4}} = \frac{\sqrt{3}}{2}$

Q4 Use $\sin^2 x + \cos^2 x \equiv 1$:

$4\sin^2 x - 3\cos x + 1 \equiv 4(1 - \cos^2 x) - 3\cos x + 1$

$\equiv 4 - 4\cos^2 x - 3\cos x + 1$

$\equiv 5 - 3\cos x - 4\cos^2 x$

Q5 $\cos^2 x \equiv 1 - \sin^2 x$, $\tan x \equiv \dfrac{\sin x}{\cos x}$

$\Rightarrow \tan x \equiv \dfrac{\sqrt{\sin^2 x}}{\sqrt{1 - \sin^2 x}} \equiv \dfrac{\frac{\sqrt{3}}{2}}{\frac{1}{2}} = \sqrt{3}$

Q6 Use $\tan x \equiv \dfrac{\sin x}{\cos x}$ and $\sin^2 x + \cos^2 x \equiv 1$:

$(\tan x + 1)(\tan x - 1) \equiv \tan^2 x - 1$

$\equiv \dfrac{\sin^2 x}{\cos^2 x} - 1$

$\equiv \dfrac{1 - \cos^2 x}{\cos^2 x} - 1$

$\equiv \dfrac{1}{\cos^2 x} - \dfrac{\cos^2 x}{\cos^2 x} - 1$

$\equiv \dfrac{1}{\cos^2 x} - 2$

Q7 Use $\sin^2\theta + \cos^2\theta \equiv 1$:

$(\sin\theta + \cos\theta)^2 + (\sin\theta - \cos\theta)^2$

$\equiv \sin^2\theta + 2\sin\theta\cos\theta + \cos^2\theta$

$\quad + \sin^2\theta - 2\sin\theta\cos\theta + \cos^2\theta$

$\equiv 2(\sin^2\theta + \cos^2\theta)$

$\equiv 2$

Don't make the mistake of writing $(\sin\theta + \cos\theta)^2 = \sin^2\theta + \cos^2\theta$

Q8 Use $\sin^2 x + \cos^2 x \equiv 1$ and $\tan x \equiv \frac{\sin x}{\cos x}$:

$$\tan x + \frac{1}{\tan x} \equiv \frac{\sin x}{\cos x} + \frac{\cos x}{\sin x}$$

$$\equiv \frac{\sin^2 x + \cos^2 x}{\sin x \cos x}$$

$$\equiv \frac{1}{\sin x \cos x}$$

Q9 Use $\sin^2 x + \cos^2 x \equiv 1$:

$$4 + \sin x - 6\cos^2 x \equiv 4 + \sin x - 6(1 - \sin^2 x)$$

$$\equiv -2 + \sin x + 6\sin^2 x$$

$$\equiv (2\sin x - 1)(3\sin x + 2)$$

If you're struggling to factorise, let $y = \sin x$, then it becomes $-2 + y + 6y^2$.

Q10 Use $\sin^2 x + \cos^2 x \equiv 1$:

$\sin^2 x\cos^2 y - \cos^2 x\sin^2 y$

$\equiv (1 - \cos^2 x)\cos^2 y - \cos^2 x(1 - \cos^2 y)$

$\equiv \cos^2 y - \cos^2 x\cos^2 y - \cos^2 x + \cos^2 x\cos^2 y$

$\equiv \cos^2 y - \cos^2 x$

4. Trig Functions

Exercise 4.1 — Graphs of trig functions

Q1 $y = \cos(x + 90°)$

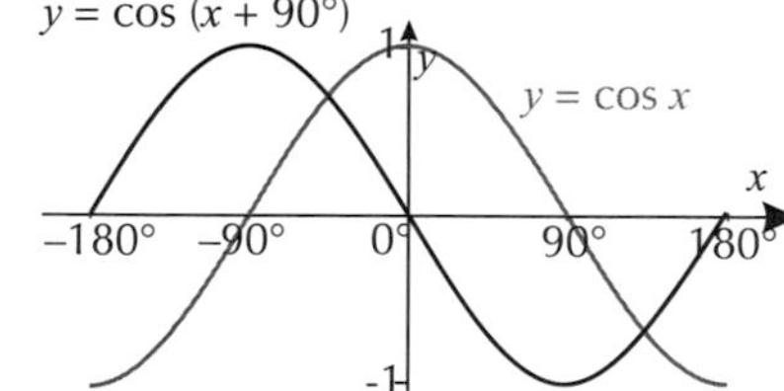

Q2

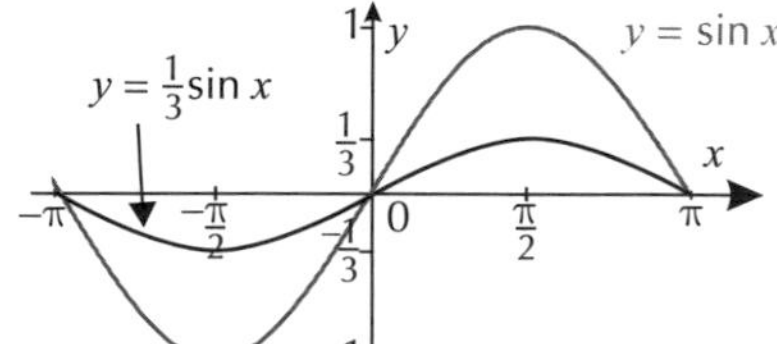

Q3

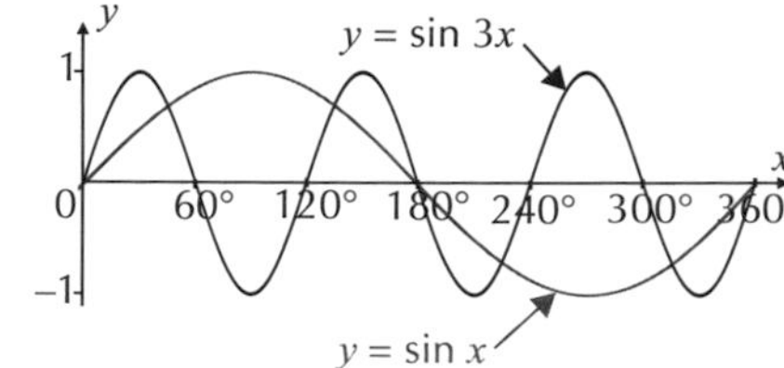

Q4

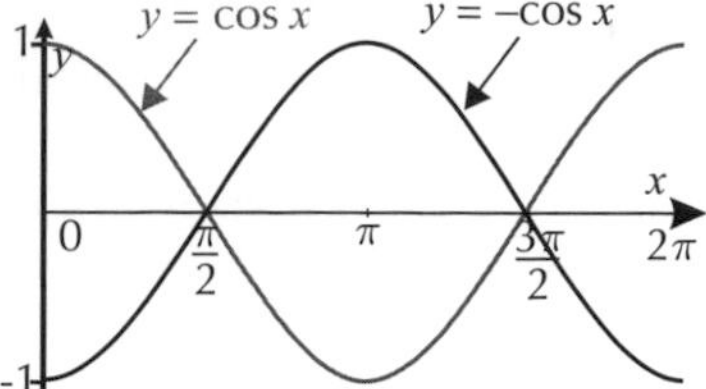

Q5 a)

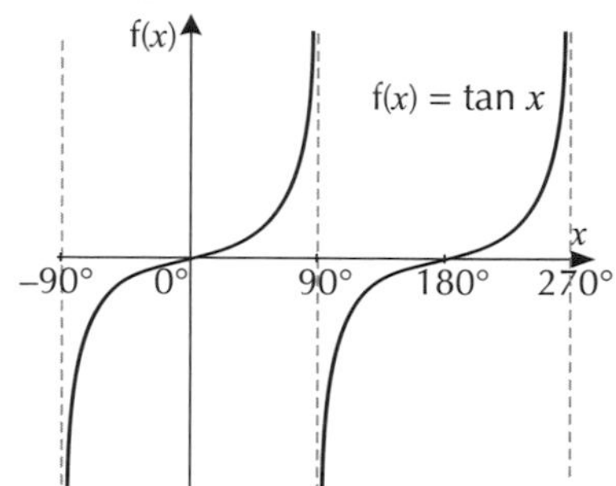

b)

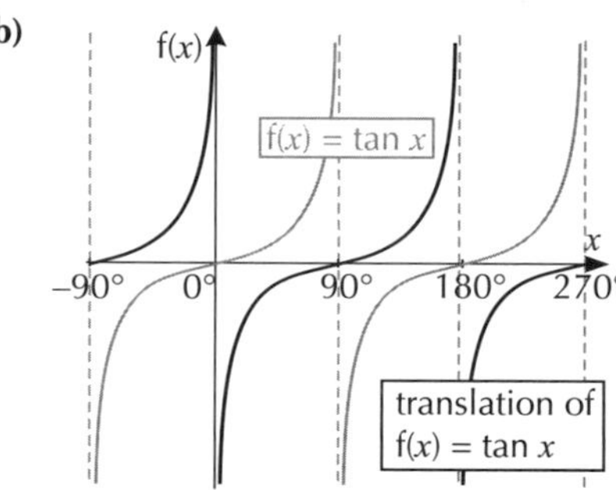

c) f(x) = tan (x + 90°)

Because the graph of tan x repeats every 180°, the transformation could also be f(x) = tan (x – 90°).

Q6 a)

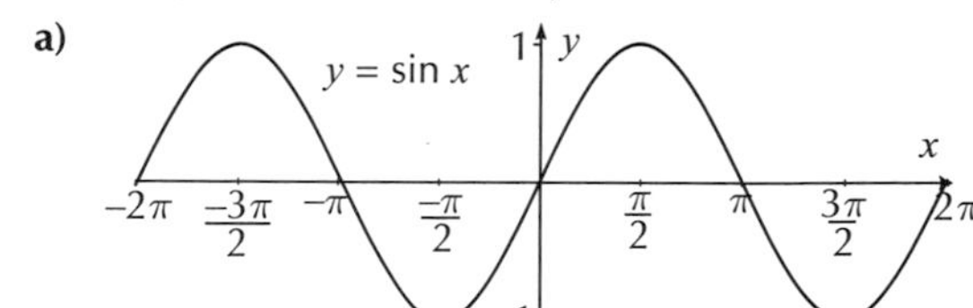

b)

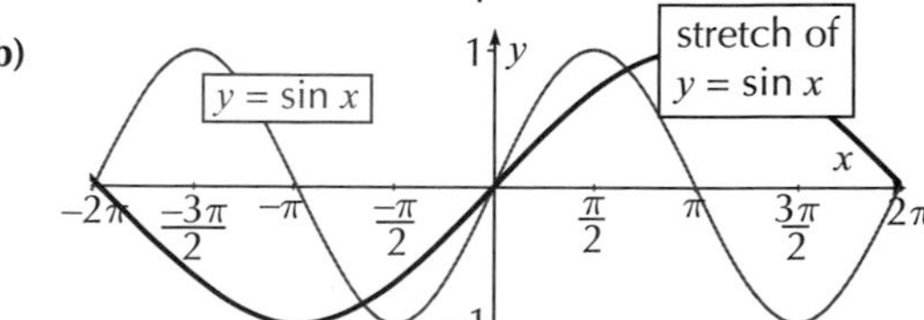

c) $y = \sin \frac{1}{2}x$.

Q7 a) The graph has been translated to the left by $\frac{\pi}{2}$.

b) $y = \sin(x + \frac{\pi}{2})$.

You might have noticed that this graph is exactly the same as the graph of $y = \cos x$.

Q8 a) The graph has been stretched vertically by a factor of 2.

b) $y = 2\cos x$.

5. Solving Trig Equations

Exercise 5.1 — Sketching a graph

Q1 a) Find the first solution using a calculator: $\sin x = 0.75 \Rightarrow x = 48.6°$ (1 d.p.).
Then sketch a graph:

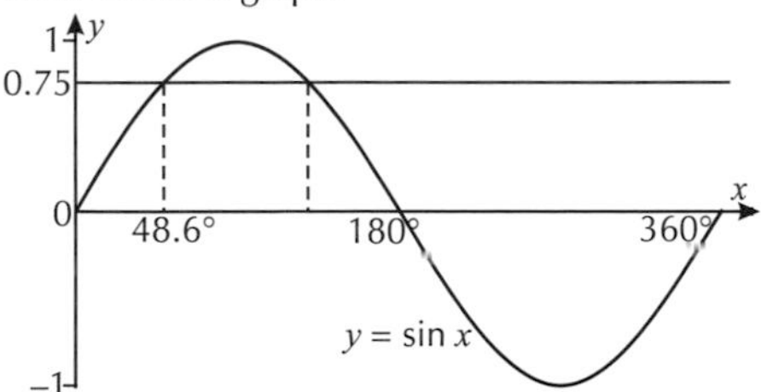

You can see from the graph that there are 2 solutions in the given interval.
Using the symmetry of the graph, if one solution is at 48.6°, the other will be at 180° – 48.6° = 131.4° (1 d.p.).

b) Find the first solution: $\cos x = 0.31 \Rightarrow x = 71.9°$ (1 d.p.). Then sketch a graph:

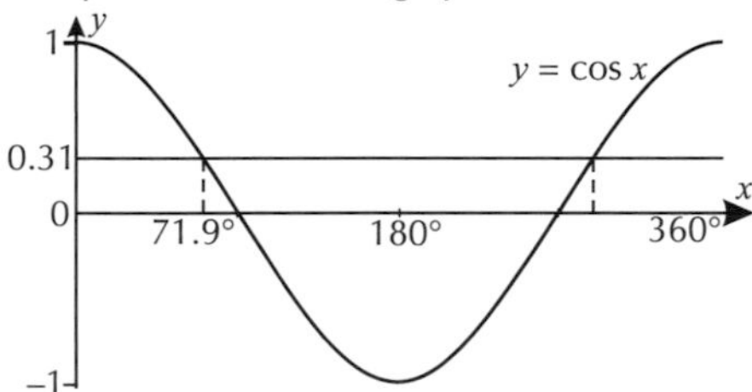

Using the symmetry of the graph to find the second solution: if one solution is at 71.9°, the other will be at 360° – 71.9° = 288.1° (1 d.p.).

c) Find the first solution: $\tan x = -1.5 \Rightarrow x = -56.3°$ (1 d.p.). This is outside the given interval, so add on 180° to find the first solution: –56.3° + 180° = 123.7° (1 d.p.). Then sketch a graph:

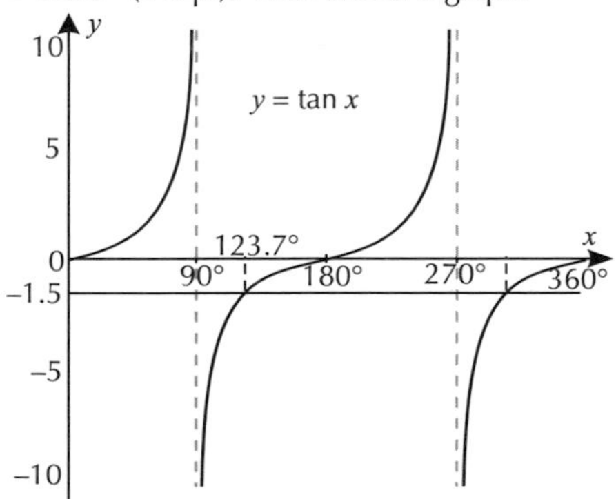

You can see from the graph that the next solution will be at 180° + 123.7° = 303.7° (1 d.p.) as $\tan x$ repeats every 180°.

d) Find the first solution: $\sin x = -0.42 \Rightarrow x = -24.8°$ (1 d.p.). This is outside the given interval, so add on 360° to find the first solution: –24.8° + 360° = 335.2° (1 d.p.). Then sketch a graph:

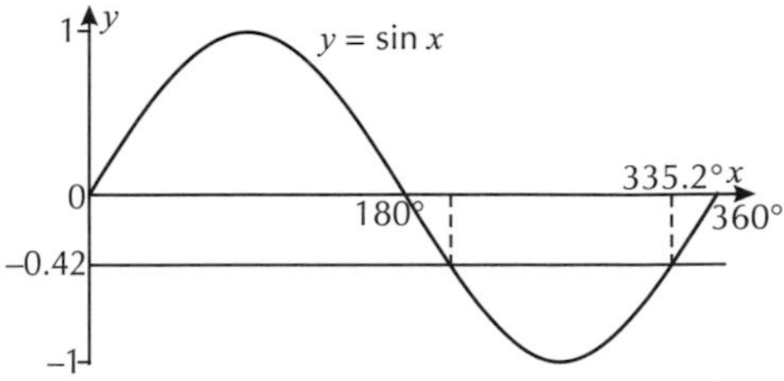

Using the symmetry of the graph, the first solution is 360° – 335.2° = 24.8° away from 360°, so the other solution will be 24.8° away from 180°, i.e. at 180° + 24.8° = 204.8° (1 d.p.).

e) Find the first solution: $\cos x = -0.56 \Rightarrow x = 124.1°$ (1 d.p.). Then sketch a graph:

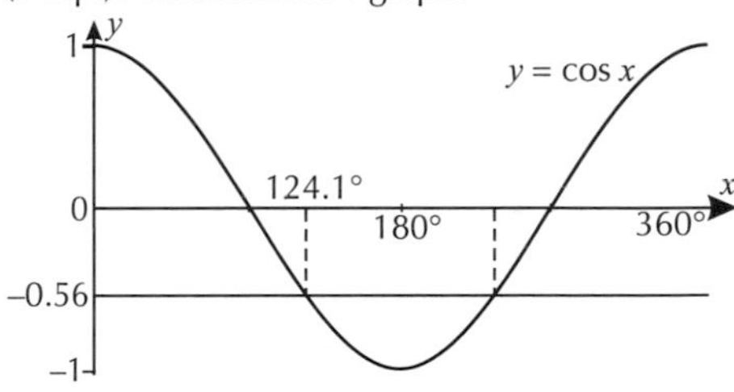

Using the symmetry of the graph to find the second solution: if one solution is at 124.1°, the other will be at 360° – 124.1° = 235.9° (1 d.p.).

f) Find the first solution: $\tan x = -0.67 \Rightarrow x = -33.8°$ (1 d.p.). This is outside the given interval, so add on 180° to find the first solution: –33.8° + 180° = 146.2° (1 d.p.). Then sketch a graph:

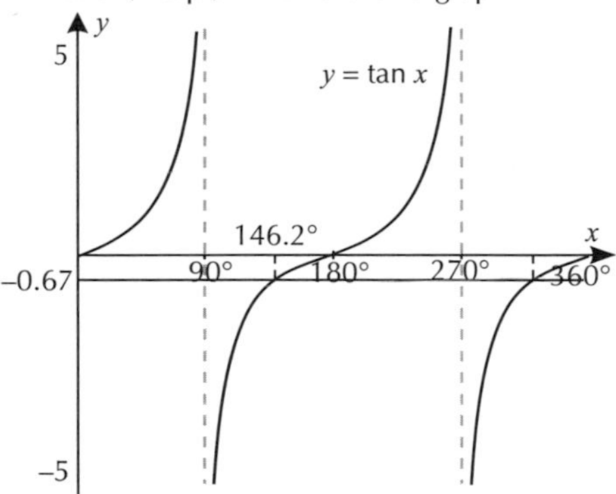

You can see from the graph that the next solution will be at 180° + 146.2° = 326.2° (1 d.p.) as $\tan x$ repeats every 180°.

Q2 a) Using your knowledge of common angles, the first solution is at $x = \frac{\pi}{4}$. Then sketch a graph:

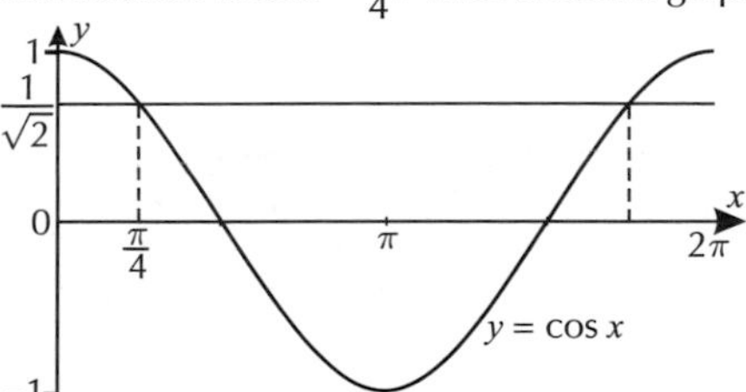

Using the symmetry of the graph, the second solution is at $2\pi - \frac{\pi}{4} = \frac{7\pi}{4}$.

You're asked for exact values, so leave your answers in terms of π.

b) Using common angles, the first solution is at $x = \frac{\pi}{3}$. Then sketch a graph:

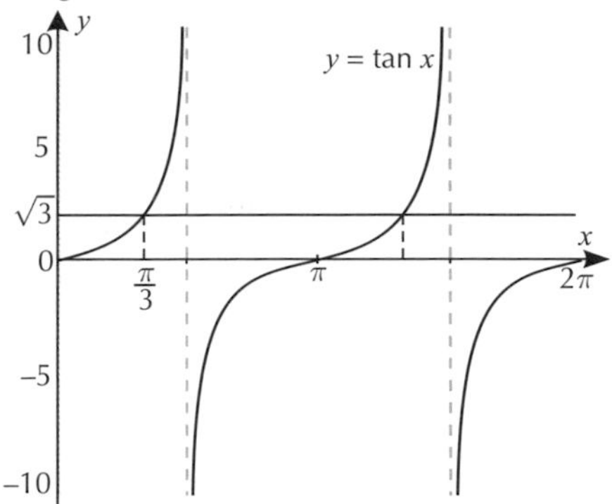

By the symmetry of the graph, the second solution is at $\pi + \frac{\pi}{3} = \frac{4\pi}{3}$.

c) Using common angles, the first solution is at $x = \frac{\pi}{6}$. Then sketch a graph:

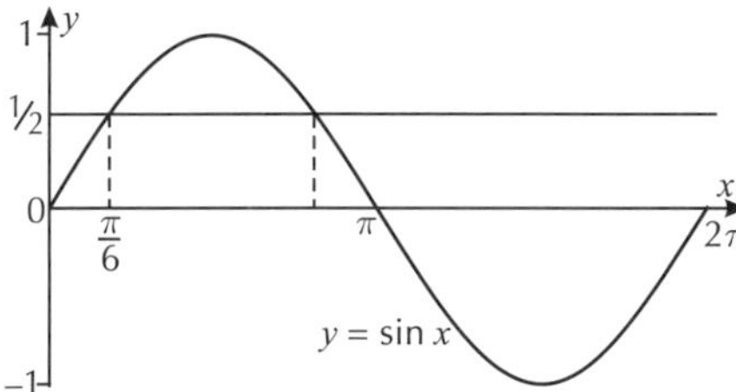

By the symmetry of the graph, the second solution is at $\pi - \frac{\pi}{6} = \frac{5\pi}{6}$.

d) Using common angles, the first solution is at $x = \frac{\pi}{6}$. Then sketch a graph:

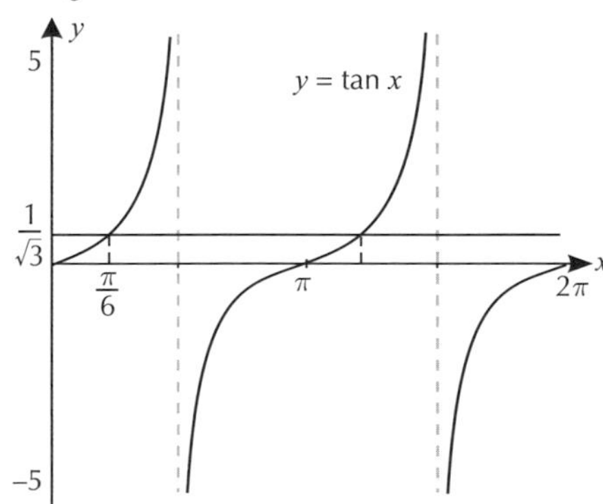

By the symmetry of the graph, the second solution is at $\pi + \frac{\pi}{6} = \frac{7\pi}{6}$.

e) Using common angles, the first solution is at $x = \frac{\pi}{4}$. Then sketch a graph:

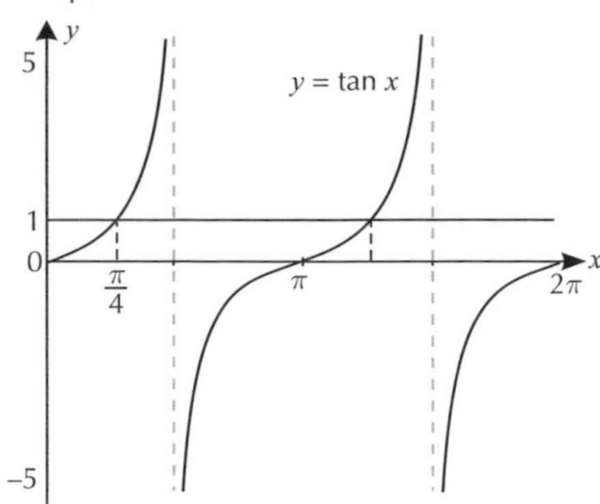

By the symmetry of the graph, the second solution is at $\pi + \frac{\pi}{4} = \frac{5\pi}{4}$.

f) Using your knowledge of common angles, the first solution is at $x = \frac{\pi}{6}$. Then sketch a graph:

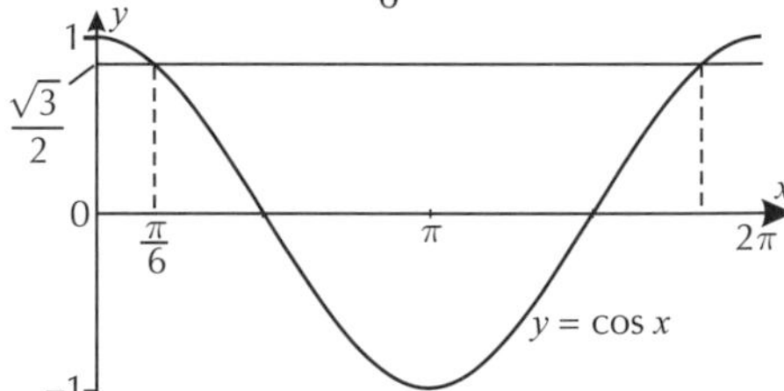

Using the symmetry of the graph, the second solution is at $2\pi - \frac{\pi}{6} = \frac{11\pi}{6}$.

Q3 You're told that there is a solution at 143.1°, and from the graph you can see that there is another solution in the given interval. The first solution is 180° – 143.1° = 36.9° away from 180°, so the other solution will be at 180° + 36.9° = 216.9° (1 d.p.).

You could also have worked this one out by doing 360° – 143.1°.

Q4 Use a calculator to find the first solution: $\tan x = 2.5 \Rightarrow x = 68.2°$ (1 d.p.). Then sketch a graph — this time the interval is bigger, so you'll need more repetitions of the tan shape:

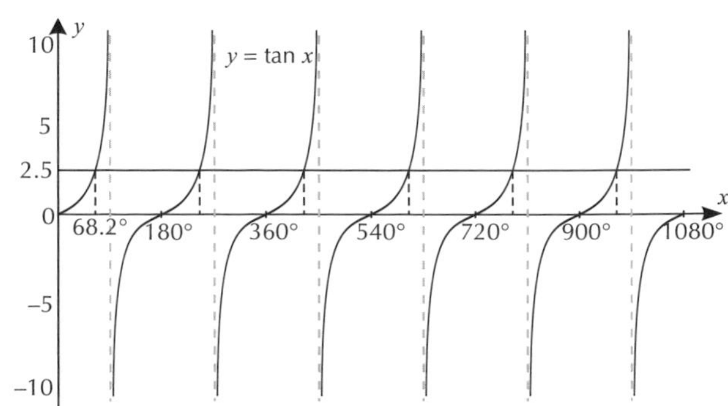

You can see from the graph that there are 6 solutions in the given interval — so just keep adding lots of 180° onto the first solution: x = 68.2°, 248.2°, 428.2°, 608.2°, 788.2°, 968.2° (all to 1 d.p.).

You don't have to draw out the whole graph if you don't want — just sketch the first part to find the first solution, then keep adding on lots of 180° until the solutions are bigger than 1080°.

Q5 Find the first solution: $\sin x = 0.81 \Rightarrow x = 0.944$ (3 s.f.). Then sketch a graph — this time for the range $-2\pi \le x \le 2\pi$:

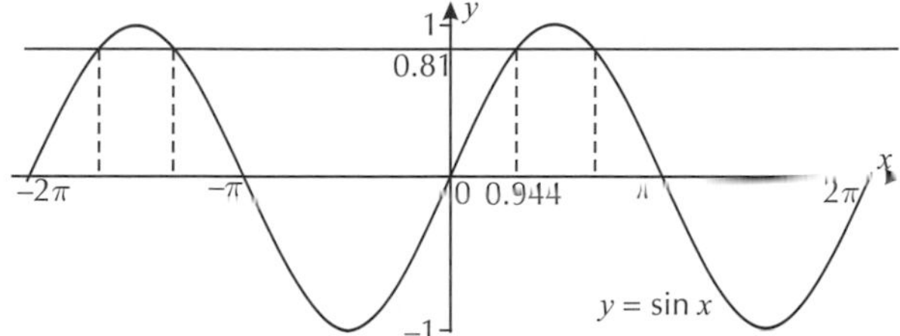

You can see from the graph that there are 4 solutions. Using the symmetry of the graph, there's another solution at $\pi - 0.944 = 2.20$ (3 s.f.). To find the other 2 solutions, subtract 2π from the values you've just found: $0.944 - 2\pi = -5.34$ (3 s.f.) and $2.20 - 2\pi = -4.09$ (3 s.f.).

Exercise 5.2 — Using a CAST diagram

Q1 0.45 is positive, so look at the quadrants where $\sin x$ is positive:

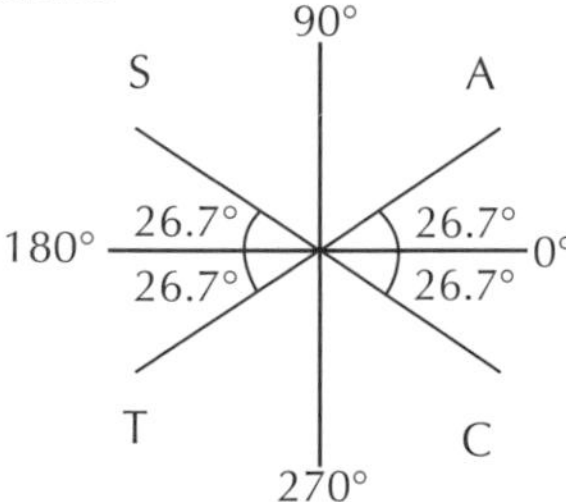

The second quadrant is the other one, so the only other solution is $180° - 26.7° = 153.3°$.

Q2 **a)** Use a calculator to find the first solution: $\cos x = 0.8 \Rightarrow x = 36.9°$ (1 d.p.). 0.8 is positive, so look at the other quadrants where cos is positive:

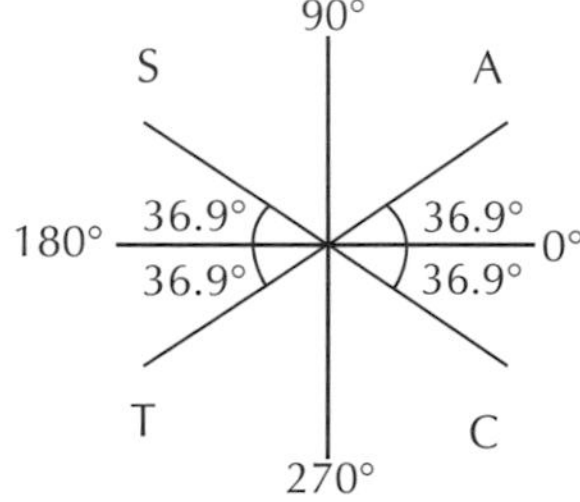

Cos is positive in the 4th quadrant, so the other solution is at $360° - 36.9° = 323.1°$ (1 d.p.).

b) Use a calculator to find the first solution: $\tan x = 2.7 \Rightarrow x = 69.7°$ (1 d.p.). 2.7 is positive, so look at the other quadrants where tan is positive:

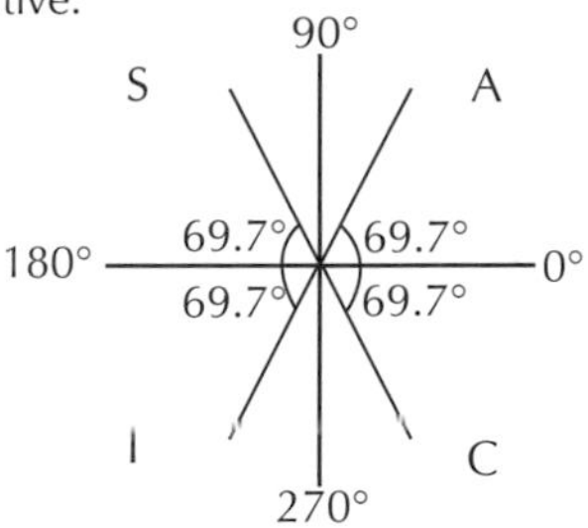

Tan is positive in the 3rd quadrant, so the other solution is at $180° + 69.7° = 249.7°$ (1 d.p.).

c) Use a calculator to find the first solution: $\sin x = -0.15 \Rightarrow x = -8.6°$ (1 d.p.). –0.15 is negative, so look at the quadrants where sin is negative:

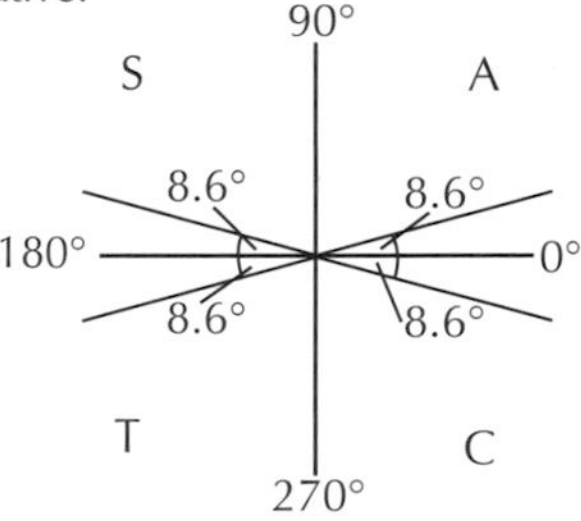

Sin is negative in the 3rd and 4th quadrants, so the solutions are at $180° + 8.6° = 188.6°$ and $360° - 8.6° = 351.4°$ (both to 1 d.p.).

d) Use a calculator to find the first solution: $\tan x = 0.3 \Rightarrow x = 16.7°$ (1 d.p.). 0.3 is positive, so look at the other quadrants where tan is positive:

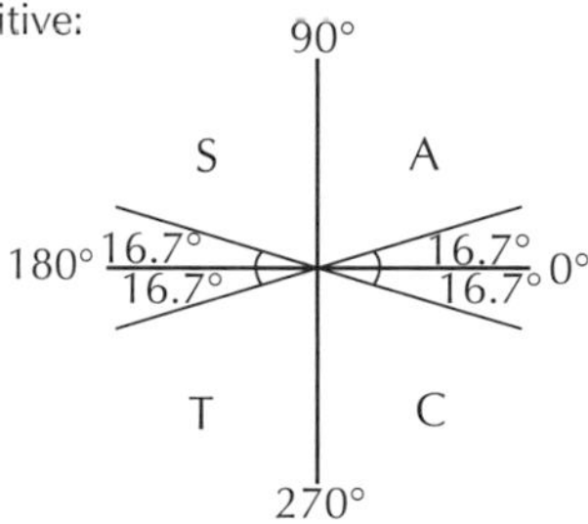

Tan is positive in the 3rd quadrant, so the other solution is at $180° + 16.7° = 196.7°$ (1 d.p.).

e) Use a calculator to find the first solution: $\tan x = -0.6 \Rightarrow x = -31.0°$ (1 d.p.). –0.6 is negative, so look at the quadrants where tan is negative:

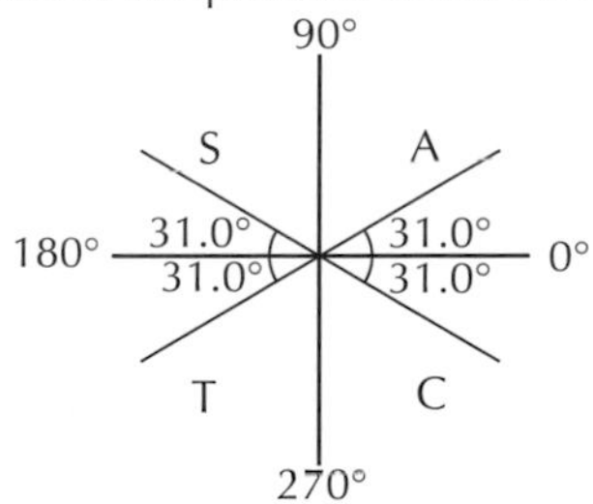

Tan is negative in the 2nd and 4th quadrants. So the solutions are at $180° - 31.0° = 149.0°$ and $360° - 31.0° = 329.0°$ (both to 1 d.p.).

f) Use a calculator to find the first solution: $\sin x = -0.29 \Rightarrow x = -16.9°$ (1 d.p.). -0.29 is negative, so look at the quadrants where sin is negative:

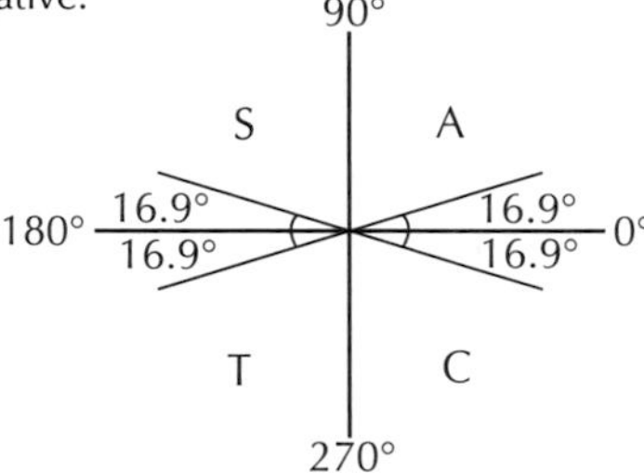

Sin is negative in the 3rd and 4th quadrants, so the solutions are at $180° + 16.9° = 196.9°$ and $360° - 16.9° = 343.1°$ (both to 1 d.p.).

g) Rearranging $4\sin x - 1 = 0$ to make $\sin x$ the subject gives $\sin x = 0.25$. Use a calculator to find the first solution: $\sin x = 0.25 \Rightarrow x = 14.5°$ (1 d.p.). 0.25 is positive, so look at the other quadrants where sin is positive:

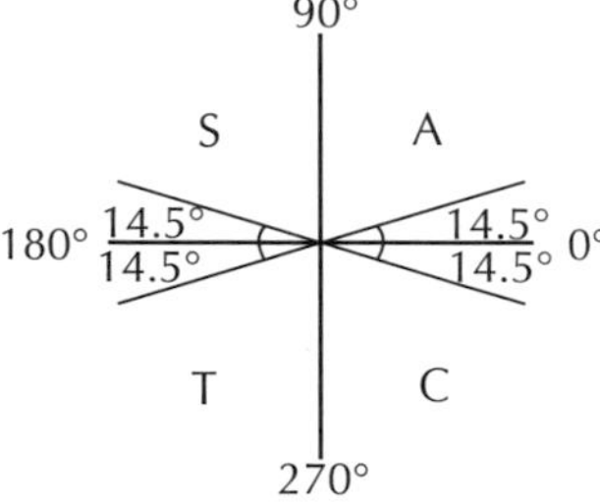

Sin is positive in the 2nd quadrant, so the other solution is at $180° - 14.5° = 165.5°$ (1 d.p.).

h) Rearranging $4\cos x - 3 = 0$ to make $\cos x$ the subject gives $\cos x = 0.75$. Use a calculator to find the first solution: $\cos x = 0.75 \Rightarrow x = 41.4°$ (1 d.p.). 0.75 is positive, so look at the other quadrants where cos is positive:

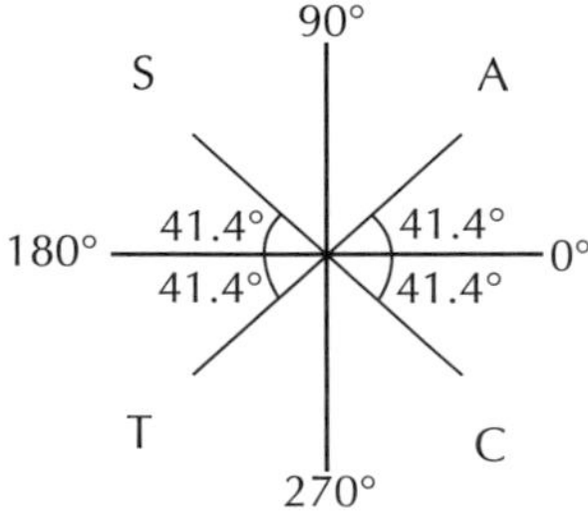

Cos is positive in the 4th quadrant, so the other solution is at $360° - 41.4° = 318.6°$ (1 d.p.).

i) Rearranging $5\tan x + 7 = 0$ to make $\tan x$ the subject gives $\tan x = -1.4$. Use a calculator to find the first solution: $\tan x = -1.4 \Rightarrow x = -54.5°$ (1 d.p.). -1.4 is negative, so look at the quadrants where tan is negative:

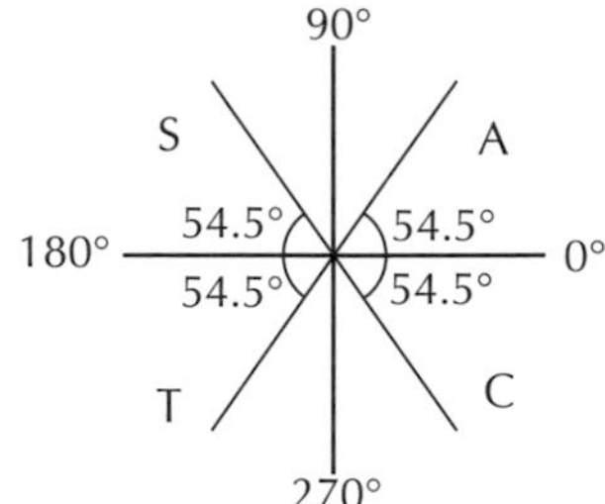

Tan is negative in the 2nd and 4th quadrants, so the solutions are at $180° - 54.5° = 125.5°$ and $360° - 54.5° = 305.5°$ (both to 1 d.p.).

Q3 Use a calculator to find the first solution: $\tan x = -8.4 \Rightarrow x = -1.45$ (3 s.f.). -8.4 is negative, so look at the quadrants where tan is negative:

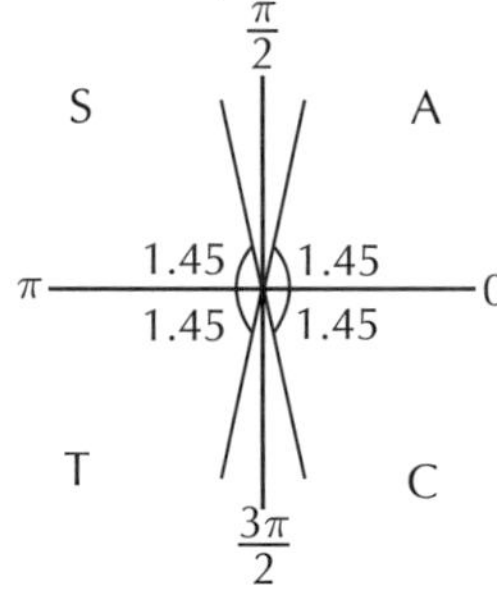

Tan is negative in the 2nd and 4th quadrants, so the solutions are at $\pi - 1.45 = 1.69$ and $2\pi - 1.45 = 4.83$ (both to 3 s.f.).

Q4 The first solution is $x = 48.6°$ (1 d.p.).

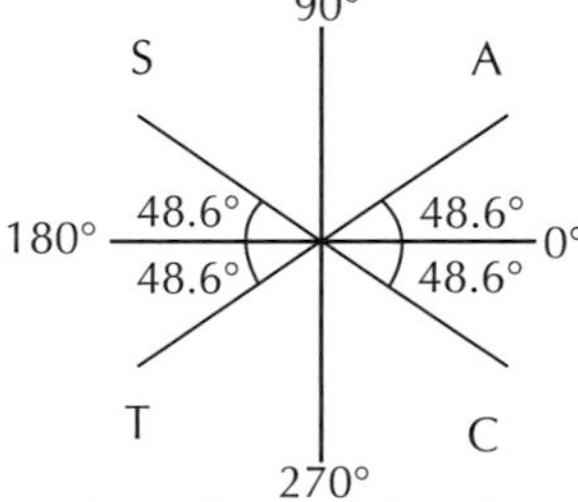

Using a CAST diagram, the solutions of $\sin x$ are also positive in the second quadrant. So the next solution is $180° - 48.6° = 131.4°$ (1 d.p.). To find the other solutions in the given interval, add on 360° to the solutions already found: $48.6° + 360° = 408.6°$ (1 d.p.) and $131.4° + 360° = 491.4°$ (1 d.p.).

Q5 The first solution is $x = 71.9°$ (1 d.p.).

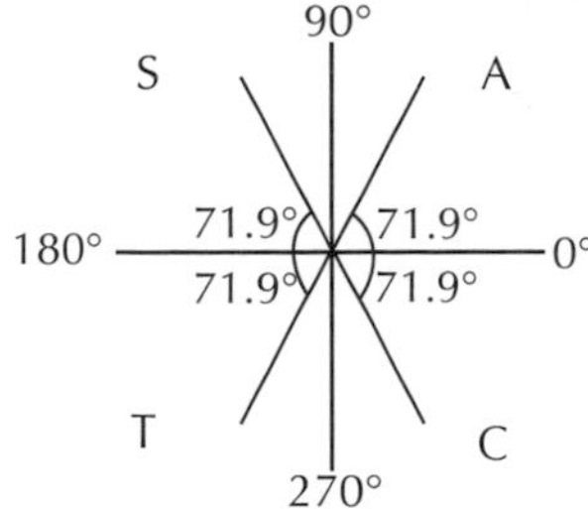

Using a CAST diagram, the solutions of $\cos x$ are also positive in the 4th quadrant. So the next solution is $360° - 71.9° = 288.1°$, but this is outside the given interval for x. To find the other solutions in the given interval, subtract 360° from the solutions already found: $71.9° - 360° = -288.1°$ (outside interval) and $288.1° - 360° = -71.9°$. So the solutions to 1 d.p. are $x = 71.9°$ and $-71.9°$.

You could have found the negative solutions more directly by reading the CAST diagram in the negative (i.e. clockwise) direction. Reading clockwise from 0°, the angle in the 4th quadrant is −71.9°.

Q6 The first solution is $x = 0.961$ (3 s.f.).

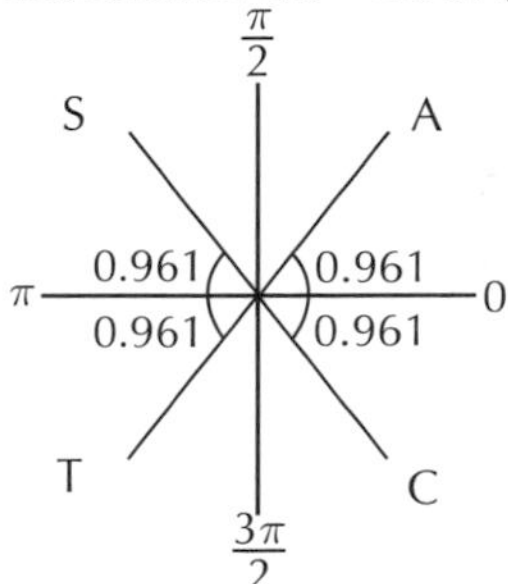

Using a CAST diagram, the solutions of $\sin x$ are also positive in the second quadrant. So the next solution is $\pi - 0.961 = 2.18$ (3 s.f.). To find the other solutions in the given interval, add on 2π to the solutions already found: $0.961 + 2\pi = 7.24$ (3 s.f.) and $2.18 + 2\pi = 8.46$ (3 s.f.).

Exercise 5.3 — Changing the interval

For all the questions in this exercise, you can either sketch a graph or use a CAST diagram.

Q1 $\sin 2x = 0.6$, so look for solutions in the interval $0° \leq 2x \leq 720°$. The first solution is $2x = 36.87°$ (2 d.p.). Using a CAST diagram, sin is also positive in the 2nd quadrant, so there's another solution at $2x = 180° - 36.87° = 143.13°$ (2 d.p.). The sin graph repeats every 360°, so add 360° onto the answers already found: $2x = 396.87°, 503.13°$ (2 d.p.). These are solutions for $2x$, so divide them all by 2: $x = 18.4°, 71.6°, 198.4°, 251.6°$ (1 d.p.).

Q2 $\tan 4x = 4.6$, so look for solutions in the interval $0° \leq 4x \leq 1440°$. The first solution is $4x = 77.74°$ (2 d.p.). From the pattern of the graph, there will be another solution at $4x = 77.74° + 180° = 257.74°$ (2 d.p.). Then just keep adding on 180° to find the rest of the solutions within the interval: $4x = 437.74°$, $617.74°, 797.74°, 977.74°, 1157.74°, 1337.74°$ (2 d.p.).

These are solutions for $4x$, so divide them all by 4: $x = 19.4°, 64.4°, 109.4°, 154.4°, 199.4°, 244.4°, 289.4°, 334.4°$ (1 d.p.).

Q3 $\cos 3x = -0.24$, so look for solutions in the interval $0° \leq 3x \leq 1080°$. The first solution is $3x = 103.89°$ (2 d.p.). Using the symmetry of the graph, there's another solution at $3x = 360° - 103.89° = 256.11°$ (2 d.p.). To find the other solutions within the interval, add on multiples of 360°: $3x = 463.89°, 616.11°, 823.89°, 976.11°$ (2 d.p.). These are solutions for $3x$, so divide them all by 3: $x = 34.6°, 85.4°, 154.6°, 205.4°, 274.6°, 325.4°$ (1 d.p.).

Q4 $\cos 2x = 0.72$, so look for solutions in the interval $0 \leq 2x \leq 4\pi$. The first solution is $2x = 0.7670$ (4 s.f.). Looking at the symmetry of the graph of $\cos x$, the other solutions are $2\pi - 0.7670 = 5.516$ (4 s.f.), $2\pi + 0.7670 = 7.050$ and $4\pi - 0.7670 = 11.80$ (4 s.f.). These are solutions for $2x$, so divide them all by 2: $x = 0.383, 2.76, 3.53, 5.90$ (3 s.f.).

Q5 $\sin 3x = -0.91$, so look for solutions in the interval $0 \leq 3x \leq 6\pi$. The first solution is $3x = -1.143$ (4 s.f.). This is outside the interval, but putting 1.143 into a CAST diagram and looking at the quadrants where sin is negative gives $3x = \pi + 1.143 = 4.285$ and $3x = 2\pi - 1.143 = 5.140$ (4 s.f.). Add on multiples of 2π to find the other solutions in the interval: $3x = 10.57, 11.42, 16.85, 17.71$ (4 s.f.). These are solutions for $3x$, so divide them all by 3: $x = 1.43, 1.71, 3.52, 3.81, 5.62, 5.90$ (3 s.f.).

Q6 $\tan \frac{x}{2} = 2.1$, so look for solutions in the interval $0° \leq \frac{x}{2} \leq 180°$. The first solution is $\frac{x}{2} = 64.54°$ (2 d.p.). This is the only solution in the interval, as tan doesn't repeat any values between 0° and 180° (looking at its graph). Multiply by 2 to get the value of x: $x = 129.1°$ (1 d.p.).

Q7 $\cos (x - 27°) = 0.64$, so look for solutions in the interval $-27° \leq x - 27° \leq 333°$. The first solution is $x - 27° = 50.2°$ (1 d.p.). Using the symmetry of the graph, there's another solution at $x - 27° = 360° - 50.2° = 309.8°$ (1 d.p.). So the solutions are $x = 77.2°$ and $336.8°$ (1 d.p.).

Q8 $\tan (x - 140°) = -0.76$, so look for solutions in the interval $-140° \leq x - 140° \leq 220°$. The first solution is $x - 140° = -37.2°$ (1 d.p.). The tan graph repeats every 180°, so there's another solution at $x - 140° = -37.2° + 180° = 142.8°$ (1 d.p.) (if you add on another 180°, the answer is outside the interval). So the solutions are $x = 102.8°$ and $282.8°$ (1 d.p.).

Q9 $\sin (x + 36°) = 0.45$, so look for solutions in the interval $36° \leq x + 36° \leq 396°$. The first solution is $x + 36° = 26.7°$ (1 d.p.). This is outside the interval, so add on 360° to find a solution in the interval: $x + 36° = 26.7° + 360° = 386.7°$ (1 d.p.). Using a CAST diagram, the other quadrant where sin is positive is the 2nd quadrant, so there's another solution at $x + 36° = 180° - 26.7° = 153.3°$. So the solutions are $x = 117.3°$ and $350.7°$ (1 d.p.).

Q10 $\tan(x + 73°) = 1.84$, so look for solutions in the interval $73° \leq x + 73° \leq 433°$. The first solution is $x + 73° = 61.5°$ (1 d.p.). This is out of the interval, but use this and the pattern of the graph of $\tan x$ to find the other solutions. $\tan x$ repeats every 180°, so the next two solutions are $x + 73° = 241.5°$ and $x + 73° = 421.5°$ (1 d.p.). So the two solutions are $x = 168.5°$ and $348.5°$ (1 d.p.).

Q11 $\sin(x - \frac{\pi}{4}) = -0.25$, so look for solutions in the interval $0 - \frac{\pi}{4} \leq x - \frac{\pi}{4} \leq 2\pi - \frac{\pi}{4}$. The first solution is $x - \frac{\pi}{4} = -0.253$ (3 s.f.). Using a CAST diagram, the other solution is at $x - \frac{\pi}{4} = \pi + 0.253$. So adding $\frac{\pi}{4}$ to each solution gives $x = 0.533$ and $x = 4.18$ (3 s.f.).

There's no solution at $2\pi - 0.25$ because it's outside the interval.

Q12 $\cos(x + \frac{\pi}{8}) = 0.13$, so look for solutions in the interval $\frac{\pi}{8} \leq x + \frac{\pi}{8} \leq 2\pi + \frac{\pi}{8}$. The first solution is $x + \frac{\pi}{8} = 1.44$ (3 s.f.). Using the symmetry of the graph, there's another solution at $x + \frac{\pi}{8} = 2\pi - 1.44 = 4.84$. So the solutions are $x = 1.05$ and 4.45 (3 s.f.).

Q13 $\sin(x + 12°) = \sin 62°$, so look for solutions in the interval $12° \leq x + 12° \leq 372°$. The first solution is $x + 12° = 62°$, so $x = 50°$. Using a CAST diagram, there is another solution at $x + 12° = 180° - 62° = 118°$. So the two solutions are $x = 50°$ and $x = 106°$.

Q14 $\cos 3x = \cos 39°$, so look for solutions in the interval $0° \leq 3x \leq 1080°$. The first solution is $3x = 39°$. Using a CAST diagram, there is another solution at $3x = 360° - 39° = 321°$. Add on multiples of 360° to get the other solutions in the interval: $3x = 399°$, 681°, 759°, 1041°. Dividing each solution by 3 gives $x = 13°$, 107°, 133°, 227°, 253°, 347°.

Exercise 5.4 — Using trig identities to solve equations

For all the questions in this exercise, you can either sketch a graph or use a CAST diagram.

Q1 **a)** This equation has already been factorised.
Either $\tan x - 5 = 0$ or $3\sin x - 1 = 0$.
$\tan x - 5 = 0 \Rightarrow \tan x = 5$
$\Rightarrow x = 78.7°$ (1 d.p.)
This is the first solution. tan repeats itself every 180°, so the other solution is 258.7° (1 d.p.).
$3\sin x = 1 \Rightarrow \sin x = \frac{1}{3}$
$\Rightarrow x = 19.5°$ (1 d.p.)
Using the symmetry of the graph, the other solution is $180° - 19.5° = 160.5°$ (1 d.p.).

b) $5\sin x \tan x - 4\tan x = 0$
$\tan x(5\sin x - 4) = 0$
So $\tan x = 0$ or $5\sin x - 4 = 0$.
$\tan x = 0 \Rightarrow x = 0°$ or $180°$
(from the graph of $\tan x$).
$5\sin x - 4 = 0 \Rightarrow \sin x = \frac{4}{5}$
$\Rightarrow x = 53.1°$ (1 d.p.)
Using the symmetry of the graph, the other solution is $180° - 53.1° = 126.9°$ (1 d.p.).

c) $\tan^2 x = 9 \Rightarrow \tan x = 3$ or -3.
$\tan x = 3 \Rightarrow x = 71.6°$ (1 d.p.)
Using the repetition of the tan graph, the other solution is $180° + 71.6° = 251.6°$ (1 d.p.).
$\tan x = -3 \Rightarrow x = -71.6°$ (1 d.p.)
This is outside the interval. Keep adding 180° until you've found all the solutions within the interval:
$-71.6° + 180° = 108.4°$ (1 d.p.) and
$108.4° + 180° = 288.4°$ (1 d.p.).

d) $4\cos^2 x = 3\cos x$
$4\cos^2 x - 3\cos x = 0$
$\cos x(4\cos x - 3) = 0$
So $\cos x = 0$ or $4\cos x - 3 = 0$
$\cos x = 0 \Rightarrow x = 90°$
Using the cos graph, the other solution is 270°.
$4\cos x - 3 = 0 \Rightarrow \cos x = \frac{3}{4}$
$\Rightarrow x = 41.4°$ (1 d.p.)
Using the symmetry of the graph, the other solution is $360° - 41.4° = 318.6°$ (1 d.p.).

e) $3\sin x = 5\cos x \Rightarrow \tan x = \frac{5}{3}$. The first solution is $x = 59.0°$ (1 d.p.). $\tan x$ repeats every 180°, so the other solution is 239.0° (1 d.p.).

f) $5\tan^2 x - 2\tan x = 0 \Rightarrow \tan x(5\tan x - 2) = 0$.
So either $\tan x = 0$ or $\tan x = 0.4$. If $\tan x = 0$ then the solutions are $x = 0°$, 180° and 360°.
If $\tan x = 0.4$, the first solution is 21.8° (1 d.p.).
The graph of $\tan x$ repeats every 180°, so another solution is $x = 201.8°$ (1 d.p.).

g) $6\cos^2 x - \cos x - 2 = 0$
$\Rightarrow (3\cos x - 2)(2\cos x + 1) = 0$
So either $\cos x = \frac{2}{3}$ or $\cos x = -0.5$. If $\cos x = \frac{2}{3}$, the first solution is 48.2° (1 d.p.). Looking at the symmetry of the graph of $\cos x$, the other solution is $x = 360° - 48.2° = 311.8°$ (1 d.p.).
If $\cos x = -0.5$, the first solution is 120°. Looking at the symmetry of the graph of $\cos x$, the other solution is $360° - 120° = 240°$.

h) $7\sin x + 3\cos x = 0 \Rightarrow 7\sin x = -3\cos x$
$\Rightarrow \tan x = -\frac{3}{7} \Rightarrow x = -23.2°$ (1 d.p.)
This is outside the required interval. Using a CAST diagram, tan is negative in the 2nd and 4th quadrants, so the solutions are $x = 180° - 23.2° = 156.8°$ (1 d.p.) and $x = 360° - 23.2° = 336.8°$ (1 d.p.).

Q2 **a)** $\tan x = \sin x \cos x \Rightarrow \frac{\sin x}{\cos x} - \sin x \cos x = 0$
$\Rightarrow \sin x - \sin x \cos^2 x = 0$
$\Rightarrow \sin x(1 - \cos^2 x) = 0$
$\Rightarrow \sin x(\sin^2 x) = 0$
$\Rightarrow \sin^3 x = 0$
So $\sin x = 0$. The solutions are $x = 0$, π and 2π.

b) $5\cos^2 x - 9\sin x = 3 \Rightarrow 5(1 - \sin^2 x) - 9\sin x = 3$
$\Rightarrow 5\sin^2 x + 9\sin x - 2 = 0$
$\Rightarrow (5\sin x - 1)(\sin x + 2) = 0$
So either $\sin x = 0.2$ or $\sin x = -2$. $\sin x$ can't be -2, so only $\sin x = 0.2$ will give solutions.

The first solution is $x = 0.201$ (3 s.f.).
The interval covers three intervals of 2π, so there will be 6 solutions. Looking at the symmetry of the sin graph and adding or subtracting 2π, the other solutions are $x = -6.08, -3.34, 2.94, 6.48$ and 9.22 (3 s.f.).
If you'd used a CAST diagram here, you'd find 0.201 and 2.94 first, then add or subtract 2π.

c) $2\sin^2 x + \sin x - 1 = 0$
$(2\sin x - 1)(\sin x + 1) = 0$
So $2\sin x - 1 = 0$ or $\sin x + 1 = 0$.
$2\sin x - 1 = 0 \Rightarrow \sin x = \frac{1}{2}$
$\Rightarrow x = \frac{\pi}{6}$. Using the symmetry of the graph, another solution is $\pi - \frac{\pi}{6} = \frac{5\pi}{6}$.
To find the other solutions in the required interval, subtract 2π from each of these:
$\frac{\pi}{6} - 2\pi = -\frac{11\pi}{6}$ and $\frac{5\pi}{6} - 2\pi = -\frac{7\pi}{6}$.
$\sin x + 1 = 0 \Rightarrow \sin x = -1$
From the graph, the solutions to this are $x = -\frac{\pi}{2}$ and $x = \frac{3\pi}{2}$.

Q3 a) $4\sin^2 x = 3 - 3\cos x$
$4(1 - \cos^2 x) = 3 - 3\cos x$
$4 - 4\cos^2 x = 3 - 3\cos x$
$\Rightarrow 4\cos^2 x - 3\cos x - 1 = 0$, as required.

b) Solve the equation from a).
$4\cos^2 x - 3\cos x - 1 = 0$
$(4\cos x + 1)(\cos x - 1) = 0$
So $4\cos x + 1 = 0$ or $\cos x - 1 = 0$
$4\cos x + 1 = 0 \Rightarrow \cos x = -\frac{1}{4}$
$\Rightarrow x = 1.82$ (3 s.f.)
Using the symmetry of the graph, the other solution is $2\pi - 1.82 = 4.46$ (3 s.f.)
$\cos x - 1 = 0 \Rightarrow \cos x = 1$
Using the cos graph, the solutions are $x = 0$ and $x = 2\pi$.

Q4 $9\sin^2 2x + 3\cos 2x = 7 \Rightarrow 9(1 - \cos^2 2x) + 3\cos 2x = 7$
$\Rightarrow 9 - 9\cos^2 2x + 3\cos 2x = 7$
$\Rightarrow 9\cos^2 2x - 3\cos 2x - 2 = 0$
$\Rightarrow (3\cos 2x + 1)(3\cos 2x - 2) = 0$

So either $\cos 2x = -\frac{1}{3}$ or $\cos 2x = \frac{2}{3}$. For $\cos 2x = -\frac{1}{3}$ look for solutions in the interval $0° \leq 2x \leq 720°$. The first solution is $2x = 109.47°$ (2 d.p.). Looking at the symmetry of the graph of $\cos x$, the other solutions are $2x = 250.53°, 469.47°$ and $610.53°$ (2 d.p.). Dividing by 2 gives the solutions: $x = 54.7°, 125.3°, 234.7°$ and $305.3°$ (1 d.p.).

For $\cos 2x = \frac{2}{3}$, again look for solutions in the interval $0° \leq 2x \leq 720°$. The first solution is $2x = 48.19°$ (2 d.p.). Looking at the symmetry of the graph of $\cos x$, the other solutions are $2x = 311.81°, 408.19°, 671.81°$ (2 d.p.). Dividing by 2 gives the solutions: $x = 24.1°, 155.9°, 204.1°$ and $335.9°$ (1 d.p.).

Review Exercise — Chapter 2

Q1 $l = r\theta = 10 \times 0.7 = 7$ cm
$\text{Area} = \frac{1}{2}r^2\theta = \frac{1}{2} \times 10^2 \times 0.7 = 35\text{ cm}^2$

Q2 Get the angle in radians:
$50° = \frac{50 \times \pi}{180} = \frac{5\pi}{18}$ radians
Find the radius, r, first:
$\text{Area} = \frac{1}{2}r^2\theta = \frac{1}{2} \times r^2 \times \frac{5\pi}{18} = 20\pi\text{ cm}^2$
$20\pi = \frac{5\pi}{36}r^2 \Rightarrow 144 = r^2 \Rightarrow r = 12$
$BC = l = r\theta = 12 \times \frac{5\pi}{18} = \frac{10\pi}{3}$ cm

Q3 $\cos 30° = \frac{\sqrt{3}}{2}$, $\sin 30° = \frac{1}{2}$, $\tan 30° = \frac{1}{\sqrt{3}}$
$\cos 45° = \frac{1}{\sqrt{2}}$, $\sin 45° = \frac{1}{\sqrt{2}}$, $\tan 45° = 1$
$\cos 60° = \frac{1}{2}$, $\sin 60° = \frac{\sqrt{3}}{2}$, $\tan 60° = \sqrt{3}$

Q4 a) Angle $B = 180° - 30° - 25° = 125°$.
Using the sine rule:
$\frac{c}{\sin C} = \frac{b}{\sin B} \Rightarrow c = \frac{6 \times \sin 25°}{\sin 125°} = 3.10\text{ m}$ (3 s.f.)
$\frac{a}{\sin A} = \frac{b}{\sin B} \Rightarrow a = \frac{6 \times \sin 30°}{\sin 125°} = 3.66\text{ m}$ (3 s.f.)

b) $\text{Area} = \frac{1}{2}ab\sin C = \frac{1}{2} \times 3.66... \times 6 \times \sin 25°$
$= 4.64\text{ m}^2$ (3 s.f.)

Q5 a) Using the cosine rule:
$r^2 = p^2 + q^2 - 2pq\cos R$
$r = \sqrt{13^2 + 23^2 - (2 \times 13 \times 23 \times \cos 20°)}$
$= 11.664... = 11.7\text{ km}$ (1d.p.)
Using the sine rule:
$\frac{\sin P}{p} = \frac{\sin R}{r} \Rightarrow P = \sin^{-1}\frac{13 \times \sin 20°}{11.664...} = 22.4°$
$Q = 180° - 20° - 22.4° = 137.6°$ (1 d.p.)
Be careful here — if you didn't realise the angle was obtuse, you'd have got the wrong value for Q. If you're not sure, sketch the triangle to check.

b) $\text{Area} = \frac{1}{2}pq\sin R = 51.1\text{ km}^2$ (1 d.p.)

Q6 Using the cosine rule:
$a^2 = b^2 + c^2 - 2bc\cos A$
$\Rightarrow A = \cos^{-1}\left(\frac{b^2 + c^2 - a^2}{2bc}\right)$
$= \cos^{-1}\left(\frac{20^2 + 25^2 - 10^2}{2 \times 20 \times 25}\right) = 22.33...°$
$= 22.3°$ (1d.p.)
It doesn't matter which angle you start with — here it was the smallest of the 3.
$B = \cos^{-1}\left(\frac{a^2 + c^2 - b^2}{2ac}\right)$
$= \cos^{-1}\left(\frac{10^2 + 25^2 - 20^2}{2 \times 10 \times 25}\right) = 49.45...°$
$= 49.5°$ (1d.p.)
$C = 180° - 49.45...° - 22.33...° = 108.218° = 108.2°$ (1 d.p.)

Q7 The two possible triangles are as shown:

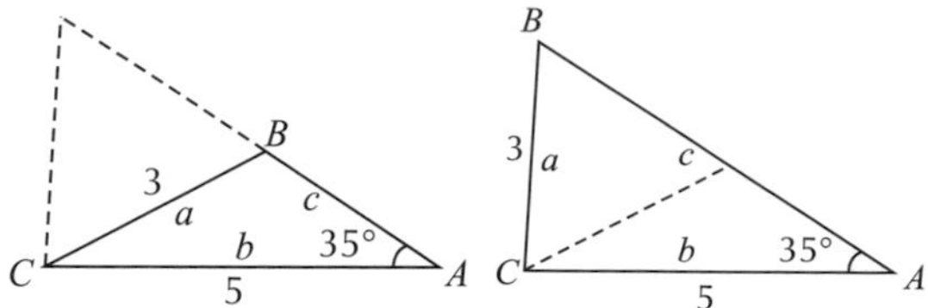

For one triangle:

$$\frac{\sin A}{a} = \frac{\sin B}{b} \Rightarrow B = \sin^{-1}\left(\frac{5 \times \sin 35^\circ}{3}\right) = 72.932...^\circ$$

$$= 72.9^\circ \text{ (1 d.p.)}$$

$C = 180° - 35° - 72.932...° = 72.067...° = 72.1°$ (1 d.p.)

$$\frac{c}{\sin C} = \frac{a}{\sin A} \Rightarrow c = \frac{3 \times \sin 72.06...^\circ}{\sin 35^\circ} = 4.976... \text{ m}$$

$$= 4.98 \text{ m (3 s.f.)}$$

For the other triangle:

$B = 180° - 72.932...° = 107.067...° = 107.1°$ (1 d.p.).

This is the other solution to $\sin^{-1}\frac{5 \times \sin 35°}{3}$ *for* $0 \le A \le 180°$.

$C = 180° - 35° - 107.067...° = 37.932...° = 37.9°$ (1 d.p.)

$$\frac{c}{\sin C} = \frac{a}{\sin A} \Rightarrow c = \frac{3 \times \sin 37.932...^\circ}{\sin 35^\circ} = 3.215... \text{ m}$$

$$= 3.22 \text{ m (3 s.f.)}$$

Whenever you find an angle using the sine rule by taking $\sin^{-1}$*, you need to make sure it's the right one and not '180° minus' the angle you want. You can usually tell by looking at the diagram.*

Q8
$$\tan x - \sin x \cos x \equiv \frac{\sin x}{\cos x} - \sin x \cos x$$
$$\equiv \frac{\sin x - \sin x \cos^2 x}{\cos x}$$
$$\equiv \frac{\sin x(1 - \cos^2 x)}{\cos x}$$
$$\equiv \frac{\sin x(\sin^2 x)}{\cos x}$$
$$\equiv \sin^2 x \tan x$$

Q9
$$\tan^2 x - \cos^2 x + 1 \equiv \frac{\sin^2 x}{\cos^2 x} - (1 - \sin^2 x) + 1$$
$$\equiv \frac{\sin^2 x}{\cos^2 x} + \sin^2 x$$
$$\equiv \frac{\sin^2 x + \sin^2 x \cos^2 x}{\cos^2 x}$$
$$\equiv \frac{\sin^2 x(1 + \cos^2 x)}{\cos^2 x}$$
$$\equiv \tan^2 x(1 + \cos^2 x)$$

Q10 $(\sin y + \cos y)^2 + (\cos y - \sin y)^2$
$$\equiv \sin^2 y + 2\sin y \cos y + \cos^2 y + \cos^2 y - 2\sin y \cos y + \sin^2 y$$
$$\equiv 2\sin^2 y + 2\cos^2 y$$
$$\equiv 2(\sin^2 y + \cos^2 y) \equiv 2$$

Q11
$$\frac{\sin^4 x + \sin^2 x \cos^2 x}{\cos^2 x - 1} \equiv \frac{\sin^4 x + \sin^2 x(1 - \sin^2 x)}{1 - \sin^2 x - 1}$$
$$\equiv \frac{\sin^4 x + \sin^2 x - \sin^4 x}{-\sin^2 x}$$
$$\equiv \frac{\sin^2 x}{-\sin^2 x} \equiv -1$$

Q12 a)

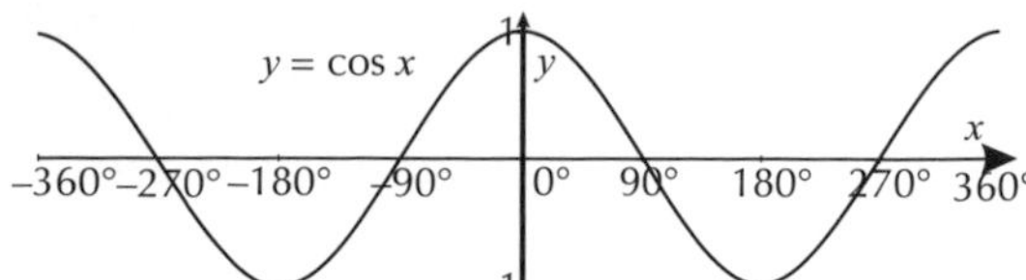

b)

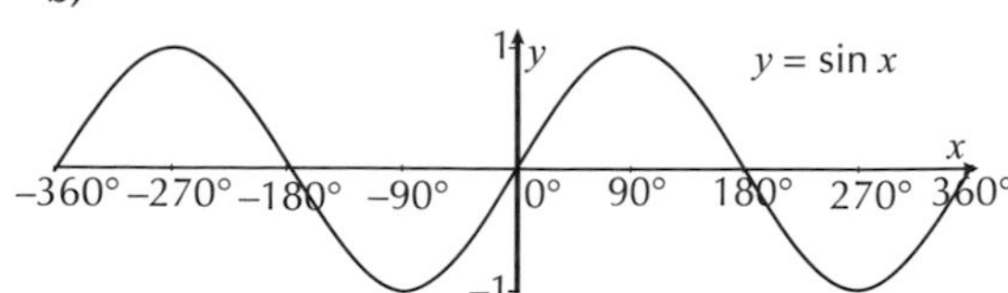

c)

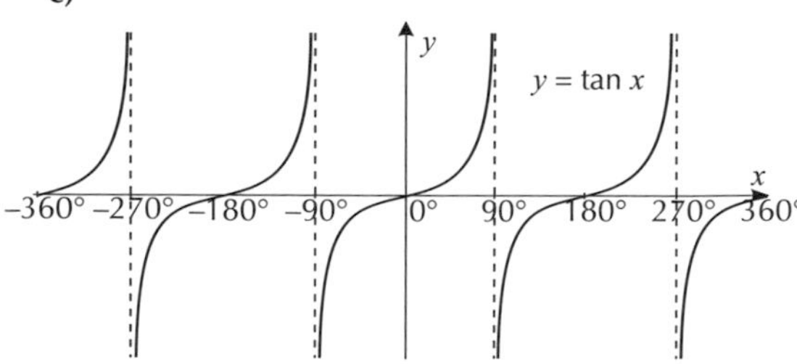

Q13 $y = -\frac{1}{2}\cos x$

Q14 $y = \sin 2x$

Q15 a)

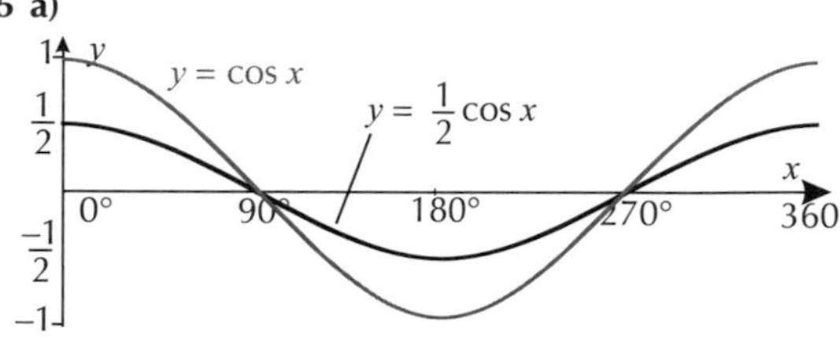

b)

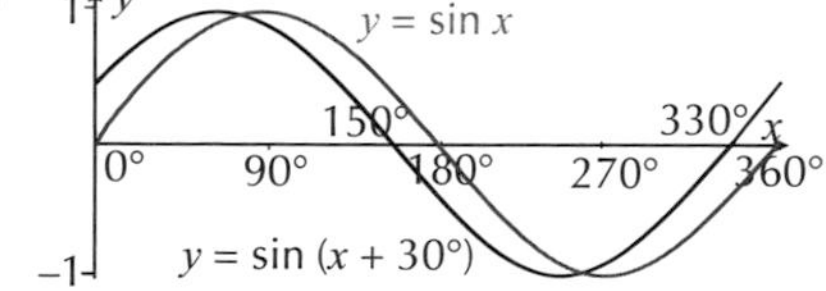

c)

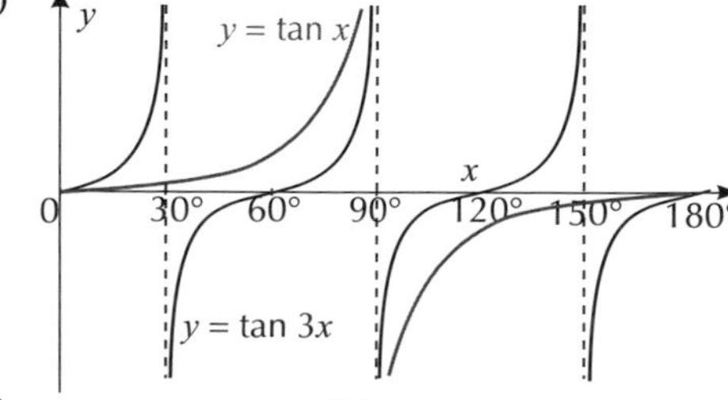

Q16 a)

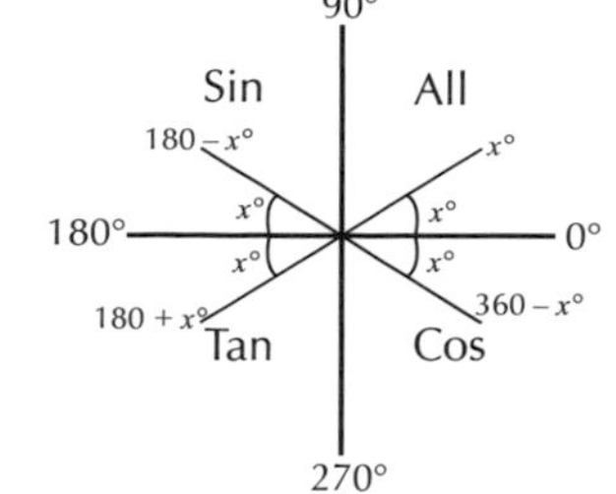

(i) The first solution is $\theta = 60°$. Looking at a CAST diagram, the other solution is $\theta = 180° - 60° = 120°$.

(ii) The first solution is $\theta = -45°$. This is out of the interval needed, but tan repeats every 180° so the two solutions are 135° and 315°.

(iii) The first solution is $\theta = 135°$. Looking at a CAST diagram, the other solution is $180° + (180° - 135°) = 225°$.
This time you want the quadrants where cos is negative.

b) (i) The first solution is $4\theta = 131.81...°$. Using the symmetry of the graph of $\cos\theta$, the other solutions in the extended interval $-720° \leq 4\theta \leq 720°$ are 228.18...°, 491.81...°, 588.18...°, −131.81...°, −228.18...°, −491.81...° and −588.18...°. These are all solutions for 4θ, so the actual solutions to 1 d.p. are $\theta = 33.0°$, 57.0°, 123.0°, 147.0°, −33.0°, −57.0°, −123.0° and −147.0°.

(ii) The first solution is $\theta + 35° = 17.5°$ (1 d.p.). Looking at the symmetry of the graph of $\sin\theta$, the other solution is $\theta + 35° = 180° - 17.5° = 162.5°$. These are solutions for $\theta + 35°$, so the actual solutions are $\theta = -17.5°$ and 127.5°

(iii) The first solution is $\frac{\theta}{2} = 89.88...°$, so $\theta = 179.77...° = 179.8°$ (1 d.p.).
As you're finding solutions for $\frac{\theta}{2}$, look in the interval $-90° \leq \frac{\theta}{2} \leq 90°$. Tan doesn't repeat any values within this interval, so there are no other solutions.

Q17 $6\sin^2 x = \cos x + 5 \Rightarrow 6(1 - \cos^2 x) = \cos x + 5$
$\Rightarrow 6\cos^2 x + \cos x - 1 = 0$
$\Rightarrow (3\cos x - 1)(2\cos x + 1) = 0$

So either $\cos x = \frac{1}{3}$ or $\cos x = -\frac{1}{2}$.
If $\cos x = \frac{1}{3}$, the first solution is $x = 1.230...$.
Looking at the symmetry of the graph of $\cos x$, the other solution is $x = 2\pi - 1.230... = 5.052...$
If $\cos x = -\frac{1}{2}$, the first solution is $x = \frac{2\pi}{3}$ (this is because $\cos\frac{\pi}{3} = \frac{1}{2}$, but you want a negative value, so as cos is negative in the second quadrant of the CAST diagram the solution is $\pi - \frac{\pi}{3} = \frac{2\pi}{3}$).
Looking at the symmetry of the graph of $\cos x$, the other solution is $x = 2\pi - \frac{2\pi}{3} = \frac{4\pi}{3}$.
So the solutions are $x = 1.23$ (3 s.f.), 5.05 (3 s.f.), $\frac{2\pi}{3}$ and $\frac{4\pi}{3}$.

Q18 $3\tan x + 2\cos x = 0 \Rightarrow 3\frac{\sin x}{\cos x} + 2\cos x = 0$
$\Rightarrow 3\sin x + 2\cos^2 x = 0$
$\Rightarrow 3\sin x + 2(1 - \sin^2 x) = 0$
$\Rightarrow 3\sin x + 2 - 2\sin^2 x = 0$
$\Rightarrow (2\sin x + 1)(\sin x - 2) = 0$
So either $\sin x = -\frac{1}{2}$ or $\sin x = 2$. $\sin x$ can't be 2, so look for solutions to $\sin x = -\frac{1}{2}$. The first solution is the only one within the interval: $x = -30°$.

Q19 $6\sin^2 x + \sin x - 1 = 0 \Rightarrow (3\sin x - 1)(2\sin x + 1) = 0$
So either $\sin x = \frac{1}{3}$ or $\sin x = -\frac{1}{2}$. If $\sin x = \frac{1}{3}$, the first solution is $x = 0.3398... = 0.340$ (3 s.f.). Looking at the symmetry of the graph of $\sin x$, the other solution is $x = \pi - 0.3398... = 2.801... = 2.80$ (3 s.f.).
If $\sin x = -\frac{1}{2}$, the first solution is $x = -\frac{\pi}{6}$.
This is outside the interval, so look at the symmetry of the graph to find the solutions within interval.
One is $\pi + \frac{\pi}{6} = \frac{7\pi}{6}$ and another is $2\pi - \frac{\pi}{6} = \frac{11\pi}{6}$.

Q20 $\tan x - 3\sin x = 0 \rightarrow \frac{\sin x}{\cos x} - 3\sin x = 0$
$\Rightarrow \sin x - 3\sin x\cos x = 0$
$\Rightarrow \sin x(1 - 3\cos x) = 0$
So either $\sin x = 0$ or $\cos x = \frac{1}{3}$. If $\sin x = 0$ the solutions are $x = 0°$, 180°, 360°, 540°, 720°.
If $\cos x = \frac{1}{3}$, the first solution is $x = 70.528...° = 70.5°$ (1 d.p.). Looking at the symmetry of the graph of $\cos x$, the other solutions to 1 d.p. are $x = 289.5°$, 430.5° and 649.5°.

Exam-Style Questions — Chapter 2

Q1 a) Using the cosine rule:
$a^2 = b^2 + c^2 - 2bc\cos A$
If XY is a, then angle $A = 180° - 100° = 80°$.
$XY^2 = 150^2 + 250^2 - (2 \times 150 \times 250 \times \cos 80°)$
$XY^2 = 71976.3867$
$XY = \sqrt{71976.3867} = 268.28$ m (to 2 d.p.)
= 268 m to the nearest m.
[2 marks available — 1 mark for correct substitution into cosine rule formula, and 1 mark for correct answer.]

b) Using the sine rule:
$\frac{a}{\sin A} = \frac{b}{\sin B}$, so $\frac{250}{\sin\theta} = \frac{268.2842}{\sin 80°}$ (from (a)).
Rearranging gives:
$\frac{\sin\theta}{\sin 80°} = \frac{250}{268.2842} = 0.93$ (2 d.p.)
[2 marks available — 1 mark for correct substitution into sine rule formula and 1 mark for correct final answer.]

Q2 a) Area of cross-section $= \frac{1}{2}r^2\theta$
$= \frac{1}{2} \times 20^2 \times \frac{\pi}{4} = 50\pi$ cm².
Volume = area of cross-section × height, so $V = 50\pi \times 10 = 500\pi$ cm³.
[3 marks available — 1 mark for correct use of area formula, 1 mark for 50π, and 1 mark for correct final answer.]

b) Surface area is made up of:
2 × cross-sectional area + 2 × side rectangles + 1 curved end rectangle.
Cross-sectional area = 50π (from part (a))
Area of each side rectangle = 10 × 20 = 200
Area of end rectangle = 10 × arc length
$= 10 \times (20 \times \frac{\pi}{4})$
$= 50\pi$.
$S = (2 \times 50\pi) + (2 \times 200) + 50\pi$
$= (150\pi + 400)$ cm².

[5 marks available — 1 mark for each correct shape area, 1 mark for correct combination, and 1 mark for correct final answer.]

Q3 a) $(1 + 2\cos x)(3\tan^2 x - 1) = 0$

$\Rightarrow 1 + 2\cos x = 0 \Rightarrow \cos x = -\frac{1}{2}$.

OR:

$3\tan^2 x - 1 = 0 \Rightarrow \tan^2 x = \frac{1}{3}$

$\Rightarrow \tan x = \frac{1}{\sqrt{3}}$ or $-\frac{1}{\sqrt{3}}$.

For $\cos x = -\frac{1}{2}$, $x = \frac{2\pi}{3}$ and $-\frac{2\pi}{3}$.

Drawing the cos x graph helps you find the second one here, and don't forget the limits are $-\pi \le x \le \pi$.

For $\tan x = \frac{1}{\sqrt{3}}$,

$x = \frac{\pi}{6}$ and $-\pi + \frac{\pi}{6} = -\frac{5\pi}{6}$.

For $\tan x = -\frac{1}{\sqrt{3}}$,

$x = -\frac{\pi}{6}$ and $-\frac{\pi}{6} + \pi = \frac{5\pi}{6}$.

Again, look at the graph of tan x if you're unsure.

[6 marks available — 1 mark for each correct solution.]

b) $3\cos^2 x = \sin^2 x \Rightarrow 3 = \frac{\sin^2 x}{\cos^2 x} \Rightarrow 3 = \tan^2 x$

$\Rightarrow \tan x = \pm\sqrt{3}$.

For $\tan x = \sqrt{3}$, $x = \frac{\pi}{3}$ and $\frac{\pi}{3} - \pi = -\frac{2\pi}{3}$.

For $\tan x = -\sqrt{3}$, $x = -\frac{\pi}{3}$ and $-\frac{\pi}{3} + \pi = \frac{2\pi}{3}$.

[4 marks available — 1 mark for each correct solution.]

Q4 a) $3\cos x = 2\sin x$, and $\tan x \equiv \frac{\sin x}{\cos x}$,

You need to substitute tan in somewhere, so look at how you can rearrange to get sin/cos in the equation...

Divide through by cos x to give:

$3\frac{\cos x}{\cos x} = 2\frac{\sin x}{\cos x} \Rightarrow 3 = 2\tan x$

$\Rightarrow \tan x = \frac{3}{2}$ (or = 1.5).

[2 marks available — 1 mark for correct substitution of tan x, 1 mark for correct final answer.]

b) Using $\tan x = 1.5$, the first solution is $x = 56.3°$ (1 d.p.) ***[1 mark]*** and a 2nd solution can be found from $x = 180° + 56.3° = 236.3°$ (1 d.p.) ***[1 mark]***.

Remember tan x repeats every 180°.

Q5 a) (i)

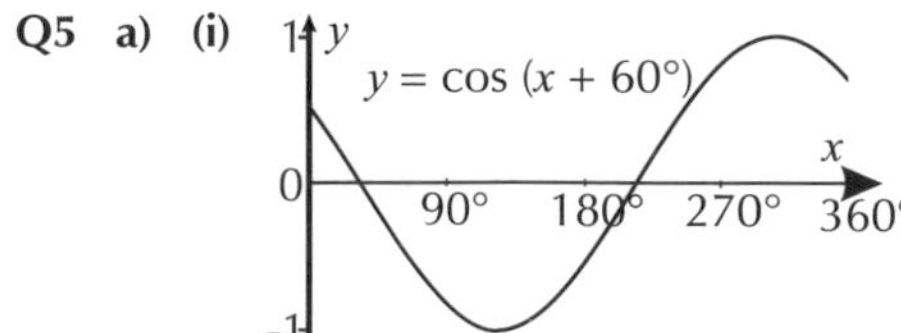

[2 marks available — 1 mark for correct shape of cos x graph, 1 mark for shift of 60° to the left.]

(ii) cos x crosses the x-axis at 90° and 270°. Shifting these left by 60° gives the solutions $x = 30°$ and 210°.

[2 marks available — 1 mark for each correct solution.]

b)

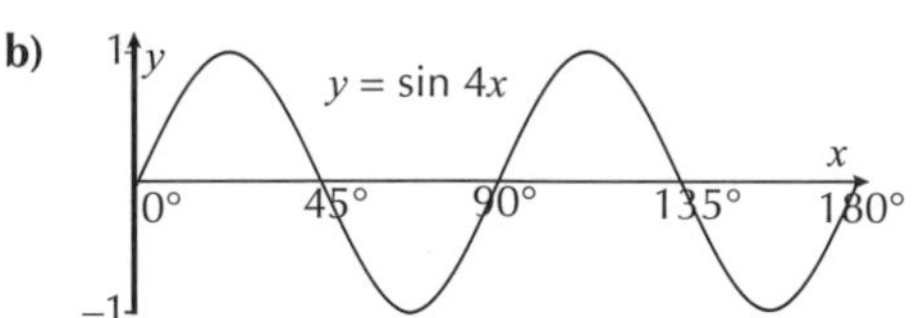

[2 marks available — 1 mark for correct shape, 1 mark for stretch of scale factor ¼.]

c) The first solution is $4x = 30°$ so $x = 7.5°$ ***[1 mark]***. The graph in (b) shows there are 4 solutions between 0° and 180°, and looking at the symmetry of the graph, they lie 7.5° from where the graph cuts the x-axis as follows:

$x = 45° - 7.5° = 37.5°$ ***[1 mark]***

$x = 90° + 7.5° = 97.5°$ ***[1 mark]***

$x = 135° - 7.5° = 127.5°$ ***[1 mark]***

If you hadn't sketched the graph, you could solve it by extending the interval.

Q6 a) $\tan\left(x + \frac{\pi}{6}\right) = \sqrt{3} \Rightarrow x + \frac{\pi}{6} = \frac{\pi}{3}$ ***[1 mark]***

tan is positive in the 3rd quadrant of a CAST diagram, so you can work out the other solution as follows...

2nd solution can be found from:

$x + \frac{\pi}{6} = \pi + \frac{\pi}{3} = \frac{4}{3}\pi$ ***[1 mark]***. So subtracting $\frac{\pi}{6}$ from each solution gives: $x = \frac{\pi}{6}$ ***[1 mark]***,

$x = \frac{7\pi}{6}$ ***[1 mark]***.

b) For this one, change the interval and look for solutions in the interval $-\frac{\pi}{4} \le x - \frac{\pi}{4} \le 2\pi - \frac{\pi}{4}$.

$2\cos(x - \frac{\pi}{4}) = \sqrt{3}$

so $\cos(x - \frac{\pi}{4}) = \frac{\sqrt{3}}{2}$.

Solving this gives $x - \frac{\pi}{4} = \frac{\pi}{6}$, which is in the interval — so it's a solution ***[1 mark]***. From the symmetry of the cos graph there's another solution at $2\pi - \frac{\pi}{6} = \frac{11\pi}{6}$. But this is outside the interval for $x - \frac{\pi}{4}$, so you can ignore it ***[1 mark]***. Using symmetry again, there's also a solution at $-\frac{\pi}{6}$ ***[1 mark]*** — and this one is in your interval. So solutions for $x - \frac{\pi}{4}$ are $-\frac{\pi}{6}$ and $\frac{\pi}{6}$

$\Rightarrow x = \frac{\pi}{12}$ and $\frac{5\pi}{12}$. ***[1 mark]***

You might find it useful to sketch the graph for this one — or you could use the CAST diagram if you prefer.

c) $\sin 2x = -\frac{1}{2}$, so look for solutions in the interval $0 \le 2x \le 4\pi$.

It's easier to see what's going on by drawing a graph.

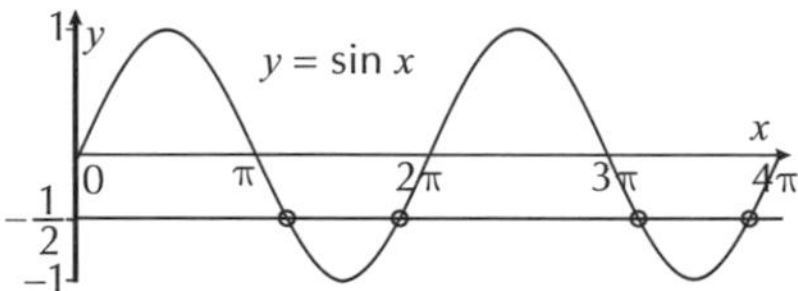

The graph shows there are 4 solutions between 0 and 4π. Using a calculator to solve $\sin 2x = -\frac{1}{2}$ gives you the solution $2x = -\frac{\pi}{6}$, but this is outside the interval.

From the graph, you can see that the solutions within the interval occur at

$\pi + \frac{\pi}{6}, 2\pi - \frac{\pi}{6}, 3\pi + \frac{\pi}{6}$ and $4\pi - \frac{\pi}{6}$ ***[1 mark]***, so $2x = \frac{7\pi}{6}, \frac{11\pi}{6}, \frac{19\pi}{6}$ and $\frac{23\pi}{6}$ ***[1 mark]***. Dividing by 2 gives: $x = \frac{7\pi}{12}, \frac{11\pi}{12}, \frac{19\pi}{12}$ and $\frac{23\pi}{12}$

[1 mark for each correct solution]

Q7 $2 - \sin x = 2\cos^2 x$, and $\cos^2 x \equiv 1 - \sin^2 x$

$\Rightarrow 2 - \sin x = 2(1 - \sin^2 x)$

$\Rightarrow 2 - \sin x = 2 - 2\sin^2 x$

$\Rightarrow 2\sin^2 x - \sin x = 0$

$\sin x(2\sin x - 1) = 0 \Rightarrow \sin x = 0$ or $\sin x = \frac{1}{2}$.

For $\sin x = 0$, $x = 0$, π and 2π.

For $\sin x = \frac{1}{2}$, $x = \frac{\pi}{6}$ and $\pi - \frac{\pi}{6} = \frac{5\pi}{6}$.

[6 marks available — 1 mark for correct substitution using trig identity, 1 mark for factorising quadratic in sin x, 1 mark for finding correct values of sin x, 1 mark for all three solutions when sin x = 0, 1 mark for each of the other 2 correct solutions.]

Q8 a) $2(1 - \cos x) = 3\sin^2 x$, and $\sin^2 x \equiv 1 - \cos^2 x$.

$\Rightarrow 2(1 - \cos x) = 3(1 - \cos^2 x)$ ***[1 mark]***.

You need to get the whole equation into either sin or cos to get something useful at the end, so get used to spotting places to use the trig identities.

$\Rightarrow 2 - 2\cos x = 3 - 3\cos^2 x$

$\Rightarrow 3\cos^2 x - 2\cos x - 1 = 0$ ***[1 mark]***.

b) From (a), the equation can be written as: $3\cos^2 x - 2\cos x - 1 = 0$

Now this looks like a quadratic equation, which can be factorised:

$(3\cos x + 1)(\cos x - 1) = 0$

$\Rightarrow \cos x = -\frac{1}{3}$ ***[1 mark]*** or $\cos x = 1$ ***[1 mark]***

For $\cos x = -\frac{1}{3}$, $x = 109.5°$ (to 1 d.p.) ***[1 mark]***, and a 2nd solution can be found from $x = (360° - 109.5°) = 250.5°$ ***[1 mark]***.

For $\cos x = 1$, $x = 0°$ ***[1 mark]*** and $360°$ ***[1 mark]***.

Chapter 3: Logarithms and Exponentials

1. Logs

Exercise 1.1 — Logs

Q1 a) $\log_2 8 = 3$ **b)** $\log_5 625 = 4$

c) $\log_{49} 7 = \frac{1}{2}$ **d)** $\log_8 4 = \frac{2}{3}$

e) $\log_{10} \frac{1}{100} = -2$ **f)** $\log_2 0.125 = -3$

Q2 a) $\log_4 9 = x$ **b)** $\log_x 40 = 3$

c) $\log_8 x = 11$

Q3 a) $5^3 = 125$ **b)** $10^4 = 10\,000$

c) $\left(\frac{1}{2}\right)^{-2} = 4$ **d)** $7^6 = a$

e) $5^{0.2} = t$ **f)** $4^1 = m$

g) $\left(\frac{1}{4}\right)^{\frac{1}{2}} = p$ **h)** $10^5 = k$

i) $x^m = a$

Q4 a) 3 **b)** –2 **c)** 0

d) 0.301 **e)** 0.477 **f)** 0.778

Use the 'log' button on your calculator to work these out.

Q5 a) 2 **b)** 3 **c)** –1

Q6 a) $x^2 = 49 \Rightarrow x = 7$

b) $x^3 = 8 \Rightarrow x = 2$

c) $x^5 = 100\,000 \Rightarrow x - 10$

d) $x^{\frac{1}{2}} = 3 \Rightarrow x = 3^2 \Rightarrow x = 9$

e) $x^{\frac{1}{3}} = 7 \Rightarrow x = 7^3 \Rightarrow x = 343$

f) $x^{\frac{1}{5}} = 2 \Rightarrow x = 2^5 \Rightarrow x = 32$

g) $3^4 = x \Rightarrow x = 81$

h) $2^6 = x \Rightarrow x = 64$

i) $7^1 = x \Rightarrow x = 7$

j) $9^{\frac{1}{2}} = x \Rightarrow x = 3$

k) $64^{\frac{1}{3}} = x \Rightarrow x = 4$

l) $27^{\frac{2}{3}} = x \Rightarrow x = 9$

Q7 a) $a^2 = x$ and $a^4 = y$, so $y = x^2$.

b) $a^3 = x$ and $(2a)^3 = y \Rightarrow 8a^3 = y$, so $y = 8x$.

c) $a^5 = x$ and $a^{20} = y$, $(a^5)^4 = y$, so $y = x^4$.

Exercise 1.2 — Laws of logs

Q1 a) $\log_a 2 + \log_a 5 = \log_a (2 \times 5) = \log_a 10$

b) $\log_m 8 + \log_m 7 = \log_m (8 \times 7) = \log_m 56$

c) $\log_b 8 - \log_b 4 = \log_b (8 \div 4) = \log_b 2$

d) $\log_m 15 - \log_m 5 = \log_m (15 \div 5) = \log_m 3$

e) $3 \log_n 4 = \log_n (4^3) = \log_n 64$

f) $2 \log_a 7 = \log_a (7^2) = \log_a 49$

g) $\frac{1}{2} \log_b 16 = \log_b (16^{\frac{1}{2}}) = \log_b 4$

h) $\frac{2}{3} \log_a 125 = \log_a (125^{\frac{2}{3}}) = \log_a 25$

i) $\log_3 a - \log_2 a$ can't be simplified any further as the bases are different.
The words 'where possible' in the question are a clue that there might be some parts which can't be simplified.

Q2 **a)** $2 \log_a 5 + \log_a 4 = \log_a (5^2) + \log_a 4$
$= \log_a (25 \times 4) = \log_a 100$

b) $3 \log_m 2 - \log_m 4 = \log_m (2^3) - \log_m 4$
$= \log_m (8 \div 4) = \log_m 2$

c) $3 \log_n 4 - 2 \log_n 8 = \log_n (4^3) - \log_n (8^2)$
$= \log_n (64 \div 64) = \log_n 1 = 0$

d) $\frac{2}{3} \log_b 216 - 2 \log_b 3 = \log_b (216^{\frac{2}{3}}) - \log_b (3^2)$
$= \log_b (36 \div 9) = \log_b 4$

e) $1 + \log_a 6 = \log_a a + \log_a 6 = \log_a 6a$

f) $2 - \log_b 5 = 2 \log_b b - \log_b 5 = \log_b b^2 - \log_b 5$
$= \log_b \left(\frac{b^2}{5}\right)$

Q3 **a)** $\log_a 6 = \log_a (2 \times 3) = \log_a 2 + \log_a 3 = x + y$

b) $\log_a 16 = \log_a 2^4 = 4 \log_a 2 = 4x$

c) $\log_a 60 = \log_a (2 \times 2 \times 3 \times 5)$
$= \log_a 2^2 + \log_a 3 + \log_a 5 = 2x + y + z$

Q4 **a)** $\log_b b^3 = 3 \log_b b = 3$

b) $\log_a \sqrt{a} = \log_a a^{\frac{1}{2}} = \frac{1}{2} \log_a a = \frac{1}{2}$

c) $\log_m 4m - 2 \log_m 2 = \log_m 4 + \log_m m - \log_m 2^2$
$= \log_m 4 + 1 - \log_m 4 = 1$

d) $\log_{2b} \left(\frac{4 \times b}{2}\right) = \log_{2b} 2b = 1$

Q5 **a)** $\log_2 4^x = x \log_2 4 = x \log_2 2^2 = 2x \log_2 2 = 2x$

b) $\frac{\log_a 54 - \log_a 6}{\log_a 3} = \frac{\log_a (54 \div 6)}{\log_a 3} = \frac{\log_a 9}{\log_a 3}$
$= \frac{\log_a 3^2}{\log_a 3} = \frac{2 \log_a 3}{\log_a 3} = 2$

Q6 **a)** $\log_6 3 = \frac{\log_{10} 3}{\log_{10} 6} = 0.613$ (3 s.f.)

b) $\log_9 2 = \frac{\log_{10} 2}{\log_{10} 9} = 0.315$ (3 s.f.)

c) $\log_3 13 = \frac{\log_{10} 13}{\log_{10} 3} = 2.33$ (3 s.f.)

d) $\log_5 4 = \frac{\log_{10} 4}{\log_{10} 5} = 0.861$ (3 s.f.)

Q7 $\log_m x = 2 + 3\log_m 2 - \log_m 5$
$\log_m x = 2\log_m m + \log_m 2^3 - \log_m 5$
$\log_m x = \log_m m^2 + \log_m 8 - \log_m 5$
$\log_m x = \log_m \left(\frac{m^2 \times 8}{5}\right)$
$\Rightarrow x = \frac{8m^2}{5}$

2. Exponentials

Exercise 2.1 — Exponentials and logs

Q1 **a)** Take logs of both sides:
$\log 2^x = \log 3 \Rightarrow x \log 2 = \log 3$
$\Rightarrow x = \frac{\log 3}{\log 2} = 1.584... = 1.58$ (3 s.f.)

b) $4^x = 16 \Rightarrow \log 4^x = \log 16 \Rightarrow x \log 4 = \log 16$
$\Rightarrow x = \frac{\log 16}{\log 4} = \frac{4 \log 2}{2 \log 2} = 2$
This one's actually pretty easy if you spot that 16 = 4^2 so x = 2.

c) $7^x = 2 \Rightarrow \log 7^x = \log 2 \Rightarrow x \log 7 = \log 2$
$\Rightarrow x = \frac{\log 2}{\log 7} = 0.3562... = 0.356$ (3 s.f.)

d) $1.8^x = 0.4 \Rightarrow \log 1.8^x = \log 0.4$
$\Rightarrow x \log 1.8 = \log 0.4$
$\Rightarrow x = \frac{\log 0.4}{\log 1.8} = -1.558... = -1.56$ (3 s.f.)
Notice that this solution is negative, because log 0.4 is negative.

e) $0.7^x = 3 \Rightarrow \log 0.7^x = \log 3 \Rightarrow x \log 0.7 = \log 3$
$\Rightarrow x = \frac{\log 3}{\log 0.7} = -3.080... = -3.08$ (3 s.f.)

f) $0.5^x = 0.2 \Rightarrow \log 0.5^x = \log 0.2$
$\Rightarrow x \log 0.5 = \log 0.2$
$\Rightarrow x = \frac{\log 0.2}{\log 0.5} = 2.321... = 2.32$ (3 s.f.)

g) Take logs of both sides:
$\log 2^{3x-1} = \log 5 \Rightarrow (3x - 1)\log 2 = \log 5$
$\Rightarrow 3x \log 2 = \log 5 + \log 2$
$= \log(5 \times 2)$
$\Rightarrow x = \frac{\log 10}{3 \log 2} = 1.11$ (3 s.f.)

h) $10^{3-x} = 8 \Rightarrow \log 10^{3-x} = \log 8$
$\Rightarrow (3 - x)\log 10 = \log 8$
$\Rightarrow 3 - x = \log 8$
$\Rightarrow x = 3 - \log 8 = 2.10$ (3 s.f.)
Remember that $\log_{10} 10 = 1$.

i) $0.4^{5x-4} = 2 \Rightarrow \log 0.4^{5x-4} = \log 2$
$\Rightarrow (5x - 4)\log 0.4 = \log 2$
$\Rightarrow 5x \log 0.4 = \log 2 + 4 \log 0.4$
$\Rightarrow x = \frac{\log 2 + 4 \log 0.4}{5 \log 0.4} = 0.649$ (3 s.f.)

Q2 **a)** Take exponentials of both sides using base 10 (since the logarithm is base 10):
$10^{\log 5x} = 10^3 \Rightarrow 5x = 1000 \Rightarrow x = 200$

b) Take exponentials of both sides (using base 2):
$\Rightarrow 2^{\log_2 (x+3)} = 2^4 \Rightarrow x + 3 = 16 \Rightarrow x = 13$

c) Take exponentials of both sides (using base 3):
$\Rightarrow 3^{\log_3 (5-2x)} = 3^{2.5} \Rightarrow 5 - 2x = 3^{2.5}$
$\Rightarrow x = \frac{5 - 3^{2.5}}{2} = -5.294... = -5.29$ (3 s.f.)

Q3 a) $4^{x+1} = 3^{2x} \Rightarrow \log 4^{x+1} = \log 3^{2x}$
$\Rightarrow (x + 1) \log 4 = 2x \log 3$
Multiply out the brackets:
$\Rightarrow x \log 4 + \log 4 = 2x \log 3$
Collect x-terms on one side:
$\Rightarrow \log 4 = 2x \log 3 - x \log 4 = x (2 \log 3 - \log 4)$
$\Rightarrow x = \dfrac{\log 4}{2 \log 3 - \log 4} = 1.709... = 1.71 \text{(3 s.f.)}$

b) $2^{5-x} = 4^{x+3} \Rightarrow \log 2^{5-x} = \log 4^{x+3}$
$\Rightarrow (5 - x) \log 2 = (x + 3) \log 4$
$\Rightarrow 5 \log 2 - x \log 2 = x \log 4 + 3 \log 4$
$\Rightarrow 5 \log 2 - 3 \log 4 = x \log 4 + x \log 2$
$\Rightarrow 5 \log 2 - 3 \log 4 = x (\log 4 + \log 2)$
$\Rightarrow x = \dfrac{5 \log 2 - 3 \log 4}{\log 4 + \log 2} = -\dfrac{1}{3}$

c) $3^{2x-1} = 6^{3-x} \Rightarrow \log 3^{2x-1} = \log 6^{3-x}$
$\Rightarrow (2x - 1) \log 3 = (3 - x) \log 6$
$\Rightarrow 2x \log 3 - \log 3 = 3 \log 6 - x \log 6$
$\Rightarrow 2x \log 3 + x \log 6 = 3 \log 6 + \log 3$
$\Rightarrow x (2 \log 3 + \log 6) = 3 \log 6 + \log 3$
$\Rightarrow x = \dfrac{3 \log 6 + \log 3}{2 \log 3 + \log 6} = 1.622... = 1.62 \text{(3 s.f.)}$

Q4 a) $\log 2x = \log(x + 1) - 1 \Rightarrow \log 2x - \log(x + 1) = -1$
$\Rightarrow \log\left(\dfrac{2x}{x+1}\right) = -1 \Rightarrow \dfrac{2x}{x+1} = 10^{-1} = \dfrac{1}{10}$
$\Rightarrow x + 1 = 20x \Rightarrow x = \dfrac{1}{19} = 0.0526$ (to 3 s.f.)

b) $\log_2 2x = 3 - \log_2 (9 - 2x)$
$\Rightarrow \log_2 2x + \log_2 (9 - 2x) = 3$
$\Rightarrow \log_2 2x (9 - 2x) = 3$
Take exponentials of base 2 of both sides to get:
$\Rightarrow 2x(9 - 2x) = 2^3 \Rightarrow 18x - 4x^2 = 8$
$\Rightarrow 4x^2 - 18x + 8 = 0 \Rightarrow 2x^2 - 9x + 4 = 0$
$\Rightarrow (2x - 1)(x - 4) = 0$
So, $x = \dfrac{1}{2}$ or $x = 4$

c) $\log_6 x = 1 - \log_6 (x + 1)$
$\Rightarrow \log_6 x + \log_6 (x + 1) = 1 \Rightarrow \log_6 x(x + 1) = 1$
Take exponentials of base 6 of both sides to get:
$\Rightarrow x(x + 1) = 6^1 \Rightarrow x^2 + x - 6 = 0$
$\Rightarrow (x + 3)(x - 2) = 0 \Rightarrow x = 2$
$x = -3$ is not a solution because logarithms of negative numbers don't exist.

d) $\log_2 (2x + 1) = 3 + 2 \log_2 x$
$\Rightarrow \log_2 (2x + 1) = 3 + \log_2 x^2$
$\Rightarrow \log_2 (2x + 1) - \log_2 x^2 = 3 \Rightarrow \log_2 \dfrac{2x+1}{x^2} = 3$
Take exponentials of base 2 of both sides to get:
$\Rightarrow \dfrac{2x+1}{x^2} = 2^3 \Rightarrow 2x + 1 = 8x^2$
$\Rightarrow 8x^2 - 2x - 1 = 0 \Rightarrow (4x + 1)(2x - 1) = 0$
So $x = \dfrac{1}{2}$.

Q5 $2^{x+y} = 8 \Rightarrow 2^{x+y} = 2^3 \Rightarrow x + y = 3$.
$\log_2 x - \log_2 y = 1 \Rightarrow \log_2 \dfrac{x}{y} = 1$
Take exponentials of base 2 of both sides to get:
$\Rightarrow \dfrac{x}{y} = 2^1 = 2 \Rightarrow x = 2y$
Solve $x + y = 3$ and $x = 2y$ simultaneously:
$x = 2y$ so put this into $x + y = 3 \Rightarrow 2y + y = 3$
$\Rightarrow 3y = 3$
$\Rightarrow y = 1$ and $x = 2$.

Q6 $9^{x-2} = 3^y \Rightarrow (3^2)^{x-2} = 3^y \Rightarrow 3^{(2(x-2))} = 3^y$ so $2(x - 2) = y$
$\log_3 2x = 1 + \log_3 y \Rightarrow \log_3 2x - \log_3 y = 1$
$\Rightarrow \log_3 \dfrac{2x}{y} = 1 \Rightarrow \dfrac{2x}{y} = 3^1 \Rightarrow 2x = 3y$
Solve $2(x - 2) = y$ and $2x = 3y$ simultaneously:
$2x = 3y$ so put this into $2(x - 2) = y \Rightarrow 3y - 4 = y$
$\Rightarrow 2y = 4 \Rightarrow y = 2$ and $x = 3$.

Q7 a) Let $y = 2^x$, then $2^{2x} - 5(2^x) + 4 = 0$ is equivalent to the quadratic equation $y^2 - 5y + 4 = 0$.
$\Rightarrow (y - 1)(y - 4) = 0$, so $y = 1$ or $y = 4$.
So $2^x = 4$ or $2^x = 1 \Rightarrow x = 2$ or $x = 0$.
The y^2 in the quadratic equation comes from $2^{2x} = (2^x)^2$.

b) Let $y = 4^x$, then $4^{2x} - 17(4^x) + 16 = 0$ is equivalent to the quadratic equation $y^2 - 17y + 16 = 0$.
$\Rightarrow (y - 1)(y - 16) = 0$, so $y = 1$ or $y = 16$.
So $4^x = 1$ or $4^x = 16 \Rightarrow x = 0$ or $x = 2$.

c) Let $y = 3^x$, then $3^{2x+2} = 3^{2x} \times 3^2 = y^2 \times 9 = 9y^2$.
So $3^{2x+2} - 82(3^x) + 9 = 0$ is equivalent to the quadratic equation $9y^2 - 82y + 9 = 0$.
$\Rightarrow (9y - 1)(y - 9) = 0$, so $y = \dfrac{1}{9}$ or $y = 9$.
So $3^x = \dfrac{1}{9}$ or $3^x = 9 \Rightarrow x = -2$ or $x = 2$.

d) Let $y = 2^x$, then $2^{2x+3} = 2^{2x} \times 2^3 = y^2 \times 8 = 8y^2$.
So $2^{2x+3} - 9(2^x) + 1 = 0$ is equivalent to the quadratic equation $8y^2 - 9y + 1 = 0$.
$\Rightarrow (8y - 1)(y - 1) = 0$, so $y = \dfrac{1}{8}$ or $y = 1$.
So $2^x = \dfrac{1}{8}$ or $2^x = 1 \Rightarrow x = -3$ or $x = 0$.

Q8 After n years, the investment is worth 500×1.08^n.
So, $500 \times 1.08^n = 1500 \Rightarrow 1.08^n = 3$.
Take logs of both sides:
$\log 1.08^n = \log 3 \Rightarrow n \log 1.08 = \log 3$
$\Rightarrow n = \dfrac{\log 3}{\log 1.08} = 14.3$
So it will take 15 years for Howard's investment to exceed £1500.
The question asks for full years, so round your answer up — after 14 years the value won't be quite high enough.

Review Exercise — Chapter 3

Q1 **a)** $\log_4 16 = 2$

b) $\log_{216} 6 = \frac{1}{3}$

c) $\log_3 \frac{1}{81} = -4$

Q2 **a)** $3^3 = 27$ so $\log_3 27 = 3$

b) To get fractions you need negative powers
$3^{-3} = \frac{1}{27}$
$\log_3 \left(\frac{1}{27}\right) = -3$

c) Logs are subtracted so divide
$\log_3 18 - \log_3 2 = \log_3 (18 \div 2)$
$= \log_3 9$
$= 2$ (as $3^2 = 9$)

Q3 **a)** Logs are added so multiply (remember $2 \log 5 = \log 5^2$).
$\log 3 + 2 \log 5 = \log (3 \times 5^2)$
$= \log 75$

b) Logs are subtracted so divide
$\frac{1}{2} \log 36 - \log 3 = \log (36^{\frac{1}{2}} \div 3)$
$= \log (6 \div 3)$
$= \log 2$

c) Logs are subtracted so divide
$\log 2 - \frac{1}{4} \log 16 = \log (2 \div 16^{\frac{1}{4}})$
$= \log (2 \div 2)$
$= \log 1 = 0$

Q4 $\log_b (x^2 - 1) - \log_b (x - 1) = \log_b \frac{x^2 - 1}{x - 1}$
$= \log_b \frac{(x + 1)(x - 1)}{x - 1} = \log_b (x + 1)$
This uses the difference of two squares.

Q5 **a)** $\log_7 12 = \frac{\log_{10} 12}{\log_{10} 7} = 1.276... = 1.28$ (3 s.f.)

b) $\log_5 8 = \frac{\log_{10} 8}{\log_{10} 5} = 1.292... = 1.29$ (3 s.f.)

c) $\log_{16} 125 = \frac{\log_{10} 125}{\log_{10} 16} = 1.741... = 1.74$ (3 s.f.)

Q6 $\log_a y = \log_a 5 + \log_a 3 + 1$
$\log_a y = \log_a 5 + \log_a 3 + \log_a a$
$\log_a y = \log_a (5 \times 3 \times a)$
$\log_a y = \log_a 15a$
$\Rightarrow y = 15a$

Q7 E.g. $\frac{2 + \log_a 4}{\log_a 2a} = \frac{2 + 2\log_a 2}{\log_a 2 + \log_a a} = \frac{2(1 + \log_a 2)}{\log_a 2 + 1} = 2$

Q8 **a)** Filling in the answers is just a case of using a calculator:

x	-3	-2	-1	0	1	2	3
y	0.0156	0.0625	0.25	1	4	16	64

b)

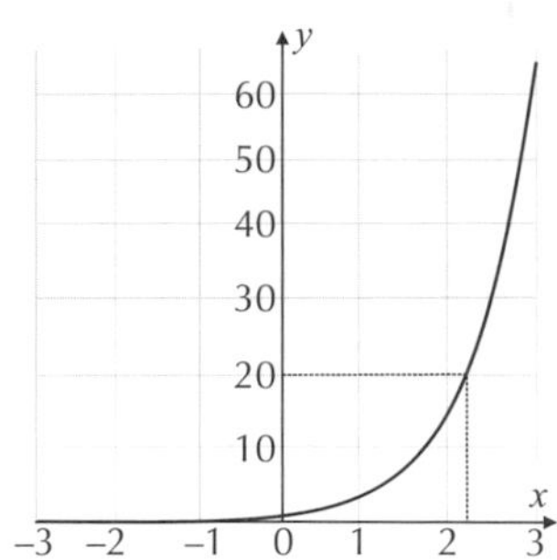

c) From the graph 2.2 is a good estimate.

d) First take logs of base 10 of both sides:
$\log_{10} 4^x = \log_{10} 20 \Rightarrow x \log_{10} 4 = \log_{10} 20$
$\Rightarrow x = \frac{\log_{10} 20}{\log_{10} 4} = 2.160... = 2.16$ (3 s.f.),
so the estimate in part c) was correct to 1 d.p.

Q9 **a)** Take logs of base 10 of both sides:
$\log_{10} 10^x = \log_{10} 240 \Rightarrow x \log_{10} 10 = \log_{10} 240$
$\Rightarrow x = \log_{10} 240 = 2.380... = 2.38$ (to 3 s.f.)
This uses the fact that $\log_{10} 10 = 1$.

b) Take exponentials of both sides using base 10:
$10^{\log_{10} x} = 10^{5.3}$
$\Rightarrow x = 10^{5.3} = 199\ 526.2... = 200\ 000$ (to 3 s.f.)

c) Take logs of base 10 of both sides:
$\log_{10} 10^{2x+1} = \log_{10} 1500$
$\Rightarrow 2x + 1 = \log_{10} 1500 = 3.176...$, so $2x = 2.176...$,
so $x = 1.088... = 1.09$ (to 3 s.f.)

d) Take logs of base 10 of both sides:
$\log 4^{x-1} = \log 200 \Rightarrow (x - 1)\log 4 = \log 200$
$\Rightarrow x = \frac{\log 200}{\log 4} + 1 = 4.821... = 4.82$ (3 s.f.)

Q10 Using $y = 10^x$, the equation becomes $2y^2 - 7y + 5 = 0$, which factorises to give $(2y - 5)(y - 1) = 0$. So $y = 2.5$ or $y = 1$, that is, $10^x = 2.5$ or $10^x = 1$.
Solving these for x gives $x = \log 2.5$ or $x = 0$.
The question asks for exact solutions so leave it in log form.

Q11 First solve for $1.5^P = 1\ 000\ 000$
$P \log_{10} 1.5 = \log_{10} 1\ 000\ 000 \Rightarrow P \log_{10} 1.5 = 6$
so $P = \frac{6}{\log_{10} 1.5}$, $P = 34.07...$
We need the next biggest integer, so $P = 35$.

Q12 In n years' time, the population will be 2000×0.75^n, so we need to find the value of n such that $2000 \times 0.75^n = 200$. Solving for n, $0.75^n = 0.1$
$\Rightarrow n \log 0.75 = \log 0.1 \Rightarrow n = \frac{\log 0.1}{\log 0.75}$
$\Rightarrow n = 8.003...$
So the spiders are in danger of extinction after 8 years.
This time you need to round down, as the spiders will face extinction in the 8th year.

Exam-Style Questions — Chapter 3

Q1 a) $2^x = 9$, so taking logs of both sides gives
$\log 2^x = \log 9$ ***[1 mark]***
$\Rightarrow x \log 2 = \log 9$ ***[1 mark]***
$\Rightarrow x = \frac{\log 9}{\log 2} = 3.17$ to 2 d.p. ***[1 mark]***

b) $2^{2x} = (2^x)^2$ (from the power laws), so let $y = 2^x$ and $y^2 = 2^{2x}$. This gives a quadratic in y: $y^2 - 13y + 36 = 0$ ***[1 mark]***
$(y - 9)(y - 4) = 0$, so $y = 9$ or $y = 4$
$\Rightarrow 2^x = 9$ ***[1 mark]*** or $2^x = 4$ ***[1 mark]***
From a), $2^x = 9 \Rightarrow x = 3.17$ to 2 d.p. ***[1 mark]***
and for $2^x = 4$, $x = 2$ (since $2^2 = 4$) ***[1 mark]***.

Q2 a) $\log_3 x = -\frac{1}{2}$, so take exponentials of base 3 of each side to remove the log:
$x = 3^{-\frac{1}{2}}$ ***[1 mark]***
$\Rightarrow x = \frac{1}{3^{\frac{1}{2}}}$ ***[1 mark]*** $\Rightarrow x = \frac{1}{\sqrt{3}}$ ***[1 mark]***.

b) $2 \log_3 x = -4$
$\Rightarrow \log_3 x = -2$, so take exponentials of base 3 of each side to remove the log:
$x = 3^{-2}$ ***[1 mark]***
$\Rightarrow x = \frac{1}{9}$ ***[1 mark]***

Q3 a) $6^{(3x+2)} = 9$, so taking logs of both sides gives:
$(3x + 2) \log 6 = \log 9$ ***[1 mark]***
$\Rightarrow 3x\log 6 = \log 9 - 2\log 6$
$\Rightarrow x = \frac{\log 9 - 2\log 6}{3\log 6}$ ***[1 mark]***
$= -0.2579... = -0.258$ (3 s.f.) ***[1 mark]***

b) $3^{y^2-4} = 7^{(y+2)}$, so taking logs of both sides gives:
$(y^2 - 4)\log 3 = (y + 2)\log 7$ ***[1 mark]***
$\Rightarrow (y + 2)(y - 2)\log 3 - (y + 2)\log 7 = 0$ ***[1 mark]***
$\Rightarrow (y + 2)[(y - 2)\log 3 - \log 7] = 0$ ***[1 mark]***
$\Rightarrow y + 2 = 0$ or $(y - 2)\log 3 - \log 7 = 0$
$\Rightarrow y = -2$ or $y = \frac{\log 7 + 2\log 3}{\log 3}$
$\Rightarrow y = -2$ ***[1 mark]*** or $y = 3.77$ (3 s.f.) ***[1 mark]***

Q4 a) (i) $\log_a 20 - 2\log_a 2$
$= \log_a 20 - \log_a 2^2$ ***[1 mark]***
$= \log_a (20 \div 2^2)$ ***[1 mark]***
$= \log_a 5$ ***[1 mark]***

(ii) $\frac{1}{2}\log_a 16 + \frac{1}{3}\log_a 27$
$= \log_a (16^{\frac{1}{2}}) + \log_a (27^{\frac{1}{3}})$ ***[1 mark]***
$= \log_a (16^{\frac{1}{2}} \times 27^{\frac{1}{3}})$ ***[1 mark]***
$= \log_a (4 \times 3) = \log_a 12$ ***[1 mark]***

b) (i) $\log_2 64 = 6$ ***[1 mark]*** (since $2^6 = 64$)

(ii) $2\log_3 9 = \log_3 9^2 = \log_3 81$ ***[1 mark]***
$\log_3 81 = 4$ ***[1 mark]*** (since $3^4 = 81$)
You could have done this by using the fact that $\log_3 9 = 2$ (since $3^2 = 9$), so $2\log_3 9 = 2 \times 2 = 4$.

c) (i) $\log_6 25 = \frac{\log 25}{\log 6} = 1.7965$ to 4 d.p. ***[1 mark]***

(ii) $\log_3 10 + \log_3 2 = \log_3 (10 \times 2) = \log_3 20$
[1 mark]
$\log_3 20 = \frac{\log 20}{\log 3} = 2.7268$ to 4 d.p. ***[1 mark]***

Q5 a) $\log_7 (y + 3) + \log_7 (2y + 1) = 1$
$\Rightarrow \log_7 ((y + 3)(2y + 1)) = 1$
To remove the $\log_7$, take exponentials of base 7:
$(y + 3)(2y + 1) = 7^1 = 7$
Multiply out, rearrange, and factorise:
$2y^2 + 7y + 3 = 7$
$\Rightarrow 2y^2 + 7y - 4 = 0$
$\Rightarrow (2y - 1)(y + 4) = 0$
$\Rightarrow y = \frac{1}{2}$ or $y = -4$,
but since $y + 3 > 0$ and $2y + 1 > 0$, $y = \frac{1}{2}$ is the only solution.
[5 marks available — 1 mark for combining the two logs, 1 mark for 7 to the power of each side, 1 mark for the correct factorisation of the quadratic, 1 mark for correct solutions and 1 mark for stating that only y = ½ is a valid solution.]

b) $3\log_5 t - \log_5 u = 1$
$\log_5 t^3 - \log_5 u = 1$ ***[1 mark]***
$\log_5 t^3 - \log_5 u = \log_5 5$ ***[1 mark]***
$\log_5 t^3 - \log_5 5 = \log_5 u$
$\log_5\left(\frac{t^3}{5}\right) = \log_5 u$ ***[1 mark]***
$\Rightarrow u = \frac{t^3}{5}$, as required. ***[1 mark]***

Q6 a) $\log_4 p - \log_4 q = \frac{1}{2}$, so using the log laws:
$\log_4 (\frac{p}{q}) = \frac{1}{2}$
Taking exponentials of base 4 gives:
$\frac{p}{q} = 4^{\frac{1}{2}} = \sqrt{4} = 2$
$\Rightarrow p = 2q$
[3 marks available — 1 mark for combining the two logs, 1 mark for taking exponentials of base 4 of each side, 1 mark for the correct final working.]

b) Since $p = 2q$ (from a)), the equation can be written: $\log_2 (2q) + \log_2 q = 7$ ***[1 mark]***
This simplifies to:
$\log_2 (2q^2) = 7$ ***[1 mark]***
Taking exponentials of base 2 gives:
$2q^2 = 2^7 = 128$ ***[1 mark]***
$\Rightarrow q^2 = 64$, $\Rightarrow q = 8$ (since p and q are positive)
[1 mark] $p = 2q \Rightarrow p = 16$ ***[1 mark]***

Chapter 4: Sequences and Series

1. Sequences

Exercise 1.1 — n^{th} term

Q1 20th term $= 3(20) - 5 = 55$

Q2 4th term $= 4(4 + 2) = 24$

Q3 1st term $= (1 - 1)(1 + 1) = 0$
2nd term $= (2 - 1)(2 + 1) = 3$
Using the same method, 3rd, 4th and 5th terms $= 8, 15, 24$

Q4 $29 = 4k - 3$
$k = 8$

Q5 Form equations for the 2nd and 5th terms:
$15 = a(2^2) + b$
$99 = a(5^2) + b$
Solve the equations simultaneously to get $a = 4$, $b = -1$

Q6 Form equations for the first 2 terms:
$9 = e(1)^2 + f(1) + 4 \Rightarrow 5 = e + f$
$20 = e(2)^2 + f(2) + 4 \Rightarrow 16 = 4e + 2f$
Solve the equations simultaneously to get $e = 3, f = 2$.

Q7 $49 = (n - 1)^2$, $n = 8$

Q8 This first 8 terms of the sequence are: 13, 11, 9, 7, 5, 3, 1, –1,... The sequence continues to decrease. So 7 terms are positive.
A different way to solve this one would be to use an inequality — set $15 - 2n > 0$ and solve for n (taking the integer value of n).

Exercise 1.2 — Recurrence relations

Q1 $u_1 = 10$
$u_2 = 3u_1 = 3(10) = 30$
$u_3 = 3u_2 = 3(30) = 90$
$u_4 = 3u_3 = 3(90) = 270$
$u_5 = 3u_4 = 3(270) = 810$

Q2 $u_1 = -2$
$u_2 = 2u_1 - 4 = 2(-2) - 4 = -8$
$u_3 = 2u_2 - 4 = 2(-8) - 4 = -20$
$u_4 = 2u_3 - 4 = 2(-20) - 4 = -44$
$u_5 = 2u_4 - 4 = 2(-44) - 4 = -92$

Q3 a) $u_1 = 2$
$u_2 = u_1^2 = 2^2 = 4$
$u_3 = u_2^2 = 4^2 = 16$
$u_4 = u_3^2 = 16^2 = 256$

b) The sequence is infinite as n can take any positive integer value, so there will be no final term.

For Q4, 5, 6, you can use any letter in place of u.

Q4 Each term is the previous term doubled. The first term is 3.
$u_{n+1} = 2u_n$, $u_1 = 3$

Q5 a) Each term is 4 more than the previous term. The first term is 12.
$u_{n+1} = u_n + 4$, $u_1 = 12$

b) Work out the number of 'jumps' of 4 needed to get from 28 to 100:
$100 - 28 = 72$, $72 \div 4 = 18$
Add on the first 5 terms given in the question:
$18 + 5 = 23$ terms
You could have written an nth term expression and used it to find the position of 100 in the sequence (it's the last term). The nth term expression would be $4n + 8$.

c) $1 \leq n \leq 23$

Q6 a) $u_{n+1} = 11 - u_n$ or $u_{n+1} = 28 \div u_n$, with $u_1 = 7$.

b) The sequence repeats every 2 terms ($u_1 = u_3 = u_5 = ...$), so the sequence has period 2.

Q7 $u_1 = 4$
$u_2 = 3(4) - 1 = 11$
$u_3 = 3(11) - 1 = 32$
$u_4 = 3(32) - 1 = 95$, so $k = 4$

Q8 $x_1 = 9$
$x_2 = (9 + 1) \div 2 = 5$
Keep substituting the result into the formula until...
$x_6 = (\frac{3}{2} + 1) \div 2 = \frac{5}{4}$, so $r = 6$

Q9 $u_1 = 7$
$u_2 = 7 + 1 = 8$
$u_3 = 8 + 2 = 10$
$u_4 = 10 + 3 = 13$
$u_5 = 13 + 4 = 17$

Q10 a) $u_2 = 4(3) + k = 12 + k$
$u_3 = 4(12 + k) + k = 48 + 5k$
So $u_4 = 4(48 + 5k) + k = 192 + 21k$

b) $u_5 = 4(192 + 21k) + k = 768 + 85k$
$768 + 85k = 598$
$85k = -170$
$k = -2$

Q11 Form an equation for getting the 2nd term from the 1st term, and an equation for getting the 3rd term from the 2nd term:
$7 = 6a + b$
$8.5 = 7a + b$
Solve the equations simultaneously to get $a = 1.5$, $b = -2$

Q12 First 5 terms:
$u_1 = 8$
$u_2 = \frac{1}{2}(8) = 4$
$u_3 = \frac{1}{2}(4) = 2$
$u_4 = \frac{1}{2}(2) = 1$
$u_5 = \frac{1}{2}(1) = \frac{1}{2}$
The terms are all powers of 2:
$8 = 2^3, 4 = 2^2, 2 = 2^1, 1 = 2^0, \frac{1}{2} = 2^{-1}$
so $u_n = 2^{(4-n)}$ or $u_n = 16 \div 2^n$

Exercise 1.3 — Convergent sequences

Q1 **a)** $a_2 = a_1 + 2 = 1 + 2 = 3$
$a_3 = 3 + 2 = 5$
$a_4 = 5 + 2 = 7$
So the sequence is 1, 3, 5, 7, ...
This sequence is divergent.

b) $a_2 = 0.5a_1 = 0.5 \times 1 = 0.5$
$a_3 = 0.5 \times 0.5 = 0.25$
$a_4 = 0.25 \times 0.5 = 0.125$
So the sequence is 1, 0.5, 0.25, 0.125, ...
This looks to be convergent.

c) $a_2 = \frac{1}{3}a_1 - 2 = (\frac{1}{3} \times 1) - 2 = -\frac{5}{3} = -1.67$ (2 d.p.)
$a_3 = \left(\frac{1}{3} \times -\frac{5}{3}\right) - 2 = -\frac{23}{9} = -2.56$ (2 d.p.)
$a_4 = \left(\frac{1}{3} \times -\frac{23}{9}\right) - 2 = -\frac{77}{27} = -2.85$ (2 d.p.)
So the sequence is $1, -\frac{5}{3}, -\frac{23}{9}, -\frac{77}{27}, \ldots$
This looks to be convergent as the differences between consecutive terms are getting smaller.

d) $a_2 = 2a_1 + 1 = 2(1) + 1 = 3$
$a_3 = 2(3) + 1 = 7$
$a_4 = 2(7) + 1 = 15$
So the sequence is 1, 3, 7, 15, ...
This sequence is divergent.

e) $2a_2 = 3a_1 + 4 = 3(1) + 4 = 7 \Rightarrow a_2 = 3.5$
$2a_3 = 3(3.5) + 4 = 14.5 \Rightarrow a_3 = 7.25$
$2a_4 = 3(7.25) + 4 = 25.75 \Rightarrow a_4 = 12.875$
So the sequence is 1, 3.5, 7.25, 12.875, ...
This sequence is divergent.

f) $3a_2 = 2a_1 - 3 = 2(1) - 3 = -1$
$\Rightarrow a_2 = -\frac{1}{3} = -0.33$ (2 d.p.)
$3a_3 = 2\left(-\frac{1}{3}\right) - 3 = -\frac{11}{3}$
$\Rightarrow a_3 = -\frac{11}{9} = -1.22$ (2 d.p.)
$3a_4 = 2\left(-\frac{11}{9}\right) - 3 = -\frac{49}{9}$
$\Rightarrow a_4 = -\frac{49}{27} = -1.81$ (2 d.p.)
So the sequence is $1, -\frac{1}{3}, -\frac{11}{9}, -\frac{49}{27}, \ldots$
This looks to be convergent as the differences between consecutive terms are getting smaller.
For parts e) and f), an alternative method would be to start by rearranging the recurrence relation to get it in terms of a_{n+1}.

Q2 **b)** $f(a_n) = 0.5a_n$
L can be found by solving $L = f(L)$:
$L = 0.5L \Rightarrow L = 0$

c) $f(a_n) = \frac{1}{3}a_n - 2$
Solving $L = f(L)$:
$L = \frac{1}{3}L - 2$
$\frac{2}{3}L = -2 \Rightarrow L = -3$

f) $f(a_n) = \frac{2}{3}a_n - 1$
Solving $L = f(L)$:
$L = \frac{2}{3}L - 1$
$\frac{1}{3}L = -1 \Rightarrow L = -3$

Q3 **a)** **(i)** $u_2 = ku_1 + 3$
$4 = 2k + 3 \Rightarrow k = 0.5$
(ii) $u_3 = 0.5u_2 + 3$
$= (0.5 \times 4) + 3 = 5$
(iii) $u_4 = 0.5u_3 + 3$
$= (0.5 \times 5) + 3 = 5.5$

b) **(i)** $u_2 = ku_1 + 3$
$7 = 2k + 3 \Rightarrow k = 2$
(ii) $u_3 = 2u_2 + 3$
$= (2 \times 7) + 3 = 17$
(iii) $u_4 = 2u_3 + 3$
$= (2 \times 17) + 3 = 37$

c) The sequence in a) is 2, 4, 5, 5.5, ...
This looks to be convergent.
The sequence in b) is 2, 7, 17, 37, ...
This is divergent.

d) $f(u_n) = ku_n + 3 = 0.5u_n + 3$
L can be found by solving $L = f(L)$:
$L = 0.5L + 3$
$0.5L = 3 \Rightarrow L = 6$

Q4 **a)** $u_2 = au_1 + b \Rightarrow 5 = 4a + b$ ...call this **eqn 1**
$u_3 = au_2 + b \Rightarrow 5\frac{3}{4} = 5a + b$ ...call this **eqn 2**
Subtract **eqn 1** from **eqn 2**: $\frac{3}{4} = a$
Substitute this value of a into **eqn 1**:
$5 = 4\left(\frac{3}{4}\right) + b \Rightarrow b = 2$

b) $f(u_n) = \frac{3}{4}u_n + 2$
$L = f(L) \Rightarrow L = \frac{3}{4}L + 2$

c) Solving $L = f(L)$:
$\frac{1}{4}L = 2 \Rightarrow L = 8$

Q5 **a)** $u_2 = \frac{3}{4}u_1 + 1 = \frac{3}{4}(4) + 1 = 4$
$u_3 = \frac{3}{4}u_2 + 1 = \frac{3}{4}(4) + 1 = 4$
$u_4 = \frac{3}{4}u_3 + 1 = \frac{3}{4}(4) + 1 = 4$

b) Each term of the sequence is 4, so $u_{20} = 4$.

c) The limit of u_n as n tends to infinity is 4.

Q6 **a)** $f(u_n) = au_n + 3$ so $L = aL + 3$
$L = 6 \Rightarrow 6 = 6a + 3 \Rightarrow a = 0.5$

b) $u_2 = 0.5u_1 + 3 = (0.5 \times 8) + 3 = 7$
$u_3 = (0.5 \times 7) + 3 = 6.5$
Keep substituting the result into the formula until...
$u_5 = 6.125$
$u_6 = 6.0625 < 6.1$, so $n = 6$

c) $u_2 = 0.5u_1 + 3 = (0.5 \times 3) + 3 = 4.5$
$u_3 = (0.5 \times 4.5) + 3 = 5.25$
Keep substituting the result into the formula until...
$u_{12} = 5.99854$
$u_{13} = 5.99927 > 5.999$, so $n = 13$
In parts b) and c), you can reduce the amount of button pressing you need to do by using the 'ANS' button on your calculator.

2. Arithmetic Sequences & Series

Exercise 2.1 — Arithmetic sequences

Q1 $a = 7, d = 5$

n^{th} term $= a + (n-1)d$
$= 7 + (n-1)5$
$= 5n + 2$

10th term $= 5(10) + 2$
$= 52$

Q2 **a)** $a = 6, d = 3$,
so n^{th} term $= 6 + (n-1)3 = 3n + 3$

b) $a = 4, d = 5$, n^{th} term $= 5n - 1$

c) $a = 12, d = -4$, n^{th} term $= -4n + 16$

d) $a = 1.5, d = 2$, n^{th} term $= 2n - 0.5$

Q3 $a = 60, d = 3$

n^{th} term $= a + (n-1)d$
$= 60 + (n-1)3$
$= 3n + 57$

12th term $= 3(12) + 57$
$= 93$

So she'll earn £93 in her 12th week.

With wordy problems, don't forget to check what the units should be and include them.

Q4 $a = 40, d = 5$

n^{th} term $= a + (n-1)d$
$= 40 + (n-1)5$
$= 5n + 35$

$80 = 5n + 35$

$n = (80 - 35) \div 5$
$= 9$

So he'll sell 80 sandwiches on the 9th day.

Q5 Form equations for 4th and 10th terms:
n^{th} term $= a + (n-1)d$

$19 = a + (4-1)d$ $\quad$ $19 = a + 3d$

$43 = a + (10-1)d$ $\quad$ $43 = a + 9d$

Solving the simultaneous equations: $a = 7, d = 4$.

Q6 **a)** The nth term is $a + (n-1)d = a + 2(n-1)$
The 7th term is 34, so:
$34 = a + 2(7-1)$
$34 = a + 12$
$\Rightarrow a = 22$

b) From part a), the nth term is:
$22 + 2(n-1) = 20 + 2n$
So the 15th term is:
$20 + 2(15) = 50$

Q7 n^{th} term $= a + (n-1)d = a + 6(n-1)$
6th term $= a + 6(6-1) = a + 30 = 88$
$\Rightarrow a = 58$
So n^{th} term $= 58 + 6(n-1) = 52 + 6n$

Q8 Form equations for 7th and 11th terms:
n^{th} term $= a + (n-1)d$

$8 = a + (7-1)d$ $\quad$ $8 = a + 6d$

$10 = a + (11-1)d$ $\quad$ $10 = a + 10d$

Solving the simultaneous equations: $a = 5, d = 0.5$
So $u_3 = 5 + 2(0.5) = 6$

Q9 Form equations for 3rd and 7th terms:
n^{th} term $= a + (n-1)d$

$15 = a + (3-1)d$ $\quad$ $15 = a + 2d$

$27 = a + (7-1)d$ $\quad$ $27 = a + 6d$

Solving the simultaneous equations: $a = 9, d = 3$.

Now write an equation for the kth term:
$66 = 9 + (k-1)3 = 6 + 3k$

And solve to find k:
$k = 20$

Q10 $a = 300\,000, d = -30\,000$

n^{th} term $= a + (n-1)d$
$= 300\,000 - 30\,000(n-1)$
$= 330\,000 - 30\,000n$

$330\,000 - 30\,000n < 50\,000$

$n > 280\,000 \div 30\,000 = 9.33...$

You want the smallest integer value of n that satisfies the inequality, so round up. Sales will have fallen below £50 000 after 10 months.

$n = 9$ doesn't satisfy the inequality.

Exercise 2.2 — Arithmetic series

Q1 $a = 8, d = 3$

n^{th} term $= a + (n-1)d$
$= 8 + (n-1)3$
$= 3n + 5$

10th term $= 3(10) + 5 = 35$

$S_n = \frac{n}{2}[2a + (n-1)d]$

$S_{10} = \frac{10}{2}[2(8) + 9(3)]$

$S_{10} = 215$

Alternatively, you could have used the $S_n = n\frac{(a+l)}{2}$ formula here. You'd worked out the last term earlier in the question.

Q2 Form equations for 2nd and 5th terms:
n^{th} term $= a + (n-1)d$
$16 = a + d$
$10 = a + 4d$

Solving the simultaneous equations: $a = 18, d = -2$.

$S_n = \frac{n}{2}[2a + (n-1)d]$

$S_8 = \frac{8}{2}[2(18) + 7(-2)]$

$S_8 = 88$

Q3 $a = 12, d = 6$

n^{th} term $= a + (n-1)d$
$= 12 + (n-1)6$
$= 6n + 6$

$u_{100} = 6(100) + 6 = 606$

$S_n = n\frac{(a+l)}{2}$

$S_{100} = 100\left(\frac{12+606}{2}\right)$

$S_{100} = 30\,900$

Q4 $a = 5(1) - 2 = 3$
$l = 5(12) - 2 = 58$

$S_n = n\frac{(a+l)}{2}$

$S_{12} = 12\left(\frac{3+58}{2}\right)$

$S_{12} = 366$

Q5 $a = 20 - 2(1) = 18$
$l = 20 - 2(9) = 2$

$S_n = n\frac{(a+l)}{2}$

$S_9 = 9\left(\frac{18+2}{2}\right)$

$S_9 = 90$

Q6 $a = 6000$
$d = 2000$
$n = 12$ (12 months in the year)

$S_n = \frac{n}{2}[2a + (n-1)d]$

$S_{12} = \frac{12}{2}[2(6000) + 11(2000)]$

$S_{12} = 204\,000$
204 000 copies will be sold.

Q7 $a = 3$
$d = 2$

$S_n = \frac{n}{2}[2a + (n-1)d]$

$960 = \frac{n}{2}[2(3) + 2(n-1)]$

$960 = n^2 + 2n$

$n^2 + 2n - 960 = 0$

You're expecting a whole number for n, so you should be able to factorise the quadratic — you need two numbers that are 2 apart and multiply to give 960.
$(n + 32)(n - 30) = 0$
Ignore the negative solution since n needs to be positive, so $n = 30$.

Q8 $S_n = \frac{n}{2}[2a + (n-1)d]$

$176 < \frac{n}{2}[2(14) + 8(n - 1)]$

$176 < \frac{n}{2}[20 + 8n]$

$176 < 10n + 4n^2$
$0 < 2n^2 + 5n - 88$
$0 < (2n - 11)(n + 8)$
Sketching a graph of $(2n - 11)(n + 8) = 0$ gives the range of solutions of the inequality as $n < -8$ and $n > 5.5$. n is a positive integer, so you can ignore the negative values. The smallest positive integer that satisfies $n > 5.5$ is $n = 6$. So 6 terms are required for their sum to exceed 176.

Q9 $a = 5(1) + 2 = 7$
$l = 5k + 2$

$S_n = n\frac{(a+l)}{2}$

$553 = k\left(\frac{7+5k+2}{2}\right)$

$1106 = 5k^2 + 9k$

$5k^2 + 9k - 1106 = 0$

Factorising gives:
$(5k + 79)(k - 14) = 0$
Now we can ignore the negative solution, so $k = 14$.

This one looked very tricky to factorise, but you can cheat a little here — you know you're trying to get to k = 14, so one of the brackets is going to be (k − 14)...

Q10 The first thing to do is to use the fact that it's an arithmetic progression to write down some equations — remember, there's a common difference, d, between each term.
$x + 11 + d = 4x + 4 \Rightarrow -3x + d = -7$
$x + 11 + 2d = 9x + 5 \Rightarrow -8x + 2d = -6$
You've now got a pair of simultaneous equations in d and x. Solving these gives $x = -4$, $d = -19$
So the first term is $a = -4 + 11 = 7$.
Now you can put $a = 7$, $d = -19$ and $n = 11$ into the formula for S_n:

$S_n = \frac{n}{2}[2a + (n-1)d]$

$S_{11} = \frac{11}{2}[2(7) + 10(-19)]$

$S_{11} = \frac{11}{2} \times -176$

$S_{11} = -968$

Exercise 2.3 — Sum of the first *n* natural numbers

Q1 **a)** $S_n = \frac{1}{2}n(n+1)$

$S_{10} = \frac{1}{2} \times 10 \times 11$

$S_{10} = 55$

b) $S_{2000} = \frac{1}{2} \times 2000 \times 2001$

$S_{2000} = 2\,001\,000$

Q2 $S_{32} = \frac{1}{2} \times 32 \times 33$

$S_{32} = 528$

Q3 $\sum_{n=11}^{20} n = \sum_{n=1}^{20} n - \sum_{n=1}^{10} n$

$S_{10} = \frac{1}{2} \times 10 \times 11$

$S_{10} = 55$

$S_{20} = \frac{1}{2} \times 20 \times 21$

$S_{20} = 210$

$\sum_{n=11}^{20} n = 210 - 55 = 155$

Q4 Frazer's series is the natural numbers up to 31.

$S_n = \frac{1}{2}n(n+1)$

$S_{31} = \frac{1}{2} \times 31 \times 32$

$S_{31} = 496$

Q5 $66 = \frac{1}{2}n(n+1)$

$132 = n^2 + n$

$0 = n^2 + n - 132$

$(n+12)(n-11) = 0$

$n = -12$ or 11 — so ignoring the negative answer, the sum of the first 11 terms is 66, so $n = 11$.

Q6 $S_n = \frac{1}{2}n(n+1)$

$120 = \frac{1}{2}k(k+1)$

$240 = k^2 + k$

$0 = k^2 + k - 240$

$(k+16)(k-15) = 0$

Ignoring the negative solution gives $k = 15$.

Q7 Subtract the sum of the first 15 natural numbers from the sum of the first 35:

$S_{35} = \frac{1}{2} \times 35 \times 36 = 630$

$S_{15} = \frac{1}{2} \times 15 \times 16 = 120$

So the sum of the series is 630 – 120 = 510.

Q8 $S_n = \frac{1}{2}n(n+1)$

$\frac{1}{2}n(n+1) > 1\,000\,000$

$n^2 + n > 2\,000\,000$

$n^2 + n - 2\,000\,000 > 0$

Put the quadratic equal to zero and solve using the quadratic formula to get $n = 1413.7...$ or $-1414.7...$ It's a u-shaped quadratic, so the quadratic is positive when $n > 1413.7$ (ignoring the negative solution). So you need 1414 natural numbers to exceed 1 000 000.

Q9 Laura's series is the natural numbers. You need to find how many are needed to exceed 1000 (£10 in pence).

$S_n = \frac{1}{2}n(n+1)$

$\frac{1}{2}(n^2+n) > 1000$

$n^2 + n > 2000$

$n^2 + n - 2000 > 0$

Putting the quadratic equal to zero and solving using the quadratic formula gives $n = 44.2$ (ignoring the negative solution), which by looking at the shape of the quadratic graph gives $n > 44.2$ as the solution to the inequality. So on the 45th day she'll have over £10.

3. Geometric Sequences & Series

Exercise 3.1 — Geometric sequences

Q1 $a = 12$, $r = 2$. Using $u_n = ar^{n-1}$:
$u_{10} = 12(2)^9 = 6144$

Q2 Common ratio $r = \frac{\text{second term}}{\text{first term}} = \frac{3}{2} = 1.5$.
Then:

5th term = 4th term × 1.5 = 6.75 × 1.5 = 10.125,
6th term = 5th term × 1.5 = 10.125 × 1.5 = 15.1875,
7th term = 6th term × 1.5 = 15.1875 × 1.5 = 22.78125.

This method isn't as slow as it looks because you can use a scientific calculator to get the terms of the series quickly: press '2 =' then '× 1.5 =' to get the second term. Pressing '=' repeatedly will give you the following terms. Even so, the method below is quicker, so unless you're asked to find the term after one you've already got, you're better off doing this:

Or: First term $a = 2$, common ratio $r = 1.5$
n^{th} term = $ar^{n-1} = 2 \times (1.5)^{n-1}$
7th term = $2 \times (1.5)^6 = 2 \times 11.390625 = 22.78125$

Q3 Common ratio $r = \frac{7^{th}\text{ term}}{6^{th}\text{ term}} = \frac{6561}{2187} = 3$.
The 6th term is $2187 = ar^5 = a \times 3^5 \Rightarrow a = \frac{2187}{3^5} = 9$.
So the first term is 9.

Q4 Common ratio: $r = \frac{\text{second term}}{\text{first term}} = \frac{12}{24} = 0.5$.
First term: $a = 24$.
n^{th} term: $u_n = ar^{n-1} = 24 \times (0.5)^{n-1}$
9th term: $u_9 = ar^8 = 24 \times (0.5)^8 = 0.09375$

Q5 First term: $a = 1.125$
n^{th} term: $u_n = ar^{n-1} = 1.125r^{n-1}$
14th term: $9216 = u_{14} = 1.125r^{13}$

$9216 = 1.125r^{13} \Rightarrow r^{13} = \frac{9216}{1.125} = 8192$

$\Rightarrow r = \sqrt[13]{8192} = 2$

Q6 Common ratio: $r = \frac{1.1}{1} = 1.1$, first term: $a = 1$.
n^{th} term: $u_n = ar^{n-1} = 1 \times 1.1^{n-1} = 1.1^{n-1}$
So to find the number of terms in the sequence that are less than 4, solve: $u_n = 1.1^{n-1} < 4$
$\Rightarrow \log 1.1^{n-1} < \log 4$
Use the log law, $\log x^n = n(\log x)$:
$\Rightarrow (n-1)\log 1.1 < \log 4$
log 1.1 > 0 so dividing through by log 1.1 doesn't change the direction of the inequality:

$\Rightarrow n - 1 < \frac{\log 4}{\log 1.1}$

$\Rightarrow n - 1 < 14.54...$

$\Rightarrow n < 15.54...$

so u_n is less than 4 when n is less than 15.54..., therefore u_{15} is the last term that's less than 4, so there are 15 terms that are less than 4.
You could solve this as an equation instead, finding the value of n such that $u_n = 4$ and rounding down.

Q7 $a = 5$, $r = 0.6$, n^{th} term: $u_n = ar^{n-1} = 5 \times (0.6)^{n-1}$

10th term: $u_{10} = 5 \times (0.6)^9 = 0.050388$ (6 d.p.)

15th term: $u_{15} = 5 \times (0.6)^{14} = 0.003918$ (6 d.p.)

Difference: $0.003918 - 0.050388 = -0.04647$ (5 d.p.)

You could also have:

Difference: 0.050388 − 0.003918 = 0.04647 (5 d.p.)

Q8 $a = 25\,000$, $r = 0.8$

n^{th} term: $u_n = ar^{n-1} = 25\,000 \times (0.8)^{n-1}$

to find the first term in the sequence less than 1000, solve: $u_n = 25\,000 \times (0.8)^{n-1} < 1000$

$$25\,000 \times (0.8)^{n-1} < 1000$$
$$\Rightarrow (0.8)^{n-1} < \frac{1000}{25\,000} = 0.04$$
$$\Rightarrow \log(0.8)^{n-1} < \log 0.04$$
$$\Rightarrow (n-1)\log 0.8 < \log 0.04$$
$$\Rightarrow n-1 > \frac{\log 0.04}{\log 0.8}$$
$$\Rightarrow n-1 > 14.425...$$
$$\Rightarrow n > 15.425...$$

so u_n is less than 1000 when n is greater than 15.425..., therefore u_{16} is the first term that's less than 1000.

0.8 < 1 so log 0.8 < 0 and dividing through by log 0.8 changes the direction of the inequality because log 0.8 is negative. Again, you could solve this as an equation by finding n such that u_n = 1000 and rounding up.

Q9 Divide consecutive terms to find the common ratio r:

e.g. $r = \frac{\text{second term}}{\text{first term}} = \frac{-5}{5} = -1$

Q10 a) Common ratio $r = \frac{\text{second term}}{\text{first term}} = \frac{\frac{3}{16}}{\frac{1}{4}} = \frac{3}{4}$

b) First term: $a = \frac{1}{4}$

n^{th} term: $u_n = ar^{n-1} = \frac{1}{4} \times \left(\frac{3}{4}\right)^{n-1}$

8th term: $u_8 = \frac{1}{4} \times \left(\frac{3}{4}\right)^7 = \frac{1}{4} \times \frac{2187}{16384} = \frac{2187}{65536}$

(= 0.03337 to 5 d.p.)

Q11 $r = 0.8$, n^{th} term: $u_n = ar^{n-1} = a(0.8)^{n-1}$

7th term: $196.608 = u_7 = a(0.8)^6$

$196.608 = a(0.8)^6 \Rightarrow a = \frac{196.608}{0.8^6} = 750$

Q12 a) 3rd term: $u_3 = ar^2 = 36$

6th term: $u_6 = ar^5 = 972$

$\frac{u_6}{u_3} = \frac{ar^5}{ar^2} = r^3$

So $r^3 = \frac{972}{36} = 27$

$\Rightarrow r = 3$

b) From part a):

$a = \frac{36}{r^2} = \frac{36}{3^2} = 4$

Q13 a) Common ratio $r = \frac{\text{second term}}{\text{first term}} = \frac{-2.4}{3} = -0.8$

b) Continuing the sequence gives –1.536, 1.2288, –0.98304. So there are 5 terms in the series before a term has modulus less than 1.

You could also answer this part of the question by writing a new series where each term is the modulus of the old series, then using logs to find the first term less than 1. But in this case it's much easier to just find the next few terms.

Exercise 3.2 — Geometric series

Q1 The sum of the first n terms is $S_n = \frac{a(1-r^n)}{(1-r)}$, $a = 8$ and $r = 1.2$, so the sum of the first 15 terms is:

$$S_{15} = \frac{a(1-r^{15})}{(1-r)} = \frac{8(1-(1.2)^{15})}{(1-1.2)} = 576.28 \text{ to 2 d.p.}$$

Q2 For a geometric series with first term a and common ratio r: $\sum_{k=0}^{n-1} ar^k = \frac{a(1-r^n)}{1-r}$,

so: $\sum_{k=0}^{9} ar^k = \sum_{k=0}^{9} 25(0.7)^k = \frac{25(1-(0.7)^{10})}{1-0.7} = 80.98$ (to 2 d.p.)

Q3 $a = 3$ and $r = 2$, the sum of the first n terms is:

$$\frac{3(1-2^n)}{(1-2)} = -3(1-2^n)$$
$$196\,605 = S_n = -3(1-2^n) \Rightarrow -65\,535 = 1-2^n$$
$$\Rightarrow 65\,536 = 2^n \Rightarrow \log 65\,536 = \log 2^n$$
$$\Rightarrow \log 65\,536 = n\log 2 \Rightarrow n = \frac{\log 65\,536}{\log 2} = 16$$

Q4 The first term is $a = 4$,

the common ratio is $r = \frac{\text{second term}}{\text{first term}} = \frac{5}{4} = 1.25$

The sum of the first x terms is

$$S_x = \frac{a(1-r^x)}{(1-r)} = \frac{4(1-(1.25)^x)}{(1-1.25)} = -16(1-(1.25)^x)$$

So: $103.2 = -16(1-(1.25)^x) \Rightarrow -6.45 = 1-(1.25)^x$

$$\Rightarrow 7.45 = 1.25^x \Rightarrow \log 7.45 = x\log 1.25$$
$$\Rightarrow x = \frac{\log 7.45}{\log 1.25} = 9.00 \text{ to 2 d.p.}$$

So $x = 9$ (as it must be an integer)

Q5 a) 3rd term $= ar^2 = 6$, 8th term $= ar^7 = 192$.

Dividing the two equations gives:

$$\frac{ar^7}{ar^2} = r^5 = \frac{192}{6} = 32 \Rightarrow r = \sqrt[5]{32} = 2$$

b) 3rd term $= ar^2 = 6$ and $r = 2$, so $a = \frac{6}{r^2} = \frac{6}{2^2} = 1.5$

c) The sum of the first 15 terms is:

$$S_{15} = \frac{a(1-r^{15})}{(1-r)} = \frac{1.5(1-2^{15})}{(1-2)} = 49\,150.5$$

Q6 a) Common ratio:

$$\frac{\text{2nd term}}{\text{1st term}} = \frac{\text{3rd term}}{\text{2nd term}}, \text{ so: } \frac{k}{k+10} = \frac{2k-21}{k}$$
$$\Rightarrow k^2 = (k+10)(2k-21)$$
$$\Rightarrow k^2 = 2k^2 - 21k + 20k - 210$$
$$\Rightarrow 0 = k^2 - k - 210$$

b) Factorising $k^2 - k - 210 = 0$ gives: $(k-15)(k+14) = 0$, so $k = 15$ or $k = -14$, since $k > 0$, $k = 15$.

c) $k = 15$ gives the first three terms 25, 15, 9.

Common ratio $= \frac{\text{second term}}{\text{first term}} = \frac{15}{25} = 0.6$

d) $a = 25$ and $r = 0.6$, so sum of first 10 terms is:

$$S_{10} = \frac{a(1-r^{10})}{(1-r)} = \frac{25(1-0.6^{10})}{(1-0.6)} = 62.12 \text{ to 2 d.p.}$$

Q7 a) $1 + x + x^2 = 3 \Rightarrow x^2 + x - 2 = 0$

$\Rightarrow (x-1)(x+2) = 0$

$\Rightarrow x = 1$ or $x = -2$.

Since the terms are all different $x \neq 1$ (as 1 is the first term and $x = 1 \Rightarrow x^2 = 1^2 = 1$), hence $x = -2$.

b) $a = 1$ and $r = \frac{\text{second term}}{\text{first term}} = \frac{-2}{1} = -2$,
so the sum of the first 7 terms is:
$$S_7 = \frac{a(1-r^7)}{(1-r)} = \frac{1(1-(-2)^7)}{(1-(-2))} = 43$$

Q8 $a = 7.2$ and $r = 0.38$, so:
$$\sum_{k=0}^{9} ar^k = \frac{a(1-r^{10})}{(1-r)} = \frac{7.2(1-0.38^{10})}{(1-0.38)} = 11.61 \text{ to 2 d.p.}$$

Q9 $$1.2 = S_8 = \frac{a(1-r^8)}{(1-r)} = \frac{a\left(1-\left(-\frac{1}{3}\right)^8\right)}{\left(1-\left(-\frac{1}{3}\right)\right)} = a(0.749...)$$
$\Rightarrow \; a = 1.60$ to 2 d.p.

Q10 The geometric sequence $a, -2a, 4a, ...$ has first term a and common ratio $r = -2$, so $\sum_{k=0}^{12} a(-2)^k$ is the sum of the first 13 terms of the sequence. Therefore:
$$\sum_{k=0}^{12} a(-2)^k = -5735.1$$
$$\sum_{k=0}^{12} a(-2)^k = \frac{a(1-r^{13})}{(1-r)} = \frac{a(1-(-2)^{13})}{(1-(-2))} = 2731a$$
$\Rightarrow \; -5735.1 = 2731a \;\Rightarrow\; a = -2.1$

Exercise 3.3 — Convergent geometric series

Q1 a) $r = \frac{1.1}{1} = 1.1, |r| = |1.1| = 1.1 > 1$,
so the sequence does not converge.

b) $r = \frac{0.8^2}{0.8} = 0.8, |r| = |0.8| = 0.8 < 1$,
so the sequence converges.

c) $r = \frac{\frac{1}{4}}{1} = \frac{1}{4}, |r| = \left|\frac{1}{4}\right| = \frac{1}{4} < 1$,
so the sequence converges.

d) $r = \frac{\frac{9}{2}}{3} = \frac{3}{2}, |r| = \left|\frac{3}{2}\right| = \frac{3}{2} > 1$,
so the sequence does not converge.

e) $r = \frac{-\frac{1}{2}}{1} = -\frac{1}{2}, |r| = \left|-\frac{1}{2}\right| = \frac{1}{2} < 1$,
so the sequence converges.

f) $r = \frac{5}{5} = 1, |r| = |1| = 1$ (and 1 is not less than 1),
so the sequence does not converge.

Q2 Find the common ratio: $r = \frac{2^{\text{nd}} \text{ term}}{1^{\text{st}} \text{ term}} = \frac{8.1}{9} = 0.9$.
The first term is $a = 9$.
The sum to infinity is:
$$S_\infty = \frac{a}{1-r} = \frac{9}{1-0.9} = \frac{9}{0.1} = 90$$

Q3 $S_\infty = \frac{a}{1-r} = 2a \;\Rightarrow\; \frac{1}{1-r} = 2 \;\Rightarrow\; 1 = 2 - 2r$
$\Rightarrow \; 2r = 1 \;\Rightarrow\; r = 0.5$

Q4 a) Sum to infinity is $13.5 = S_\infty = \frac{a}{1-r}$
Sum of the first three terms is $13 = S_3 = \frac{a(1-r^3)}{(1-r)}$
Divide S_3 by S_∞: $\frac{13}{13.5} = \frac{a(1-r^3)}{1-r} \div \frac{a}{1-r}$
$= \frac{a(1-r^3)}{1-r} \times \frac{1-r}{a} = 1 - r^3$
You can cancel the $1 - r$ because r can't be 1 (as the series converges), so $1 - r \neq 0$.
So $1 - r^3 = \frac{13}{13.5} = \frac{26}{27} \;\Rightarrow\; r^3 = \frac{1}{27} \;\Rightarrow\; r = \frac{1}{3}$.

b) $13.5 = S_\infty = \frac{a}{1-r} \;\Rightarrow\; a = 13.5(1 - r)$
$= 13.5 \times \frac{2}{3} = 9$.

Q5 $ar = 3, 12 = S_\infty = \frac{a}{1-r} \;\Rightarrow\; 12 - 12r = a$
The first equation gives $a = \frac{3}{r}$,
plugging this into the second equation gives:
$12 - 12r = \frac{3}{r} \;\Rightarrow\; 12r - 12r^2 = 3$
$\Rightarrow \; 12r^2 - 12r + 3 = 0$
$\Rightarrow \; 4r^2 - 4r + 1 = 0$
This factorises to $(2r - 1)(2r - 1) = 0$
Hence $2r - 1 = 0 \;\Rightarrow\; r = 0.5$
Then $a = \frac{3}{r} = \frac{3}{0.5} = 6$.

Q6 a) $a = 6, 10 = S_\infty = \frac{a}{1-r} = \frac{6}{1-r}$
$\Rightarrow \; 1 - r = \frac{6}{10} = 0.6 \;\Rightarrow\; r = 0.4$

b) 5th term: $u_5 = ar^4 = 6 \times 0.4^4 = 0.1536$.

Q7 a) Second term $= ar = -48$, 5th term $= ar^4 = 0.75$.
Dividing gives: $r^3 = \frac{ar^4}{ar} = \frac{0.75}{-48} = -0.015625$
$\Rightarrow \; r = -0.25$

b) $ar = -48 \;\Rightarrow\; a = \frac{-48}{r} = \frac{-48}{-0.25} = 192$

c) $|r| < 1$ so you can find the sum to infinity:
$$S_\infty = \frac{a}{1-r} = \frac{192}{1-(-0.25)} = \frac{192}{1.25} = 153.6.$$

Q8 The sum of terms after the 10th is $S_\infty - S_{10}$. So the question tells you that $S_\infty - S_{10} < \frac{1}{100}S_\infty$
$\Rightarrow \frac{99}{100}S_\infty - S_{10} < 0 \Rightarrow \frac{99}{100}S_\infty < S_{10}$
Then:
$$0.99(S_\infty) = \frac{0.99a}{1-r} < \frac{a(1-r^{10})}{(1-r)} = S_{10}$$
You can cancel and keep the inequality sign because the series is convergent so $|r| < 1 \;\Rightarrow\; 1 - r > 0$, and you know $a > 0$ from the question:
$\Rightarrow \; 0.99 < 1 - r^{10} \;\Rightarrow\; r^{10} < 0.01$
$\Rightarrow \; |r| < \sqrt[10]{0.01} \;\Rightarrow\; |r| < 0.631$ (to 3 s.f.)

4. Sequences & Series Problems

Exercise 4.1 — Sequences & series problems

Q1 a) $S_n = \frac{n}{2}[2a + (n-1)d]$ and $S_4 = 24$, so:
$24 = \frac{4}{2}[2a + (4-1)d] \;\Rightarrow\; 12 = 2a + 3d$ ...**eqn 1**
$u_n = a + (n-1)d$ and $u_5 = 11$, so:
$11 = a + (5-1)d \;\Rightarrow\; 11 = a + 4d$ ...**eqn 2**
($2 \times$ **eqn 2**) – **eqn 1** gives:
$10 = 5d \;\Rightarrow\; d = 2$

b) Substituting $d = 2$ into **eqn 2**:
$11 = a + 8 \;\Rightarrow\; a = 3$

c) $u_n = a + (n-1)d$
$u_7 = 3 + 2(7 - 1) = 15$

Q2 a) $S_n = \frac{n}{2}[2a + (n-1)d]$ and $S_5 = 155$, so:
$155 = \frac{5}{2}[2a + (5-1)d]$
$\Rightarrow 155 = 5(a + 2d) \Rightarrow 31 = a + 2d$ ...**eqn 1**
$u_n = a + (n-1)d$ and $u_5 = 47$, so:
$47 = a + (5-1)d \Rightarrow 47 = a + 4d$ ...**eqn 2**
eqn 2 – eqn 1 gives:
$16 = 2d \Rightarrow d = 8$
Substituting $d = 8$ into **eqn 1**:
$31 = a + (2 \times 8) \Rightarrow a = 15$
So $u_2 = 15 + (1)8 = 23$
$u_3 = 15 + (2)8 = 31$
$u_4 = 15 + (3)8 = 39$
The first five terms of the progression are:
15, 23, 31, 39, 47

b) $u_n > 200 \Rightarrow a + (n-1)d > 200$
So, $15 + 8(n-1) > 200$. Solve the inequality:
$8(n-1) > 185$
$8n > 193 \Rightarrow n > 24.125$
So the first term to exceed 200 is the 25th term.
You can check this answer by calculating the 24th and 25th terms — you'll find that $u_{24} = 199$ and $u_{25} = 207$.

Q3 a) The sum of the 5th, 6th and 7th terms can be found using $S_7 - S_4$, so:
$S_7 = \frac{7}{2}[2a + 6d] = 7a + 21d$ and
$S_4 = 2[2a + 3d] = 4a + 6d$.
$\Rightarrow S_7 - S_4 = 3a + 15d$
$3a + 15d = 111 \Rightarrow a + 5d = 37$ ...**eqn 1**
$u_{10} = 57 \Rightarrow a + 9d = 57$ ...**eqn 2**
eqn 2 – eqn 1 gives:
$4d = 20 \Rightarrow d = 5$
Substituting $d = 5$ into **eqn 1**:
$a + (5 \times 5) = 37 \Rightarrow a = 12$
So first term is 12 and common difference is 5.
Here, you could have found the sum of the 5th, 6th and 7th terms as $(a + 4d) + (a + 5d) + (a + 6d) = 3a + 15d$. That's OK for a small number of terms, but to add up a lot of terms, the method we've used here is much quicker and easier.

b) $u_{15} = 12 + (15 - 1)5 = 82$

Q4 $u_1 + u_2 + u_7 = 0 \Rightarrow (a) + (a + d) + (a + 6d) = 0$
So, $3a + 7d = 0$ ...**eqn 1**
Rearrange **eqn 1** to give $d = -\frac{3a}{7}$.
Now find expressions for u_4 and u_{10} in terms of a:
$u_4 = a + 3d = a - \frac{9a}{7} = -\frac{2a}{7}$
$u_{10} = a + 9d = a - \frac{27a}{7} = -\frac{20a}{7} \Rightarrow u_{10} = 10u_4$
Or you could rearrange to get a in terms of d and then find expressions for u_4 and u_{10} in terms of d. You'll still find that $u_{10} = 10u_4$.

Q5 a) $u_4 = a + 3d$ and $u_8 = a + 7d$
Given that $u_8 = 2u_4$:
$a + 7d = 2(a + 3d)$
$a + 7d = 2a + 6d$
$d = a$
So the common difference is the same as the first term.

b) $u_{30} = 60 \Rightarrow a + 29d = 60$
$a = d$, so $30d = 60 \Rightarrow d = a = 2$
So, the first term in the progression is 2, and the common difference is 2. This describes the set of positive even numbers.

c) $S_{30} - S_5 = \frac{30}{2}[2a + (30-1)d] - \frac{5}{2}[2a + (5-1)d]$
$= 15[4 + (29 \times 2)] - 2.5[4 + (4 \times 2)]$
$= 930 - 30 = 900$
You need to subtract S_5 not S_6 from S_{30} here because you're trying to find $u_6 + u_7 + ... + u_{30}$. If you subtracted S_6, you'd be missing the term u_6.

Q6 a) $S_\infty = \frac{a}{1-r} = 16 \Rightarrow a = 16(1-r)$ ...**eqn 1**
$u_2 = ar = 4 \Rightarrow a = \frac{4}{r}$ ...**eqn 2**
Combining **eqn 1** and **eqn 2**:
$\frac{4}{r} = 16(1-r) \Rightarrow 1 = 4r - 4r^2$
So $4r^2 - 4r + 1 = 0$.
This factorises to $(2r-1)^2 = 0$, so $r = 0.5$.

b) Substitute this value of r into **eqn 2**:
$a = \frac{4}{0.5} = 8$

c) $u_n = ar^{n-1}$, so need to find the lowest n such that:
$8(0.5)^{n-1} < 0.01$ i.e. $(0.5)^{n-1} < 0.00125$.
Solve $(0.5)^{n-1} = 0.00125$ by taking logs:
$(n-1)\log(0.5) = \log(0.00125)$
$\Rightarrow n - 1 = \frac{\log 0.00125}{\log 0.5} = 9.6438...$
$\Rightarrow n = 10.6438...$
So the first term to go below 0.01 is the 11th.

Q7 $S_\infty = \frac{a}{1-r}$, so $\frac{a}{1-r} = 40.5$ ...**eqn 1**
$S_4 = \frac{a(1-r^4)}{1-r}$, so $\frac{a(1-r^4)}{1-r} = 40$ ...**eqn 2**
Dividing **eqn 2** by **eqn 1** gives:
$1 - r^4 = \frac{40}{40.5} \Rightarrow r^4 = \frac{1}{81}$, so $r = \frac{1}{3}$.
You're told that the first four terms are positive, so you can ignore the negative solution of $r^4 = \frac{1}{81}$, as this would give negative terms.

Substitute this value of r into **eqn 1**:
$a = 40.5(1 - \frac{1}{3}) = 27$.
Now find the 2nd to 4th terms:
$u_2 = 27 \times \frac{1}{3} = 9$
$u_3 = 27\left(\frac{1}{3}\right)^2 = 3$
$u_4 = 27\left(\frac{1}{3}\right)^3 = 1$
Dividing eqn 2 by eqn 1 here is quite tricky, so an alternative method to solve the simultaneous equations is to rearrange one of the equations and then substitute into the other to eliminate a.

Q8 $S_\infty = \frac{a}{1-r}$, so $\frac{a}{1-r} = 4a$
$1 = 4 - 4r \Rightarrow r = \frac{3}{4}$

Q9 a) $S_\infty = \frac{a}{1-r}$, so $\frac{a}{1-r} = 1562.5$ ...**eqn 1**
$S_3 = \frac{a(1-r^3)}{1-r}$, so $\frac{a(1-r^3)}{1-r} = 1225$ ...**eqn 2**
Dividing **eqn 2** by **eqn 1** gives:
$1 - r^3 = \frac{1225}{1562.5} \Rightarrow r^3 = 0.216$, so $r = 0.6$.

b) $\sum_{n=4}^{\infty} u_n = S_\infty - S_3 = 1562.5 - 1225 = 337.5$

Q10 a) The 8th, 4th and 2nd terms of the arithmetic progression (AP) will be:
$u_8 = A + 7d,\ u_4 = A + 3d,\ u_2 = A + d$
These are the first three terms of the geometric progression (GP): $[A + 7d], [A + 3d], [A + d], \ldots$
Divide consecutive terms to find two expressions for r: $r = \frac{A+3d}{A+7d} = \frac{A+d}{A+3d}$.
Now cross-multiply:
$(A + 3d)^2 = (A + d)(A + 7d)$
$A^2 + 6Ad + 9d^2 = A^2 + 8Ad + 7d^2$
$2d^2 = 2Ad \Rightarrow d = A$
So, $r = \frac{A+3d}{A+7d} = \frac{4d}{8d} = 0.5$

b) A, the first term of the AP is 2. Hence, as $A = d$, the first term of the GP is:
$G = [A + 7d] = 8A = 16$.
So, the sum to infinity of the GP is:
$S_\infty = \frac{G}{1-r} = \frac{16}{0.5} = 32$

5. Binomial Expansions

Exercise 5.1 — Binomial expansions — $(1 + x)^n$

Q1 Pascal's triangle is

1
1 1
1 2 1
1 3 3 1
1 4 6 4 1

The expansion of $(1 + x)^4$ takes its coefficients of each term, in ascending powers of x, from the 5th row:
$(1 + x)^4 = 1 + 4x + 6x^2 + 4x^3 + x^4$

Q2 a) ${}^6C_2 = 15$ **b)** $\binom{12}{5} = {}^{12}C_5 = 792$

c) $\frac{30!}{4!26!} = {}^{30}C_4 = 27\,405$ **d)** ${}^8C_8 = 1$

Q3 a) $\frac{9!}{4!5!} = \frac{9 \times 8 \times 7 \times 6 \times 5 \times 4 \times 3 \times 2 \times 1}{(4 \times 3 \times 2 \times 1)(5 \times 4 \times 3 \times 2 \times 1)}$
$= \frac{9 \times 8 \times 7 \times 6}{4 \times 3 \times 2 \times 1} = 3 \times 7 \times 6 = 126$

b) ${}^{10}C_3 = \frac{10!}{3!(10-3)!} = \frac{10 \times 9 \times 8}{3 \times 2 \times 1}$
$= 10 \times 3 \times 4 = 120$

c) $\frac{15!}{11!4!} = \frac{15 \times 14 \times 13 \times 12}{4 \times 3 \times 2 \times 1} = 15 \times 7 \times 13 = 1365$

d) $\binom{8}{6} = \frac{8!}{6!(8-6)!} = \frac{8 \times 7}{2 \times 1} = 4 \times 7 = 28$

Q4 $(1 + x)^{10} = 1 + {}^{10}C_1x + {}^{10}C_2x^2 + {}^{10}C_3x^3 + \ldots$
You can work out the coefficients ${}^nC_r$ using a calculator, or using the method below. Using the notation $\binom{n}{r}$ instead of ${}^nC_r$ for the coefficients is fine too. The formula for ${}^nC_r$ only works when n and r are positive integers — which is fine in C2, but in C4 you'll need to use the formula on p.93 instead.

${}^nC_r = \frac{n!}{r!(n-r)!}$,

${}^{10}C_1 = \frac{10!}{1!(10-1)!} = \frac{10 \times 9 \times 8 \times \ldots 1}{1 \times 9 \times 8 \times \ldots 1} = 10$

${}^{10}C_2 = \frac{10!}{2!(10-2)!} = \frac{10 \times 9 \times 8 \times \ldots 1}{2 \times 1 \times 8 \times 7 \times \ldots 1}$
$= \frac{10 \times 9}{2} = 45$

${}^{10}C_3 = \frac{10!}{3!(10-3)!} = \frac{10 \times 9 \times 8 \times 7 \times \ldots 1}{3 \times 2 \times 1 \times 7 \times \ldots 1}$
$= \frac{10 \times 9 \times 8}{3 \times 2}$
$= 10 \times 3 \times 4 = 120$

$(1 + x)^{10} = 1 + 10x + 45x^2 + 120x^3 + \ldots.$
For the rest of this exercise you can use one of the methods shown in question 1 or 4 to find the coefficients ${}^nC_r$, or you can use a calculator.

Q5 $(1 + x)^6 = 1 + {}^6C_1x + {}^6C_2x^2 + {}^6C_3x^3 + {}^6C_4x^4 + {}^6C_5x^5 + {}^6C_6x^6$
$= 1 + 6x + 15x^2 + 20x^3 + 15x^4 + 6x^5 + x^6$

Q6 $(1 + x)^7 = 1 + {}^7C_1x + {}^7C_2x^2 + {}^7C_3x^3 + \ldots$
$= 1 + 7x + 21x^2 + 35x^3 + \ldots$

Q7 ${}^{15}C_8 = 6435$

Exercise 5.2 — Binomial expansions — $(1 + ax)^n$

Q1 a) $(1 - x)^6 = 1 + {}^6C_1(-x) + {}^6C_2(-x)^2 + {}^6C_3(-x)^3 + {}^6C_4(-x)^4 + {}^6C_5(-x)^5 + {}^6C_6(-x)^6$
$= 1 - 6x + 15x^2 - 20x^3 + 15x^4 - 6x^5 + x^6$
Or you could just use the formula for the expansion of $(1 - x)^n$: $(1 - x)^n = 1 - {}^nC_1x + {}^nC_2x^2 - {}^nC_3x^3 + \ldots$

b) $(1 + x)^9$
$= 1 + {}^9C_1x + {}^9C_2x^2 + {}^9C_3x^3 + {}^9C_4x^4 + {}^9C_5x^5 + \ldots$
$(1 - x)^9$
$= 1 - {}^9C_1x + {}^9C_2x^2 - {}^9C_3x^3 + {}^9C_4x^4 - {}^9C_5x^5 + \ldots$
So:
$(1 + x)^9 - (1 - x)^9 = 2({}^9C_1x + {}^9C_3x^3 + {}^9C_5x^5 + \ldots)$
The even powers cancel out, so only the terms with odd powers appear (and they're doubled because one term comes from each expansion).
$= 2(9x + 84x^3 + 126x^5 + 36x^7 + x^9)$
$= 18x + 168x^3 + 252x^5 + 72x^7 + 2x^9$

Q2 The first 3 terms will include 1 and the terms in x and x^2 so expand each bracket up to and including the term in x^2:
$(1 + x)^3(1 - x)^4$
$= (1 + 3x + 3x^2 + \ldots)(1 - 4x + 6x^2 - \ldots)$
$= 1 - 4x + 6x^2 + \ldots + 3x - 12x^2 + \ldots. + 3x^2 +$ (*higher power terms*)
$= 1 - x - 3x^2 + \ldots.$

Q3 The expansion of $(1 + x)^5(1 + y)^7$ is the expansions of $(1 + x)^5$ and $(1 + y)^7$ multiplied together. We need the x^3 term from $(1 + x)^5$ and the y^2 term from $(1 + y)^7$. Multiplying the coefficients gives the x^3y^2 coefficient:
x^3 coefficient: $\frac{5!}{3!(5-3)!} = \frac{5 \times 4}{2 \times 1} = 10$
y^2 coefficient: $\frac{7!}{2!(7-2)!} = \frac{7 \times 6}{2 \times 1} = 21$
x^3y^2 coefficient: $10 \times 21 = 210$

Q4 $(1-3x)^6 = 1 + {}^6C_1(-3x) + {}^6C_2(-3x)^2 + {}^6C_3(-3x)^3 + ...$
$= 1 - 18x + 135x^2 - 540x^3 + ...$

Q5 $(1-2x)^5 = 1 + {}^5C_1(-2x) + {}^5C_2(-2x)^2 + {}^5C_3(-2x)^3 + {}^5C_4(-2x)^4 + {}^5C_5(-2x)^5$
$= 1 + 5(-2x) + 10(4x^2) + 10(-8x^3) + 5(16x^4) + 1(-32x^5)$
$= 1 - 10x + 40x^2 - 80x^3 + 80x^4 - 32x^5$

Q6 $(1+kx)^8$
$= 1 + {}^8C_1kx + {}^8C_2(kx)^2 + {}^8C_3(kx)^3 + ...$
$= 1 + 8kx + 28k^2x^2 + 56k^3x^3 + ...$

Q7 $\left(1+\frac{x}{2}\right)^{12} = 1 + {}^{12}C_1\left(\frac{x}{2}\right) + {}^{12}C_2\left(\frac{x}{2}\right)^2 + {}^{12}C_3\left(\frac{x}{2}\right)^3 + {}^{12}C_4\left(\frac{x}{2}\right)^4 + ...$
$= 1 + 6x + \frac{33}{2}x^2 + \frac{55}{2}x^3 + \frac{495}{16}x^4 + ...$

Exercise 5.3 — Binomial expansions — $(a + b)^n$

Q1 Using the formula for the expansion of $(a+b)^n$:
$$(a+b)^n = a^n + \binom{n}{1}a^{n-1}b + \binom{n}{2}a^{n-2}b^2 + ... + b^n$$
In this case $a = 3$ and $b = x$:
$(3+x)^6 = 3^6 + {}^6C_13^5x + {}^6C_23^4x^2 + {}^6C_33^3x^3 + ...$
$= 729 + 6(243x) + 15(81x^2) + 20(27x^3) + ...$
$= 729 + 1458x + 1215x^2 + 540x^3 + ...$

Q2 In this case $a = 2$ and $b = x$:
$(2+x)^4 = 2^4 + {}^4C_12^3x + {}^4C_22^2x^2 + {}^4C_32x^3 + {}^4C_4x^4$
$= 16 + 4(8x) + 6(4x^2) + 4(2x^3) + x^4$
$= 16 + 32x + 24x^2 + 8x^3 + x^4$

Q3 **a)** The term in x^5 is ${}^8C_5(\lambda x)^5 = 56\lambda^5x^5$
Therefore $56\lambda^5 = 57\,344$
$\Rightarrow \lambda^5 = 1024 \Rightarrow \lambda = \sqrt[5]{1024} = 4$

b) $(1+4x)^8 = 1 + {}^8C_1(4x) + {}^8C_2(4x)^2 + ...$
$= 1 + 32x + 448x^2 + ...$

Q4 $(3+5x)^7$
$= 3^7 + {}^7C_13^6(5x) + {}^7C_23^5(5x)^2 + {}^7C_33^4(5x)^3 + ...$
$= 2187 + 25515x + 127575x^2 + 354375x^3 + ...$

Q5 **a)** $(3+2x)^6 = 3^6 + {}^6C_13^5(2x) + {}^6C_23^4(2x)^2 + {}^6C_33^3(2x)^3 + {}^6C_43^2(2x)^4 + ...$
$= 729 + 2916x + 4860x^2 + 4320x^3 + 2160x^4 + ...$

b) $(1+x)(3+2x)^6 = (3+2x)^6 + x(3+2x)^6$
$= (729 + 2916x + 4860x^2 + 4320x^3 + 2160x^4 + ...)$
$+ (729x + 2916x^2 + 4860x^3 + 4320x^4 + 2160x^5 + ...)$
$= 729 + 3645x + 7776x^2 + 9180x^3 + 6480x^4 + ...$
(The term in x^5 is the 6th term.)

Q6 **a)** Expansion of $(1+x)^n = 1 + nx + \frac{n(n-1)}{2}x^2 + ...$
So: $\frac{n(n-1)}{2} = 231$
$\Rightarrow n(n-1) = 462$
$\Rightarrow n^2 - n - 462 = 0$
$\Rightarrow (n+21)(n-22) = 0$
$\Rightarrow n = -21$ or $n = 22$
Hence $n = 22$ since $n > 0$.
This factorisation was a bit tricky, but you know that 462 is the product of two consecutive numbers. So to give you an idea of the factors, try square rooting 462. $\sqrt{462} = 21.49...$ so the roots are 21 and 22.

b) Coefficient of term in x^3 is:
$\frac{22!}{3!(22-3)!} = \frac{22 \times 21 \times 20}{3 \times 2 \times 1} = 1540$
So the term in x^3 is: $1540x^3$

Q7 $(1+4x^2)^3 = 1 + {}^3C_1(4x^2) + {}^3C_2(4x^2)^2 + {}^3C_3(4x^2)^3$
$= 1 + 3(4x^2) + 3(4x^2)^2 + (4x^2)^3$
$= 1 + 12x^2 + 48x^4 + 64x^6$

Q8 **a)** Use the formula for the expansion of $(a+b)^n$.
In this case $a = x$ and $b = \frac{1}{x}$:
$(a+b)^n = a^n + {}^nC_1a^{n-1}b + {}^nC_2a^{n-2}b^2 + ... + b^n,$
$(x+\frac{1}{x})^4 = x^4 + 4x^3\left(\frac{1}{x}\right) + 6x^2\left(\frac{1}{x}\right)^2 + 4x\left(\frac{1}{x}\right)^3 + \left(\frac{1}{x}\right)^4$
$= x^4 + 4x^2 + 6 + \frac{4}{x^2} + \frac{1}{x^4}$

b) In this case $a = x^2$ and $b = -y$:
$(x^2-y)^5 = (x^2)^5 + 5(x^2)^4(-y) + 10(x^2)^3(-y)^2 + 10(x^2)^2(-y)^3 + 5(x^2)(-y)^4 + (-y)^5$
$= x^{10} - 5x^8y + 10x^6y^2 - 10x^4y^3 + 5x^2y^4 - y^5$

Q9 The expansion of $(1-2x^3)^7$ will give terms in $1, x^3, x^6, x^9, x^{12}, ...$
The term in x^{12} is the 5th term: ${}^7C_4(-2x^3)^4$.
So the coefficient of x^{12} is:
${}^7C_4 \times (-2)^4 = 35 \times 16 = 560$

Q10 Use the formula for the expansion of $(a+b)^n$.
In this case $a = 3x$ and $b = -\frac{2}{x}$:
$(3x-\frac{2}{x})^4 = (3x)^4 + 4(3x)^3\left(-\frac{2}{x}\right) + 6(3x)^2\left(-\frac{2}{x}\right)^2 + 4(3x)\left(-\frac{2}{x}\right)^3 + \left(-\frac{2}{x}\right)^4$
$= 81x^4 - 216x^2 + 216 - \frac{96}{x^2} + \frac{16}{x^4}$

Q11 $(2x-\frac{3}{x})^8 = (2x)^8 + {}^8C_1(2x)^7\left(-\frac{3}{x}\right) + {}^8C_2(2x)^6\left(-\frac{3}{x}\right)^2 + {}^8C_3(2x)^5\left(-\frac{3}{x}\right)^3 + {}^8C_4(2x)^4\left(-\frac{3}{x}\right)^4 + ...$
So the constant term is the 5th term:
${}^8C_4(2x)^4\left(-\frac{3}{x}\right)^4 = 70(16x^4)\left(\frac{81}{x^4}\right)$
$= 70 \times 16 \times 81 = 90\,720$
You could work out that you can go straight to the 5th term if you spot that x^4 will cancel with $\frac{1}{x^4}$. Be careful if you do this way though, it's easy to make a mistake. If in doubt, expand fully.

Q12 $(1 + 4x)^5 - (1 - 4x)^4$
$= [1 + 5(4x) + 10(4x)^2 + 10(4x)^3 + 5(4x)^4 + (4x)^5]$
$- [1 + 4(-4x) + 6(-4x)^2 + 4(-4x)^3 + (-4x)^4]$
$= [1 + 20x + 160x^2 + 640x^3 + 1280x^4 + 1024x^5]$
$- [1 - 16x + 96x^2 - 256x^3 + 256x^4]$
$= 36x + 64x^2 + 896x^3 + 1024x^4 + 1024x^5$

Q13 The coefficient of x^2 is ${}^8C_2a^63^2$
The coefficient of x^5 is ${}^8C_5a^33^5$
Therefore:
$$28 \times a^6 \times 3^2 = \frac{32}{27} \times 56 \times a^3 \times 3^5$$
$$\Rightarrow 28a^3 = \frac{32}{27} \times 56 \times 3^3$$
$$\Rightarrow a^3 = \frac{32 \times 56 \times 27}{27 \times 28} = 64$$
$$\Rightarrow a = \sqrt[3]{64} = 4.$$

Q14 Expand each bracket up to the term in x^3:
$(1 + 2x)^5 = 1 + 5(2x) + 10(2x)^2 + 10(2x)^3 + ...$
$= 1 + 10x + 40x^2 + 80x^3 + ...$
$(3 - x)^4 = 3^4 + 4(3)^3(-x) + 6(3)^2(-x)^2 + 4(3)(-x)^3 + ...$
$= 81 - 108x + 54x^2 - 12x^3 + ...$
Multiply the terms that will give a result in x^3:
$(1 \times -12x^3) + (10x \times 54x^2) + (40x^2 \times -108x)$
$+ (80x^3 \times 81) = 2688x^3$
So the coefficient of x^3 is 2688.

Q15 a) The coefficient of x^3 is:
$$\frac{n!}{3!(n-3)!} = \frac{n(n-1)(n-2)}{3 \times 2 \times 1}$$
The coefficient of x^2 is:
$$\frac{n!}{2!(n-2)!} = \frac{n(n-1)}{2}$$
The coefficient of x^3 is three times the coefficient of x^2, so:
$$\frac{n(n-1)(n-2)}{3 \times 2 \times 1} = 3 \times \frac{n(n-1)}{2}.$$
$$\Rightarrow \frac{n-2}{3} = 3$$
$$\Rightarrow n = 11$$

b) $(1 + x)^{11} = 1 + 11x + 55x^2 + ...$
The coefficient of x^2 is $a \times$ (coefficient of x), so $55 = 11a \Rightarrow a = 5$.

Q16 a) $(2 + \mu x)^8 = 2^8 + {}^8C_12^7(\mu x) + {}^8C_22^6(\mu x)^2 + ...$
$= 256 + (8 \times 128)(\mu x) + (28 \times 64)(\mu x)^2 + ...$
$= 256 + 1024\mu x + 1792\mu^2x^2 + ...$

b) The coefficient of x^2 is:
$87\,808 = 1792\mu^2 \Rightarrow \mu^2 = 49 \Rightarrow \mu = 7$ or -7.

Q17 a) $(x + \frac{1}{x})^6 = x^6 + 6x^5\left(\frac{1}{x}\right) + 15x^4\left(\frac{1}{x}\right)^2 + ...$
$= x^6 + 6x^4 + 15x^2 + ...$
Coefficient of term in $x^2 = 15$

b) $(2x + \frac{1}{x})^7 = (2x)^7 + 7(2x)^6\left(\frac{1}{x}\right) + ...$
$... + 7(2x)\left(\frac{1}{x}\right)^6 + \left(\frac{1}{x}\right)^7$
Coefficient of term in $\frac{1}{x^5} = 14$
Again, you could go straight to the terms you need without expanding fully.

Q18 a) $(x - \frac{k}{x})^8 = x^8 + 8x^7\left(-\frac{k}{x}\right) + ...$
$... + {}^8C_4x^4\left(-\frac{k}{x}\right)^4 + {}^8C_5x^3\left(-\frac{k}{x}\right)^5 + ...$
The constant term is:
${}^8C_4x^4\left(-\frac{k}{x}\right)^4 = 70 \times (-k)^4 = 1120$
So, $k^4 = 16 \Rightarrow k = 2$

b) The term in $\frac{1}{x^2}$ is ${}^8C_5x^3\left(-\frac{k}{x}\right)^5$, with coefficient:
$56 \times (-k)^5 = 56 \times (-2)^5 = -1792$

Review Exercise — Chapter 4

Q1 a) n^{th} term $= 4n - 2$
b) n^{th} term $= 0.5n - 0.3$
c) n^{th} term $= -3n + 24$
d) n^{th} term $= -6n + 82$

Q2 8th term $= 8^2 - 3 = 61$

Q3 $44 = k^2 + 3k + 4$
$k^2 + 3k - 40 = 0$
$(k + 8)(k - 5) = 0$
Ignoring the negative solution, $k = 5$.
It's the only positive solution — you can't have the -8th term.

Q4 Substituting $n = 1, 2, 3, 4, 5$ in the formula $(-1)^n n$ generates the first 5 terms: $-1, 2, -3, 4, -5$

Q5 a) Each term is the square root of the term before:
$a_{k+1} = \sqrt{a_k}$, $a_1 = 65\,536$

b) Each term is equal to the previous term minus double the previous term's position.
$a_{k+1} = a_k - 2k$, $a_1 = 40$

c) Each term (from the third onwards) is equal to the sum of the previous two terms.
$u_{n+2} = u_n + u_{n+1}$, $u_1 = 1$, $u_2 = 1$
This one is a bit different. You have to state two consecutive terms to establish the relation. Oh, and you can use a variety of letters for variables in recurrence relations, so I used some different ones here.

Q6 $f(u_n) = -\frac{1}{4}u_n + 3$. L can be found by solving $L = f(L)$:
$L = -\frac{1}{4}L + 3$
$\frac{5}{4}L = 3 \Rightarrow L = \frac{12}{5}$

Q7 Form an equation for getting the 2nd term from the 1st term, and an equation for getting the 3rd term from the 2nd term:
$8 = 2a + b$
$26 = 8a + b$
Solving the equations simultaneously: $a = 3$, $b = 2$

Q8 $l = a + (n - 1)d$
$19 = -2 + (29 - 1)d$
$21 = 28d \Rightarrow d = 0.75$

Q9 Form equations for the 7th and 11th terms:
$8 = a + (7 - 1)d \Rightarrow 8 = a + 6d$
$10 = a + (11 - 1)d \Rightarrow 10 = a + 10d$
Solving the equations gives $a = 5$, $d = 0.5$
3rd term $= 5 + (3 - 1)0.5 = 6$

You could also do this 'by inspection'. The difference between the 7th and 11th terms is 2, so the difference between the 3rd and 7th terms must also be 2.
So $u_3 = 8 - 2 = 6$.

Q10 Form equations for the 3rd and 7th terms:
$15 = a + (3 - 1)d \Rightarrow 15 = a + 2d$
$27 = a + (7 - 1)d \Rightarrow 27 = a + 6d$
Solving the equations gives $a = 9$, $d = 3$
Now form an equation for the kth term and solve:
$66 = 9 + (k - 1)3 \Rightarrow k = 20$

Q11 a) $a = 3(1) - 1 = 2$
$l = 3(20) - 1 = 59$
$$S_n = n\frac{(a+l)}{2}$$
$$S_{20} = 20\left(\frac{2+59}{2}\right)$$
$$S_{20} = 610$$

b) $S_n = \frac{1}{2}n(n+1)$
$630 = \frac{1}{2}k(k+1)$
$1260 = k^2 + k$
$0 = k^2 + k - 1260$
$(k+36)(k-35) = 0$
So $k = 35$ (ignoring negative solution)

Q12 First term $= a$, second term $= ar$
$$r = \frac{\text{second term}}{\text{first term}} = \frac{1875}{3125} = 0.6$$

Q13 First term is $a = 3$,
common ratio is $r = \frac{\text{second term}}{\text{first term}} = \frac{-9}{3} = -3$
n^{th} term of a geometric sequence is: $u_n = ar^{n-1}$
So the nth term of this sequence is:
$u_n = 3(-3)^{n-1} = -(-3)^n$

Q14 a) $a = 2$, $r = \frac{\text{second term}}{\text{first term}} = \frac{-6}{2} = -3$
10th term, $u_{10} = ar^9 = 2 \times (-3)^9 = -39366$

b) The sum of the first 10 terms is:
$$S_{10} = \frac{a(1-r^{10})}{(1-r)} = \frac{2(1-(-3)^{10})}{1-(-3)} = -29524$$

Q15 For $a = 7$, $r = 0.6$
$$\sum_{k=0}^{5} 7(0.6)^k = S_6 = \frac{a(1-r^6)}{(1-r)}$$
$$= \frac{7(1-(0.6)^6)}{(1-0.6)} = 16.68 \text{ to 2 d.p.}$$

For the rest of this exercise the common ratio r is found by dividing two consecutive terms, unless another method is given.

Q16 a) $r = \frac{2}{1} = 2, |2| > 1$, so series is divergent.

b) $r = \frac{27}{81} = \frac{1}{3}, \left|\frac{1}{3}\right| < 1$, so series is convergent.

c) $r = \frac{\frac{1}{3}}{1} = \frac{1}{3}, \left|\frac{1}{3}\right| < 1$, so series is convergent.

d) $r = \frac{1}{4}, \left|\frac{1}{4}\right| < 1$, so series is convergent.

Q17 a) $r = \frac{\text{second term}}{\text{first term}} = \frac{12}{24} = \frac{1}{2}$

b) 7th term $= ar^6 = 24 \times \left(\frac{1}{2}\right)^6 = 0.375$ or $\frac{3}{8}$

c) $S_{10} = \frac{a(1-r^{10})}{1-r} = \frac{24\left(1-\left(\frac{1}{2}\right)^{10}\right)}{1-\frac{1}{2}} = 47.953$ to 3 d.p.

d) $S_\infty = \frac{a}{1-r} = \frac{24}{1-\frac{1}{2}} = 48$

Q18 $a = 2$, $r = \frac{6}{2} = 3$
Need to find n so that $ar^{n-1} = 1458$,
$2 \times 3^{n-1} = 1458 \Rightarrow 3^{n-1} = 729$.
Then, use logs to find that: $\log 3^{n-1} = \log 729$
$$(n-1)\log 3 = \log 729$$
$$n - 1 = \frac{\log 729}{\log 3}$$
$\Rightarrow n - 1 = 6 \Rightarrow n = 7$, so the 7th term equals 1458.

Q19 $\sum_{k=0}^{\infty} ar^k = S_\infty = \frac{a}{1-r}$
In this case $a = 33$ and $r = 0.25$, so:
$$\sum_{k=0}^{\infty} ar^k = \sum_{k=0}^{\infty} 33(0.25)^k$$
$$= \frac{33}{1-0.25} = \frac{33}{0.75} = 44$$

Q20 $(1+x)^{12} = 1 + {}^{12}C_1x + {}^{12}C_2x^2 + {}^{12}C_3x^3 + \ldots$
$= 1 + 12x + 66x^2 + 220x^3 + \ldots$

Q21 ${}^{16}C_4(-2x)^4 = 1820 \times 16x^4 = 29120x^4$

Q22 $\left(1+\frac{x}{3}\right)^9 = 1 + {}^9C_1\left(\frac{x}{3}\right) + {}^9C_2\left(\frac{x}{3}\right)^2 + {}^9C_3\left(\frac{x}{3}\right)^3 + \ldots$
$= 1 + 9\left(\frac{x}{3}\right) + 36\left(\frac{x}{3}\right)^2 + 84\left(\frac{x}{3}\right)^3 + \ldots$
$= 1 + 3x + 4x^2 + \frac{28}{9}x^3 + \ldots$

Q23 $(1+3x)^5 = 1 + {}^5C_1(3x) + {}^5C_2(3x)^2 + {}^5C_3(3x)^3 + {}^5C_4(3x)^4 + {}^5C_5(3x)^5$
$= 1 + 5(3x) + 10(3x)^2 + 10(3x)^3 + 5(3x)^4 + (3x)^5$
$= 1 + 15x + 90x^2 + 270x^3 + 405x^4 + 243x^5$

Q24 a) $(1+ax)^8 = 1 + {}^8C_1(ax) + {}^8C_2(ax)^2 + {}^8C_3(ax)^3 + {}^8C_4(ax)^4 + \ldots$
$= 1 + 8ax + 28a^2x^2 + 56a^3x^3 + 70a^4x^4 + \ldots$

b) The coefficient of x^2 is double the coefficient of x^3, so $28a^2 = 2 \times 56a^3 = 112a^3$
$\Rightarrow \frac{28}{112} = a \Rightarrow a = \frac{1}{4}$

c) The coefficient of x is $8a = 8 \times \frac{1}{4} = 2$

Q25 $(4-5x)^7 = 4^7 + {}^7C_14^6(-5x) + {}^7C_24^5(-5x)^2 + \ldots$
$= 16\,384 + (7 \times 4096)(-5x) + (21 \times 1024)(-5x)^2 + \ldots$
$= 16\,384 - 143\,360x + 537\,600x^2 + \ldots$
This method uses the $(a + b)^n$ formula. You could also rearrange the bracket so you can expand it using the $(1 + x)^n$ formula — if you do it this way make sure you multiply through by 4^7 at the end. For the rest of this exercise the $(a + b)^n$ formula is used, but you can use the other method for all of these questions.

Q26 a) $(2+kx)^{13} = 2^{13} + {}^{13}C_12^{12}(kx) + {}^{13}C_22^{11}(kx)^2 + \ldots$
$= 8192 + 53\,248kx + 159\,744k^2x^2 + \ldots$

b) The coefficient of x is $\frac{1}{6}$ of the coefficient of x^2:

$6(53\,248k) = 159\,744k^2$

$\Rightarrow \ k = 6 \times \frac{53\,248}{159\,744} = 2$

Q27 Expand each bracket up to and including the term in a^3 and then multiply the two expansions and give only the terms up to a^3:

$(2 + a)^4 = 2^4 + {}^4C_1 2^3(a) + {}^4C_2 2^2(a^2) + {}^4C_3 2(a^3) + ...$
$= 16 + 32a + 24a^2 + 8a^3 + ...$

$(3 - 4a)^5 = 3^5 + {}^5C_1 3^4(-4a) + {}^5C_2 3^3(-4a)^2 + {}^5C_3 3^2(-4a)^3 + ...$
$= 243 - 1620a + 4320a^2 - 5760a^3 + ...$

$(2 + a)^4(3 - 4a)^5 = 16(243 - 1620a + 4320a^2 - 5760a^3 + ...) + 32a(243 - 1620a + 4320a^2 - 5760a^3 + ...) + 24a^2(243 - 1620a + 4320a^2 - 5760a^3 + ...) + 8a^3(243 - 1620a + 4320a^2 - 5760a^3 + ...) + ...$
$= 3888 - 25920a + 69120a^2 - 92160a^3 + 7776a - 51840a^2 + 138240a^3 + 5832a^2 - 38880a^3 + 1944a^3$ + terms in higher powers of a
$= 3888 - 18144a + 23112a^2 + 9144a^3$ (up to a^3)

Q28 $(1 - \frac{2}{x^3})^4 = 1 + 4\left(\frac{-2}{x^3}\right) + 6\left(\frac{-2}{x^3}\right)^2 + 4\left(\frac{-2}{x^3}\right)^3 + \left(\frac{-2}{x^3}\right)^4$
$= 1 - \frac{8}{x^3} + \frac{24}{x^6} - \frac{32}{x^9} + \frac{16}{x^{12}}$

So, $a = 8$, $b = 24$, $c = 32$, $d = 16$.

Exam Questions — Chapter 4

Q1 a) The series is defined by $u_{n+1} = 12 \times 1.3^n$ so the common ratio = 1.3, which is greater than 1, so the sequence is divergent. ***[1 mark]***

b) $u_3 = 12 \times 1.3^2 = 20.28$ ***[1 mark]***

$u_{10} = 12 \times 1.3^9 = 127.25$ to 2 d.p. ***[1 mark]***

Q2 a) $a_{31} = 22 + (31 - 1)(-1.1)$ ***[1 mark]***
$= 22 + 30(-1.1)$
$= 22 - 33 = -11$ ***[1 mark]***

b) $a_k = 0$
$a_1 + (k - 1)d = 0$
$22 + (k - 1) \times -1.1 = 0$ ***[1 mark]***
$k - 1 = \frac{-22}{-1.1} = \frac{220}{11} = 20$
$k = 20 + 1 = 21$ ***[1 mark]***

c) We want to find the first value of n for which $S_n < 0$. Using the formula for sum of a series:

$S_n = \frac{n}{2}[2 \times 22 + (n - 1)(-1.1)] < 0$ ***[1 mark]***

$S_n = \frac{n}{2}(44 - 1.1n + 1.1) < 0$

$\frac{n}{2}(45.1 - 1.1n) < 0$ ***[1 mark]***

Consider $\frac{n}{2}(45.1 - 1.1n) = 0$

$\Rightarrow \frac{n}{2} = 0$ or $45.1 - 1.1n = 0$

$\Rightarrow n = 0$ or $n = \frac{45.1}{1.1} = 41$

The coefficient of n^2 is negative so graph is n-shaped.

Need to find negative part, so $n < 0$ or $n > 41$.
Since n cannot be negative then $n > 41$.
Now we just want the first (i.e. lowest) value of n for which this is true, which is $n = 42$. ***[1 mark]***

Q3 a) $(1 + 3x)^5 = 1 + {}^5C_1(3x) + {}^5C_2(3x)^2 + {}^5C_3(3x)^3 + {}^5C_4(3x)^4 + (3x)^5$
$= 1 + 15x + 90x^2 + 270x^3 + 405x^4 + 243x^5$.
[2 marks available — 1 mark for using binomial expansion, 1 mark for correct answer.]

b) When you multiply $(1 + 3x)^5$ by $(1 + x)$, the only terms which are going to multiply together to give an x^2 term are $(1 \times 90x^2)$ and $(x \times 15x)$ ***[1 mark]***.
So the x^2 term will be $(1 \times 90x^2) + (x \times 15x)$ ***[1 mark]*** $= (90 + 15)x^2 = 105x^2$ ***[1 mark]***.
So the coefficient of x^2 is 105, as required.

Q4 a) $S_\infty = \frac{a}{1-r} = \frac{20}{1-\frac{3}{4}} = \frac{20}{\frac{1}{4}} = 80$

[2 marks available — 1 mark for formula, 1 mark for correct answer]

b) $u_{15} = ar^{14} = 20 \times \left(\frac{3}{4}\right)^{14} = 0.356$ (to 3 sig. fig.)

[2 marks available — 1 mark for formula, 1 mark for correct answer]

c) Use the formula for the sum of a geometric series to write an expression for S_n:

$S_n = \frac{a(1-r^n)}{1-r} = \frac{20\left(1-\left(\frac{3}{4}\right)^n\right)}{1-\frac{3}{4}}$ ***[1 mark]***

so $\frac{20\left(1-\left(\frac{3}{4}\right)^n\right)}{1-\frac{3}{4}} > 79.76$

Now rearrange and use logs to get n on its own:

$\frac{20\left(1-\left(\frac{3}{4}\right)^n\right)}{1-\frac{3}{4}} > 79.76 \Rightarrow 20\left(1-\frac{3^n}{4}\right) > 19.94$

$\Rightarrow 1-\left(\frac{3}{4}\right)^n > 0.997 \Rightarrow 0.003 > 0.75^n$ ***[1 mark]***

$\Rightarrow \log 0.003 > n \log 0.75$ ***[1 mark]***

$\Rightarrow \frac{\log 0.003}{\log 0.75} < n$ ***[1 mark]***

Remember — if $x < 1$, then log x has a negative value.

$\frac{\log 0.003}{\log 0.75} = 20.1929....$ so $n > 20.1929....$

But n must be an integer, so $n = 21$ ***[1 mark]***

Q5 a) $S_\infty = \frac{a}{1-r}$ and $u_2 = ar$ ***[1 mark]***

So $36 = \frac{a}{1-r}$ i.e. $36 - 36r = a$ ***[1 mark]***

and $5 = ar$. ***[1 mark]***

Substituting for a gives:

$5 = (36 - 36r)r = 36r - 36r^2$

i.e. $36r^2 - 36r + 5 = 0$ ***[1 mark]***

b) Factorising gives: $(6r - 1)(6r - 5) = 0$
So: $r = \frac{1}{6}$ or $r = \frac{5}{6}$.
[1 mark for each correct value]
If $r = \frac{1}{6}$ and $ar = 5$ then $\frac{a}{6} = 5$ i.e. $a = 30$
If $r = \frac{5}{6}$ and $ar = 5$ then $\frac{5a}{6} = 5$ i.e. $a = 6$
[1 mark for each correct value]

Q6 $(4 + 3x)^{10} = 4^{10} + {}^{10}C_1 4^9(3x) + {}^{10}C_2 4^8(3x)^2 + {}^{10}C_3 4^7(3x)^3 + {}^{10}C_4 4^6(3x)^4 + \ldots$

So: x coefficient $= 10 \times 4^9 \times 3 = 7\,864\,320$ ***[1 mark]***
x^2 coefficient $= 45 \times 4^8 \times 9 = 26\,542\,080$ ***[1 mark]***
x^3 coefficient $= 120 \times 4^7 \times 27 = 53\,084\,160$ ***[1 mark]***
x^4 coefficient $= 210 \times 4^6 \times 81 = 69\,672\,960$ ***[1 mark]***

Q7 a) Common ratio: $r = \frac{\text{second term}}{\text{first term}} = \frac{5}{2} = 2.5$
First term $a = 2$
$S_8 = \frac{a(1 - r^8)}{1 - r} = \frac{2(1 - 2.5^8)}{1 - 2.5} = 2033.17$ to 2 d.p.
[3 marks available — 1 mark for correct values of a and r, 1 mark for putting values into formula, 1 mark for correct answer]

b) An infinite geometric series with common ratio r is convergent when $|r| < 1$. ***[1 mark]***
You could also have 'when $-1 < r < 1$'.

c) $S_\infty = \frac{a}{1 - r} = \frac{8}{1 - \left(-\frac{3}{4}\right)} = \frac{8}{1.75} = 4.57$ to 2 d.p.
[2 marks available — 1 mark for using formula, 1 mark for correct answer]

Q8 a) $u_1 = 10$
$u_2 = au_1 + b = 10a + b = -1$
$u_3 = au_2 + b = -a + b = \frac{6}{5}$
You now have a pair of simultaneous equations:
$10a + b = -1$ **(eqn. 1)** ***[1 mark]***
$-a + b = \frac{6}{5}$ **(eqn. 2)** ***[1 mark]***
Eliminate b by subtracting **eqn. 2** from **eqn. 1**:
$11a = -\frac{11}{5}$ ***[1 mark]***
$\Rightarrow a = -\frac{1}{5}$ ***[1 mark]***
And so (from **eqn. 2**):
$b = \frac{6}{5} + a = \frac{6}{5} - \frac{1}{5} = 1$ ***[1 mark]***.
So, $u_{n+1} = -\frac{1}{5}u_n + 1$

b) First find the value of u_4:
$u_4 = au_3 + b = -\frac{1}{5}u_3 + 1$
$= -\frac{1}{5}\left(\frac{6}{5}\right) + 1 = \frac{19}{25}$ ***[1 mark]***
So $u_5 = -\frac{1}{5}u_4 + 1 = -\frac{1}{5}\left(\frac{19}{25}\right) + 1 = \frac{106}{125}$ ***[1 mark]***.

c) The sequence is defined by the function
$f(u_n) = -\frac{1}{5}u_n + 1$
Setting $L = f(L)$ gives $L = -\frac{1}{5}L + 1$ ***[1 mark]***.
$\Rightarrow \frac{6}{5}L = 1 \Rightarrow L = \frac{5}{6}$ ***[1 mark]***.

Q9 a) $h_2 = h_{1+1} = 2 \times 5 + 2 = 12$ ***[1 mark]***
$h_3 = h_{2+1} = 2 \times 12 + 2 = 26$ ***[1 mark]***
$h_4 = h_{3+1} = 2 \times 26 + 2 = 54$ ***[1 mark]***

b) $\sum_{r=3}^{6} h_r = h_3 + h_4 + h_5 + h_6$
$h_5 = 2h_4 + 2 = 110$ ***[1 mark]***
$h_6 = 2(110) + 2 = 222$ ***[1 mark]***
so $\sum_{r=3}^{6} h_r = 26 + 54 + 110 + 222 = 412$ ***[1 mark]***

Q10 a) $S_\infty = \frac{a}{1 - r} = -9 \Rightarrow a = -9(1 - r)$ ***[1 mark]***
and $ar = -2 \Rightarrow a = \frac{-2}{r}$
$\Rightarrow \frac{-2}{r} = -9(1 - r)$ ***[1 mark]***
$\Rightarrow -2 = -9r + 9r^2 \Rightarrow 9r^2 - 9r + 2 = 0$ ***[1 mark]***

b) $9r^2 - 9r + 2 = 0$,
factorising: $(3r - 1)(3r - 2) = 0$ ***[1 mark]***
$\Rightarrow r = \frac{1}{3}$ or $r = \frac{2}{3}$ ***[1 mark]***

c) $ar = -2 \Rightarrow a = \frac{-2}{r}$
$r = \frac{1}{3} \Rightarrow a = \frac{-2}{\frac{1}{3}} = -6$ ***[1 mark]***
$r = \frac{2}{3} \Rightarrow a = \frac{-2}{\frac{2}{3}} = -3$ ***[1 mark]***

d) r takes its smallest possible value,
so $r = \frac{1}{3} \Rightarrow a = -6$.
The 7th term is: $u_7 = ar^6$ ***[1 mark]***
$= -6 \times \left(\frac{1}{3}\right)^6 = -0.0082$ to 4 d.p. ***[1 mark]***

e) $S_5 = \frac{a(1 - r^5)}{1 - r} = \frac{-6\left(1 - \left(\frac{1}{3}\right)^5\right)}{1 - \frac{1}{3}}$ ***[1 mark]***
$= -8.96$ to 2 d.p. ***[1 mark]***

Q11 a) $\left(\frac{1}{2x} + \frac{x}{2}\right)^3$
$= \left(\frac{1}{2x}\right)^3 + 3\left(\frac{1}{2x}\right)^2\left(\frac{x}{2}\right) + 3\left(\frac{1}{2x}\right)\left(\frac{x}{2}\right)^2 + \left(\frac{x}{2}\right)^3$
$= \frac{1}{8x^3} + \frac{3}{8x} + \frac{3x}{8} + \frac{x^3}{8}$
[3 marks available — 1 mark for correct use of formula, 1 mark for correct coefficients, 1 mark for correct simplified final answer].

b) $(2 + x^2)\left(\frac{1}{2x} + \frac{x}{2}\right)^3$
$= (2 + x^2)\left(\frac{1}{8x^3} + \frac{3}{8x} + \frac{3x}{8} + \frac{x^3}{8}\right)$
The only parts of this multiplication which will give an x term are $2\left(\frac{3x}{8}\right)$ and $x^2\left(\frac{3}{8x}\right)$ ***[1 mark]***.
So, x term will be: $2\left(\frac{3x}{8}\right) + x^2\left(\frac{3}{8x}\right) = x\left(\frac{6}{8} + \frac{3}{8}\right)$
[1 mark] and the coefficient of x is $\frac{9}{8}$ ***[1 mark]***.

Chapter 5: Differentiation

1. Differentiating x^n

Exercise 1.1 — When n is negative or a fraction

Q1 **a)** $\frac{dy}{dx} = 8x^7$ **b)** $\frac{dy}{dx} = -2x^{-3} = -\frac{2}{x^3}$

c) $\frac{dy}{dx} = 10x^4$ **d)** $\frac{dy}{dx} = \frac{3}{2}x^{-\frac{1}{2}} = \frac{3}{2\sqrt{x}}$

e) $\frac{dy}{dx} = 0$ **f)** $\frac{dy}{dx} = -2x^{-2} = -\frac{2}{x^2}$

g) $\frac{dy}{dx} = -6x^{-4} = -\frac{6}{x^4}$ **h)** $\frac{dy}{dx} = \frac{1}{4}x^{-\frac{3}{4}} = -\frac{1}{4\sqrt[4]{x^3}}$

Q2 **a)** $f'(x) = 4$ **b)** $f'(x) = -4x^{-5} = -\frac{4}{x^5}$

c) $f'(x) = 4x^{-\frac{1}{2}} = \frac{4}{\sqrt{x}}$ **d)** $f'(x) = x^{-\frac{2}{3}} = \frac{1}{\sqrt[3]{x^2}}$

e) $f'(x) = 3x^5$ **f)** $f'(x) = -8x^{-3} = -\frac{8}{x^3}$

g) $f'(x) = -20x^{-3} = -\frac{20}{x^3}$ **h)** $f'(x) = -x^{-\frac{3}{2}} = -\frac{1}{\sqrt{x^3}}$

Q3 **a)** $\frac{dy}{dx} = 3x^2 \Rightarrow$ At $x = 3$, $\frac{dy}{dx} = 27$

b) $\frac{dy}{dx} = -x^{-2} = -\frac{1}{x^2} \Rightarrow$ At $x = 2$, $\frac{dy}{dx} = -\frac{1}{4}$

c) $f'(x) = x^{-\frac{1}{2}} = \frac{1}{\sqrt{x}} \Rightarrow f'(9) = \frac{1}{3}$

d) $\frac{dy}{dx} = 4x^5 \Rightarrow$ At $x = -1$, $\frac{dy}{dx} = -4$

e) $f'(x) = 3x^{\frac{1}{2}} = 3\sqrt{x} \Rightarrow f'(4) = 6$

f) $f'(x) = -12x^{-4} = -\frac{12}{x^4}$

$f(x) = -\frac{1}{2} \Rightarrow \frac{4}{x^3} = -\frac{1}{2} \Rightarrow x^3 = -8 \Rightarrow x = -2$

$f'(-2) = -\frac{12}{16} = -\frac{3}{4}$

Exercise 1.2 — Differentiating functions

Q1 **a)** $\frac{dy}{dx} = 6x + 25x^4$

b) $\frac{dy}{dx} = 1 + (-x^{-2}) = 1 - \frac{1}{x^2}$

c) $\frac{dy}{dx} = 6x + \frac{1}{2}x^{-\frac{1}{2}} = 6x + \frac{1}{2\sqrt{x}}$

d) $f'(x) = -10x^4 + 4 - (-2x^{-3}) = -10x^4 + 4 + \frac{2}{x^3}$

e) $f'(x) = \frac{3}{2}x^{\frac{1}{2}} - 1 = \frac{3}{2}\sqrt{x} - 1$

f) $f'(x) = 5 - 2(-3x^{-4}) + \frac{1}{3}x^{-\frac{2}{3}} = 5 + \frac{6}{x^4} + \frac{1}{3\sqrt[3]{x^2}}$

Q2 **a)** $\frac{dy}{dx} = -4x^3 + 12x^2$

At $x = 2$, $\frac{dy}{dx} = -32 + 48 = 16$

b) $\frac{dy}{dx} = 10x^4 + (-x^{-2}) = 10x^4 - \frac{1}{x^2}$

At $x = -2$, $\frac{dy}{dx} = 160 - \frac{1}{4} = \frac{639}{4}$

c) $y = x(x^2 + 4x + 3) = x^3 + 4x^2 + 3x$

$\frac{dy}{dx} = 3x^2 + 8x + 3$

At $x = 4$, $\frac{dy}{dx} = 48 + 32 + 3 = 83$

d) $y = x^{-1} + 2x^{-2} - 2x - 4$

$\frac{dy}{dx} = -x^{-2} - 4x^{-3} - 2 = -\frac{1}{x^2} - \frac{4}{x^3} - 2$

At $x = 1$, $\frac{dy}{dx} = -1 - 4 - 2 = -7$

e) $y = \sqrt{x}(x - 1) = x^{\frac{1}{2}}(x - 1) = x^{\frac{3}{2}} - x^{\frac{1}{2}}$

$\frac{dy}{dx} = \frac{3}{2}x^{\frac{1}{2}} - \frac{1}{2}x^{-\frac{1}{2}} = \frac{3}{2}\sqrt{x} - \frac{1}{2\sqrt{x}}$

At $x = 4$, $\frac{dy}{dx} = 3 - \frac{1}{4} = \frac{11}{4}$

f) $f(x) = \frac{2x^2}{x} + \frac{3x^2}{x^3} = 2x + \frac{3}{x} = 2x + 3x^{-1}$

$f'(x) = 2 - 3x^{-2} = 2 - \frac{3}{x^2}$

$f'(-1) = 2 - 3 = -1$

g) $f(x) = \frac{1}{x^2}(x^3 - x) = x - x^{-1}$

$f'(x) = 1 + x^{-2} = 1 + \frac{1}{x^2}$

$f'(5) = \frac{26}{25}$

h) $f(x) = \frac{3x^3}{x^2} + \frac{10x^2}{x^2} - \frac{2x}{x^2} = 3x + 10 - 2x^{-1}$

$f'(x) = 3 + 2x^{-2} = 3 + \frac{2}{x^2}$

$f'(2) = 3 + \frac{1}{2} = \frac{7}{2}$

Q3 **a)** $f(x) = 2x^2 + 9x - 18$

$f'(x) = 4x + 9$

So $f'(x) = -3 \Rightarrow 4x + 9 = -3 \Rightarrow 4x = -12$

$\Rightarrow x = -3$

$f(-3) = 18 - 27 - 18 = -27$

$f'(x) = -3$ at $(-3, -27)$

b) $f(x) = x + 12\sqrt{x} + 32 = x + 12x^{\frac{1}{2}} + 32$

$f'(x) = 1 + 6x^{-\frac{1}{2}} = 1 + \frac{6}{\sqrt{x}}$

So $f'(x) = 3 \Rightarrow 1 + \frac{6}{\sqrt{x}} = 3 \Rightarrow \frac{6}{\sqrt{x}} = 2$

$\Rightarrow \sqrt{x} = 3 \Rightarrow x = 9$

$f(9) = 9 + 36 + 32 = 77$

$f'(x) = 3$ at $(9, 77)$

c) $f(x) = \frac{x^3}{x^2} - \frac{3x^2}{x^2} + \frac{2x}{x^2} = x - 3 + 2x^{-1}$

$f'(x) = 1 - 2x^{-2} = 1 - \frac{2}{x^2}$

So $f'(x) = \frac{1}{2} \Rightarrow 1 - \frac{2}{x^2} = \frac{1}{2} \Rightarrow \frac{2}{x^2} = \frac{1}{2}$

$\Rightarrow x^2 = 4 \Rightarrow x = 2$ (as $x > 0$)

$f(2) = \frac{8}{4} - \frac{12}{4} + \frac{4}{4} = 2 - 3 + 1 = 0$

$f'(x) = \frac{1}{2}$ at $(2, 0)$

Q4 **a)** $f(x) = \frac{x^5 - 16x^3}{x + 4} = \frac{x^3(x + 4)(x - 4)}{x + 4} = x^3(x - 4)$

$= x^4 - 4x^3 \Rightarrow f'(x) = 4x^3 - 12x^2$

b) $y = \frac{1}{x}(x-3)(x-4)$

$= \frac{1}{x}(x^2 - 7x + 12)$

$= x - 7 + \frac{12}{x} = x - 7 + 12x^{-1}$

$\Rightarrow \frac{dy}{dx} = 1 - 12x^{-2} = 1 - \frac{12}{x^2}$

c) $y = \sqrt{x}(x^3 - \sqrt{x}) = x^{\frac{1}{2}}(x^3 - x^{\frac{1}{2}}) = x^{\frac{7}{2}} - x$

$\Rightarrow \frac{dy}{dx} = \frac{7}{2}x^{\frac{5}{2}} - 1 = \frac{7}{2}\sqrt{x^5} - 1$

d) $f(x) = \frac{3 - \sqrt{x}}{\sqrt{x}} = \frac{3 - x^{\frac{1}{2}}}{x^{\frac{1}{2}}} = \frac{3}{x^{\frac{1}{2}}} - \frac{x^{\frac{1}{2}}}{x^{\frac{1}{2}}} = 3x^{-\frac{1}{2}} - 1$

$f'(x) = 3(-\frac{1}{2}x^{-\frac{3}{2}}) = -\frac{3}{2}x^{-\frac{3}{2}} = -\frac{3}{2\sqrt{x^3}}$

e) $f(x) = \frac{x + 5\sqrt{x}}{\sqrt{x}} = \frac{x + 5x^{\frac{1}{2}}}{x^{\frac{1}{2}}} = \frac{x}{x^{\frac{1}{2}}} + \frac{5x^{\frac{1}{2}}}{x^{\frac{1}{2}}} = x^{\frac{1}{2}} + 5$

$f'(x) = \frac{1}{2}x^{-\frac{1}{2}} = \frac{1}{2\sqrt{x}}$

f) Factorising the numerator:

$f(x) = \frac{x - 3\sqrt{x} + 2}{\sqrt{x} - 1} = \frac{(\sqrt{x} - 2)(\sqrt{x} - 1)}{\sqrt{x} - 1}$

$= \sqrt{x} - 2 = x^{\frac{1}{2}} - 2$

$f'(x) = \frac{1}{2}x^{-\frac{1}{2}} = \frac{1}{2\sqrt{x}}$

2. Using Differentiation

Exercise 2.1 — Finding tangents and normals

Q1 a) $y = -x^3 + 3x^2 + 4$

$\frac{dy}{dx} = -3x^2 + 6x$

At (3, 4), $\frac{dy}{dx} = -9 \Rightarrow$ tangent has a gradient of -9 and has an equation of the form $y = -9x + c$.

Using the point (3, 4), $4 = -27 + c \Rightarrow c = 31$.

So the tangent's equation is $y = -9x + 31$

$\Rightarrow 9x + y - 31 = 0$

b) $y = 2x^2 - 11x + 5$

$\frac{dy}{dx} = 4x - 11$

At (2, –9), $\frac{dy}{dx} = -3 \Rightarrow$ tangent has a gradient of -3 and has an equation of the form $y = -3x + c$.

Using the point (2, –9), $-9 = -6 + c \Rightarrow c = -3$.

So the tangent's equation is $y = -3x - 3$

$\Rightarrow 3x + y + 3 = 0$

c) $y = x^{-1} + x + 3$

$\frac{dy}{dx} = -x^{-2} + 1$

At $(2, 5\frac{1}{2})$, $\frac{dy}{dx} = \frac{3}{4} \Rightarrow$ tangent has a gradient of $\frac{3}{4}$ and has an equation of the form $y = \frac{3}{4}x + c$.

Using the point $(2, 5\frac{1}{2})$, $5\frac{1}{2} = 1\frac{1}{2} + c \Rightarrow c = 4$.

So the tangent's equation is $y = \frac{3}{4}x + 4$

$\Rightarrow 4y = 3x + 16 \Rightarrow 3x - 4y + 16 = 0$

d) $y = 4x^2 - 3x^{\frac{1}{2}}$

$\frac{dy}{dx} = 8x - 3(\frac{1}{2}x^{-\frac{1}{2}}) = 8x - \frac{3}{2}x^{-\frac{1}{2}}$

At (1, 1), $\frac{dy}{dx} = 6\frac{1}{2} \Rightarrow$ tangent has a gradient of $6\frac{1}{2}$ and has an equation of the form $y = 6\frac{1}{2}x + c$.

Using the point (1, 1), $1 = 6\frac{1}{2} + c \Rightarrow c = -5\frac{1}{2}$.

So the tangent's equation is $y = 6\frac{1}{2}x - 5\frac{1}{2}$

$\Rightarrow 2y = 13x - 11 \Rightarrow 13x - 2y - 11 = 0$

e) $y = 3x^{-1} + 2x^{\frac{1}{2}}$

$\frac{dy}{dx} = 3(-x^{-2}) + 2(\frac{1}{2}x^{-\frac{1}{2}}) = -3x^{-2} + x^{-\frac{1}{2}}$

At $(4, 4\frac{3}{4})$, $\frac{dy}{dx} = \frac{5}{16} \Rightarrow$ tangent has a gradient of $\frac{5}{16}$ and has an equation of the form $y = \frac{5}{16}x + c$.

Using the point $(4, 4\frac{3}{4})$, $4\frac{3}{4} = \frac{5}{4} + c \Rightarrow c = 3\frac{1}{2}$.

So the tangent's equation is $y = \frac{5}{16}x + 3\frac{1}{2}$

$\Rightarrow 16y = 5x + 56 \Rightarrow 5x - 16y + 56 = 0$

f) $y = x^{-1} + 4x^{-2}$

$\frac{dy}{dx} = -x^{-2} + 4(-2x^{-3}) = -x^{-2} - 8x^{-3}$

At $(2, 1\frac{1}{2})$, $\frac{dy}{dx} = -\frac{5}{4}$

$\Rightarrow$ tangent has a gradient of $-\frac{5}{4}$ and has an equation of the form $y = -\frac{5}{4}x + c$.

Using the point $(2, 1\frac{1}{2})$, $1\frac{1}{2} = -\frac{5}{2} + c \Rightarrow c = 4$.

So the tangent's equation is $y = -\frac{5}{4}x + 4$

$\Rightarrow 4y = -5x + 16 \Rightarrow 5x + 4y - 16 = 0$

g) $y = \frac{1}{3}x^2 - 4x^{\frac{1}{2}} - \frac{1}{3}$

$\frac{dy}{dx} = \frac{1}{3}(2x) - 4(\frac{1}{2}x^{-\frac{1}{2}}) = \frac{2}{3}x - 2x^{-\frac{1}{2}}$

At (4, –3), $\frac{dy}{dx} = \frac{5}{3}$

$\Rightarrow$ tangent has a gradient of $\frac{5}{3}$ and has an equation of the form $y = \frac{5}{3}x + c$.

Using the point (4, –3), $-3 = \frac{20}{3} + c \Rightarrow c = -\frac{29}{3}$.

So the tangent's equation is $y = \frac{5}{3}x - \frac{29}{3}$

$\Rightarrow 3y = 5x - 29 \Rightarrow 5x - 3y - 29 = 0$

h) $y = x - 2x^{-1} + 3x^{-2}$

$\frac{dy}{dx} = 1 + 2x^{-2} - 6x^{-3}$

At (–3, –2), $\frac{dy}{dx} = \frac{13}{9}$

$\Rightarrow$ tangent has a gradient of $\frac{13}{9}$ and has an equation of the form $y = \frac{13}{9}x + c$.

Using the point (–3, –2), $-2 = -\frac{13}{3} + c \Rightarrow c = \frac{7}{3}$.

So the tangent's equation is $y = \frac{13}{9}x + \frac{7}{3}$

$\Rightarrow 9y = 13x + 21 \Rightarrow 13x - 9y + 21 = 0$

Q2 a) $y = \frac{2x^5 - 2x^4}{3x^3} = \frac{2}{3}x^2 - \frac{2}{3}x$

Remember — if the denominator is a single term, you can split the equation up into separate terms.

$\frac{dy}{dx} = \frac{2}{3}(2x) - \frac{2}{3} = \frac{4}{3}x - \frac{2}{3}$

At (–2, 4), $\frac{dy}{dx} = -\frac{10}{3}$.

So the normal has a gradient of $\frac{3}{10}$ and an equation of the form $y = \frac{3}{10}x + c$.

Using the point (–2, 4), $4 = -\frac{6}{10} + c \Rightarrow c = \frac{23}{5}$

So the normal's equation is

$y = \frac{3}{10}x + \frac{23}{5} \Rightarrow 10y = 3x + 46$

$\Rightarrow 3x - 10y + 46 = 0$

b) $y = \frac{5x^2 - 2x + 3}{x^2} = 5 - \frac{2}{x} + \frac{3}{x^2}$

$\frac{dy}{dx} = -2(-x^{-2}) + 3(-2x^{-3}) = \frac{2}{x^2} - \frac{6}{x^3}$

At $(2, 4\frac{3}{4})$, $\frac{dy}{dx} = -\frac{1}{4}$.

So the normal has a gradient of 4 and an equation of the form $y = 4x + c$.

Using the point $(2, 4\frac{3}{4})$, $4\frac{3}{4} = 8 + c \Rightarrow c = -\frac{13}{4}$.

So the normal's equation is

$y = 4x - \frac{13}{4} \Rightarrow 4y = 16x - 13 \Rightarrow 16x - 4y - 13 = 0$

c) $y = 3xx^{-\frac{1}{2}} - x^2x^{-\frac{1}{2}} = 3x^{\frac{1}{2}} - x^{\frac{3}{2}}$

$\frac{dy}{dx} = 3(\frac{1}{2}x^{-\frac{1}{2}}) - \frac{3}{2}x^{\frac{1}{2}} = \frac{3}{2\sqrt{x}} - \frac{3}{2}\sqrt{x}$

At (4, –2), $\frac{dy}{dx} = -\frac{9}{4}$.

So the normal has a gradient of $\frac{4}{9}$ and an equation of the form $y = \frac{4}{9}x + c$.

Using the point (4, –2), $-2 = \frac{16}{9} + c \Rightarrow c = -\frac{34}{9}$.

So the normal's equation is

$y = \frac{4}{9}x - \frac{34}{9} \Rightarrow 9y = 4x - 34$

$\Rightarrow 4x - 9y - 34 = 0$

d) $y = \frac{1}{x} - \frac{3}{x^2} - \frac{4}{x^3} + \frac{7}{4} = x^{-1} - 3x^{-2} - 4x^{-3} + \frac{7}{4}$

$\frac{dy}{dx} = -x^{-2} - 3(-2x^{-3}) - 4(-3x^{-4})$

$= -x^{-2} + 6x^{-3} + 12x^{-4}$

At (–2, 1), $\frac{dy}{dx} = -\frac{1}{4}$.

So the normal has a gradient of 4 and an equation of the form $y = 4x + c$.

Using the point (–2, 1), $1 = -8 + c \Rightarrow c = 9$.

So the normal's equation is $y = 4x + 9$.

e) $y = \frac{x^3 - 5x^2 - 4x}{x^{\frac{3}{2}}} = x^{\frac{3}{2}} - 5x^{\frac{1}{2}} - 4x^{-\frac{1}{2}}$

$\frac{dy}{dx} = \frac{3}{2}x^{\frac{1}{2}} - 5(\frac{1}{2}x^{-\frac{1}{2}}) - 4(-\frac{1}{2}x^{-\frac{3}{2}})$

$= \frac{3}{2}\sqrt{x} - \frac{5}{2\sqrt{x}} + \frac{2}{x\sqrt{x}}$

At (4, –4), $\frac{dy}{dx} = 2$

So the normal has a gradient of $-\frac{1}{2}$ and an equation of the form $y = -\frac{1}{2}x + c$.

Using the point (4, –4), $-4 = -2 + c \Rightarrow c = -2$.

So the normal's equation is $y = -\frac{1}{2}x - 2$

$\Rightarrow 2y = -x - 4 \Rightarrow x + 2y + 4 = 0$

Q3 a) Putting $x = -2$ into the equation gives:

$y = \frac{x^3 + x^2 + x + 5}{x^2}$

$= \frac{(-2)^3 + (-2)^2 + (-2) + 5}{(-2)^2}$

$= \frac{-8 + 4 - 2 + 5}{4} = -\frac{1}{4}$

so $(2, -\frac{1}{4})$ is a point on the curve.

b) $y = \frac{x^3 + x^2 + x + 5}{x^2} = x + 1 + \frac{1}{x} + \frac{5}{x^2}$

$\frac{dy}{dx} = 1 + 0 + (-x^{-2}) + 5(-2x^{-3})$

$= 1 - \frac{1}{x^2} - \frac{10}{x^3}$

At $(-2, -\frac{1}{4})$, $\frac{dy}{dx} = 2$. So the gradient of the tangent at this point is 2 and it has equation $y = 2x + c$. Using the point $(-2, -\frac{1}{4})$, $-\frac{1}{4} = -4 + c \Rightarrow c = \frac{15}{4}$.

So the equation of the tangent is $y = 2x + \frac{15}{4}$

$\Rightarrow 4y = 8x + 15 \Rightarrow 8x - 4y + 15 = 0$

c) The gradient of the normal at $(-2, -\frac{1}{4})$ is $-\frac{1}{2}$ and so it has equation $y = -\frac{1}{2}x + c$.

Using the point $(-2, -\frac{1}{4})$, $-\frac{1}{4} = 1 + c \Rightarrow c = -\frac{5}{4}$.

So the equation of the normal is $y = -\frac{1}{2}x - \frac{5}{4}$

$\Rightarrow 4y = -2x - 5 \Rightarrow 2x + 4y + 5 = 0$

Exercise 2.2 — Finding second order derivatives

Q1 a) $\frac{dy}{dx} = 12x$ and $\frac{d^2y}{dx^2} = 12$

b) $\frac{dy}{dx} = 6x^5$ and $\frac{d^2y}{dx^2} = 30x^4$

c) $y = x^{-1}$, so $\frac{dy}{dx} = -x^{-2} = -\frac{1}{x^2}$

and $\frac{d^2y}{dx^2} = 2x^{-3} = \frac{2}{x^3}$

d) $y = x^{\frac{1}{2}}$, so $\frac{dy}{dx} = \frac{1}{2}x^{-\frac{1}{2}} = \frac{1}{2\sqrt{x}}$

and $\frac{d^2y}{dx^2} = -\frac{1}{4}x^{-\frac{3}{2}} = -\frac{1}{4(\sqrt{x})^3}$

e) $y = x^{-2}$, so $\frac{dy}{dx} = -2x^{-3} = -\frac{2}{x^3}$

and $\frac{d^2y}{dx^2} = 6x^{-4} = \frac{6}{x^4}$

f) $y = x\sqrt{x} = x^1x^{\frac{1}{2}} = x^{1+\frac{1}{2}} = x^{\frac{3}{2}}$,

so $\frac{dy}{dx} = \frac{3}{2}x^{\frac{1}{2}} = \frac{3}{2}\sqrt{x}$ and $\frac{d^2y}{dx^2} = \frac{3}{4}x^{-\frac{1}{2}} = \frac{3}{4\sqrt{x}}$

Q2 a) $f(x) = -5x^3 - 3x - 1$
$f'(x) = -15x^2 - 3$
$f''(x) = -30x$

b) $f(x) = 3x^{\frac{1}{2}} + xx^{\frac{1}{2}} = 3x^{\frac{1}{2}} + x^{\frac{3}{2}}$
$f'(x) = \frac{3}{2}x^{-\frac{1}{2}} + \frac{3}{2}x^{\frac{1}{2}} = \frac{3}{2\sqrt{x}} + \frac{3}{2}\sqrt{x}$
$f''(x) = \frac{3}{2}(-\frac{1}{2}x^{-\frac{3}{2}}) + \frac{3}{2}(\frac{1}{2}x^{-\frac{1}{2}}) = -\frac{3}{4}x^{-\frac{3}{2}} + \frac{3}{4}x^{-\frac{1}{2}}$
$= -\frac{3}{4(\sqrt{x})^3} + \frac{3}{4\sqrt{x}} \left(= -\frac{3}{4x\sqrt{x}} + \frac{3}{4\sqrt{x}}\right)$

c) $f(x) = \frac{1}{x}(3x^4 - 2x^3) = 3x^3 - 2x^2$
$f'(x) = 9x^2 - 4x$
$f''(x) = 18x - 4$

d) $f(x) = \frac{x^2 - xx^{\frac{1}{2}} + 7x}{x^{\frac{1}{2}}} = x^2x^{-\frac{1}{2}} - xx^{\frac{1}{2}}x^{-\frac{1}{2}} + 7xx^{-\frac{1}{2}}$
$= x^{\frac{3}{2}} - x + 7x^{\frac{1}{2}}$
$f'(x) = \frac{3}{2}x^{\frac{1}{2}} - 1 + 7(\frac{1}{2}x^{-\frac{1}{2}}) = \frac{3}{2}\sqrt{x} - 1 + \frac{7}{2\sqrt{x}}$
$f''(x) = \frac{3}{2}(\frac{1}{2}x^{-\frac{1}{2}}) + \frac{7}{2}(-\frac{1}{2}x^{-\frac{3}{2}}) = \frac{3}{4\sqrt{x}} - \frac{7}{4(\sqrt{x})^3}$

Q3 a) $f'(x) = 36x^3 - 20x$ and $f''(x) = 108x^2 - 20$
So $f''(-1) = 108 - 20 = 88$

b) $y = xx^{\frac{1}{2}} - x^{-1} = x^{\frac{3}{2}} - x^{-1}$ so $\frac{dy}{dx} = \frac{3}{2}x^{\frac{1}{2}} + x^{-2}$
so $\frac{d^2y}{dx^2} = \frac{3}{2}(\frac{1}{2}x^{-\frac{1}{2}}) - 2x^{-3} = \frac{3}{4\sqrt{x}} - \frac{2}{x^3}$
so at $x = 4$, $\frac{d^2y}{dx^2} = \frac{11}{32}$

c) $f(x) = \frac{9x^2 + 3x}{3\sqrt{x}} = 3x^{\frac{3}{2}} + x^{\frac{1}{2}}$ so
$f'(x) = 3(\frac{3}{2}x^{\frac{1}{2}}) + \frac{1}{2}x^{-\frac{1}{2}} = \frac{9}{2}\sqrt{x} + \frac{1}{2\sqrt{x}}$ and so
$f''(x) = \frac{9}{2}(\frac{1}{2}x^{-\frac{1}{2}}) + \frac{1}{2}(-\frac{1}{2}x^{-\frac{3}{2}}) = \frac{9}{4\sqrt{x}} - \frac{1}{4(\sqrt{x})^3}$
$f''(1) = 2$

d) $y = (x^{-2} + x^{-1})(5 - x)$
$= 5x^{-2} - x^{-2}x + 5x^{-1} - xx^{-1}$
$= 5x^{-2} - x^{-1} + 5x^{-1} - 1 = 5x^{-2} + 4x^{-1} - 1$
$\frac{dy}{dx} = 5(-2x^{-3}) + 4(-x^{-2}) = -10x^{-3} - 4x^{-2}$
so $\frac{d^2y}{dx^2} = 30x^{-4} + 8x^{-3} = \frac{30}{x^4} + \frac{8}{x^3}$
At $x = -3$, $\frac{d^2y}{dx^2} = \frac{2}{27}$

Q4 a) $x = 4t^{\frac{3}{2}} \Rightarrow \frac{dx}{dt} = 6t^{\frac{1}{2}} = 6\sqrt{t}$ ms^{-1}

b) (i) $t = 1 \Rightarrow \frac{dx}{dt} = 6\sqrt{1} = 6$ ms^{-1}

(ii) $t = 9 \Rightarrow \frac{dx}{dt} = 6\sqrt{9} = 18$ ms^{-1}

c) $\frac{d^2x}{dt^2} = 3t^{-\frac{1}{2}} = \frac{3}{\sqrt{t}}$ ms^{-2}

d) $t = 4 \Rightarrow \frac{d^2x}{dt^2} = \frac{3}{\sqrt{4}} = 1.5$ ms^{-2}

e) If $\frac{d^2x}{dt^2} = 0.5 \Rightarrow \frac{3}{\sqrt{t}} = 0.5 \Rightarrow 6 = \sqrt{t}$
$\Rightarrow t = 36$ s

$t = 36 \Rightarrow \frac{dx}{dt} = 6\sqrt{36} = 36$ ms^{-1}

Exercise 2.3 — Stationary points

Q1 a) $\frac{dy}{dx} = 4x - 3$
So $\frac{dy}{dx} = 0 \Rightarrow 4x - 3 = 0 \Rightarrow x = \frac{3}{4}$
$x = \frac{3}{4} \Rightarrow y = 2\left(\frac{9}{16}\right) - 3\left(\frac{3}{4}\right) + 5 = \frac{31}{8}$
So the curve has one stationary point, at $\left(\frac{3}{4}, \frac{31}{8}\right)$.

b) $\frac{dy}{dx} = 3x^2 - 27$
So $\frac{dy}{dx} = 0 \Rightarrow 3x^2 = 27 \Rightarrow x^2 = 9 \Rightarrow x = \pm 3$
$x = -3 \Rightarrow y = -27 + 81 + 4 = 58$
$x = 3 \Rightarrow y = 27 - 81 + 4 = -50$
So the curve has stationary points at $(-3, 58)$ and $(3, -50)$.

c) $y = -3x^2 + 5x + 2 \Rightarrow \frac{dy}{dx} = -6x + 5$
So $\frac{dy}{dx} = 0 \Rightarrow 6x = 5 \Rightarrow x = \frac{5}{6}$
$x = \frac{5}{6} \Rightarrow y = -3\left(\frac{25}{36}\right) + 5\left(\frac{5}{6}\right) + 2 = \frac{49}{12}$
So the curve has one stationary point, at $\left(\frac{5}{6}, \frac{49}{12}\right)$.

d) $y = 4x^{-2} + x \Rightarrow \frac{dy}{dx} = -8x^{-3} + 1 = -\frac{8}{x^3} + 1$
So $\frac{dy}{dx} = 0 \Rightarrow \frac{8}{x^3} = 1 \Rightarrow x^3 = 8 \Rightarrow x = 2$
$x = 2 \Rightarrow y = \frac{4}{4} + 2 = 3$
So the curve has one stationary point, at $(2, 3)$.

e) $y = x^{-2} + 54x + 3 \Rightarrow \frac{dy}{dx} = -2x^{-3} + 54 = -\frac{2}{x^3} + 54$
So $\frac{dy}{dx} = 0 \Rightarrow \frac{2}{x^3} = 54 \Rightarrow x^3 = \frac{1}{27} \Rightarrow x = \frac{1}{3}$
$x = \frac{1}{3} \Rightarrow y = 9 + 18 + 3 = 30$
So the curve has one stationary point, at $\left(\frac{1}{3}, 30\right)$.

f) $y = 8x^{-1} + 18x - 9 \Rightarrow \frac{dy}{dx} = -8x^{-2} + 18 = -\frac{8}{x^2} + 18$
So $\frac{dy}{dx} = 0 \Rightarrow 18 = \frac{8}{x^2} \Rightarrow x^2 = \frac{4}{9} \Rightarrow x = \pm\frac{2}{3}$
$x = -\frac{2}{3} \Rightarrow y = 8\left(-\frac{3}{2}\right) + 18\left(-\frac{2}{3}\right) - 9$
$= -12 - 12 - 9 = -33$
$x = \frac{2}{3} \Rightarrow y = 8\left(\frac{3}{2}\right) + 18\left(\frac{2}{3}\right) - 9$
$= 12 + 12 - 9 = 15$

So the curve has stationary points at $\left(-\frac{2}{3}, -33\right)$ and $\left(\frac{2}{3}, 15\right)$.

Q2 $y = \frac{3}{2}x^{\frac{1}{3}} - \frac{1}{4}x^2 + 4 \Rightarrow \frac{dy}{dx} = \frac{1}{2}x^{-\frac{2}{3}} - \frac{1}{2}x = \frac{1}{2\sqrt[3]{x^2}} - \frac{x}{2}$

So $\frac{dy}{dx} = 0 \Rightarrow \frac{1}{2\sqrt[3]{x^2}} = \frac{x}{2} \Rightarrow x^{\frac{5}{3}} = 1 \Rightarrow x = 1$

$x = 1 \Rightarrow y = \frac{3}{2} - \frac{1}{4} + 4 = \frac{21}{4}$

So the curve has one stationary point, at $\left(1, \frac{21}{4}\right)$.

Q3 $y = \frac{1}{3}x^2 + 27x^{-2} + 6 \Rightarrow \frac{dy}{dx} = \frac{2}{3}x - 54x^{-3} = \frac{2}{3}x - \frac{54}{x^3}$

So $x = -3 \Rightarrow \frac{dy}{dx} = -\frac{6}{3} - \frac{54}{-27} = -2 + 2 = 0$

and $x = 3 \Rightarrow \frac{dy}{dx} = \frac{6}{3} - \frac{54}{27} = 2 - 2 = 0$

So the graph has stationary points at $x = -3$ and $x = 3$.

$x = -3 \Rightarrow y = 3 + 3 + 6 = 12$
$x = 3 \Rightarrow y = 3 + 3 + 6 = 12$
So (–3, 12) and (3, 12) are stationary points of the graph.

Q4 $y = 3x - 21x^{-1} - 1 \Rightarrow \frac{dy}{dx} = 3 + 21x^{-2} = 3 + \frac{21}{x^2}$

So $\frac{dy}{dx} = 0 \Rightarrow \frac{21}{x^2} = -3 \Rightarrow x^2 = -7$

$x^2 \geq 0$, so $\frac{dy}{dx}$ is never equal to zero and the graph has no stationary points.

Exercise 2.4 — Maximum and minimum points

Q1 a) $y = 5 - 7x + x^2 \Rightarrow \frac{dy}{dx} = -7 + 2x \Rightarrow \frac{d^2y}{dx^2} = 2$

When $\frac{dy}{dx} = 0, -7 + 2x = 0 \Rightarrow x = \frac{7}{2}$

When $x = \frac{7}{2}, y = 5 - \frac{49}{2} + \frac{49}{4} = -\frac{29}{4}$

So there's one stationary point, at $\left(\frac{7}{2}, -\frac{29}{4}\right)$.

$\frac{d^2y}{dx^2} = 2$, so at $\left(\frac{7}{2}, -\frac{29}{4}\right)$, $\frac{d^2y}{dx^2} = 2$

$\frac{d^2y}{dx^2} > 0$, so $\left(\frac{7}{2}, -\frac{29}{4}\right)$ is a minimum.

$\frac{d^2y}{dx^2} = 2$, so it's positive for all values of x.

b) $f(x) = (x + 2)(3x - 4) = 3x^2 + 2x - 8$
$\Rightarrow f'(x) = 6x + 2 \Rightarrow f''(x) = 6$

When $f'(x) = 0, 6x + 2 = 0 \Rightarrow x = -\frac{1}{3}$

When $x = -\frac{1}{3}, y = 3\left(\frac{1}{9}\right) + 2\left(-\frac{1}{3}\right) - 8 = -\frac{25}{3}$

So there's one stationary point, at $\left(-\frac{1}{3}, -\frac{25}{3}\right)$.

$f''(x) = 6$, so $f''\left(-\frac{1}{3}\right) = 6$.

$f''(x) > 0$, so $\left(-\frac{1}{3}, -\frac{25}{3}\right)$ is a minimum.

c) $f(x) = \frac{27}{x^3} + x = 27x^{-3} + x$
$\Rightarrow f'(x) = -81x^{-4} + 1 \Rightarrow f''(x) = 324x^{-5}$

When $f'(x) = 0, x^4 = 81 \Rightarrow x = \pm 3$.

When $x = 3, f(x) = \frac{27}{27} + 3 = 4$.

When $x = -3, f(x) = -\frac{27}{27} - 3 = -4$.

So there are stationary points at (3, 4) and (–3, –4).

$f''(x) = 324x^{-5}$, so $f''(3) = \frac{4}{3}$

$f''(x) > 0$, so (3, 4) is a minimum.

$f''(-3) = -\frac{4}{3}$, so (–3, –4) is a maximum.

d) $y = 15x^{\frac{1}{3}} - 5x - 10 \Rightarrow \frac{dy}{dx} = 5x^{-\frac{2}{3}} - 5 = \frac{5}{x^{\frac{2}{3}}} - 5$

$\Rightarrow \frac{d^2y}{dx^2} = -\frac{10}{3}x^{-\frac{5}{3}} = -\frac{10}{3x^{\frac{5}{3}}}$

When $\frac{dy}{dx} = 0, \frac{5}{x^{\frac{2}{3}}} = 5 \Rightarrow \sqrt[3]{x^2} = 1 \Rightarrow x = \pm 1$

When $x = 1, y = 15 - 5 - 10 = 0$
When $x = -1, y = -15 + 5 - 10 = -20$
So there are stationary points at (1, 0) and (–1, –20).

$\frac{d^2y}{dx^2} = -\frac{10}{3x^{\frac{5}{3}}}$, so at (1, 0), $\frac{d^2y}{dx^2} = -\frac{10}{3}$

$\frac{d^2y}{dx^2} < 0$, so (1, 0) is a maximum.

At (–1, –20), $\frac{d^2y}{dx^2} = \frac{10}{3}$, so (–1, –20) is a minimum.

e) $f(x) = 2x^{-1} - x^2 \Rightarrow f'(x) = -2x^{-2} - 2x$
$\Rightarrow f''(x) = 4x^{-3} - 2$
When $f'(x) = 0, -2x^{-2} - 2x = 0 \Rightarrow x = -1$
When $x = -1, y = 2(-1)^{-1} - (-1)^2 = -3$
So there's one stationary point, at (–1, –3).
$f''(x) = 4x^{-3} - 2$, so $f''(-1) = 4(-1)^{-3} - 2 = -6$.
$f''(x) < 0$, so (–1, –3) is a maximum.

f) $f(x) = 2x^{\frac{1}{2}} - 3x \Rightarrow f'(x) = x^{-\frac{1}{2}} - 3$
$\Rightarrow f''(x) = -\frac{1}{2}x^{-\frac{3}{2}}$

When $f'(x) = 0, x^{-\frac{1}{2}} - 3 = 0 \Rightarrow x = \frac{1}{9}$.

When $x = \frac{1}{9}, y = 2\left(\frac{1}{3}\right) - 3\left(\frac{1}{9}\right) = \frac{1}{3}$.

So there's one stationary point, at $\left(\frac{1}{9}, \frac{1}{3}\right)$.

$f''(x) = -\frac{1}{2}x^{-\frac{3}{2}}$, so $f''\left(\frac{1}{9}\right) = -\frac{1}{2}\left(\frac{1}{9}\right)^{-\frac{3}{2}} = -13.5$

$f''(x) < 0$, so $\left(\frac{1}{9}, \frac{1}{3}\right)$ is a maximum.

Q2 a) $V = r^2 + \frac{2000}{r} = r^2 + 2000r^{-1} \Rightarrow \frac{dV}{dr} = 2r - \frac{2000}{r^2}$

When $\frac{dV}{dr} = 0, 2r = \frac{2000}{r^2} \Rightarrow r^3 = 1000 \Rightarrow r = 10$

b) $\frac{d^2V}{dr^2} = 2 + \frac{4000}{r^3}$. When $r = 10$,

$\frac{d^2V}{dr^2} = 2 + 4 = 6$, so it's a minimum.

Q3 $f(x) = x^2 + ax + b + cx^{-1}$
$\Rightarrow f'(x) = 2x + a - cx^{-2} = 2x + a - \frac{c}{x^2}$
$\Rightarrow f''(x) = 2 + 2cx^{-3} = 2 + \frac{2c}{x^3}$
$f''(x) = 10$ at the point (1, 3)
$\Rightarrow f''(1) = 2 + 2c = 10 \Rightarrow c = 4$
(1, 3) is a stationary point, so $f'(1) = 0$
$\Rightarrow 2 + a - c = 0 \Rightarrow 2 + a - 4 = 0 \Rightarrow a = 2$
(1, 3) is a point on the curve, so $f(1) = 3$
$\Rightarrow 1 + a + b + c = 3 \Rightarrow 1 + 2 + b + 4 = 3 \Rightarrow b = -4$
So $f(x) = x^2 + 2x - 4 + 4x^{-1}$

Exercise 2.5 — Increasing and decreasing functions

Q1 a) $y = x^2 - 6x + 1 \Rightarrow \frac{dy}{dx} = 2x - 6$

y is decreasing when $\frac{dy}{dx} < 0$

$\Rightarrow 2x - 6 < 0 \Rightarrow 2x < 6 \Rightarrow x < 3$

b) $y = 9x + x^{-1} - 2 \Rightarrow \frac{dy}{dx} = 9 - x^{-2} = 9 - \frac{1}{x^2}$

$\frac{dy}{dx} < 0 \Rightarrow 9 - \frac{1}{x^2} < 0 \Rightarrow 9x^2 - 1 < 0$

$\Rightarrow (3x + 1)(3x - 1) < 0$

The graph of $y = (3x + 1)(3x - 1)$ is below the x-axis for $-\frac{1}{3} < x < \frac{1}{3}$.

$y = 9x + \frac{1}{x} - 2$ is undefined for $x = 0$, so the function is decreasing for $-\frac{1}{3} < x < 0$ and $0 < x < \frac{1}{3}$.

c) $y = 4x^{\frac{1}{2}} - x \Rightarrow \frac{dy}{dx} = 2x^{-\frac{1}{2}} - 1 = \frac{2}{\sqrt{x}} - 1$

$\frac{dy}{dx} < 0 \Rightarrow \frac{2}{\sqrt{x}} - 1 < 0 \Rightarrow \frac{2}{\sqrt{x}} < 1 \Rightarrow \frac{4}{x} < 1$

$\Rightarrow x > 4$

Q2 a) $y = x^2 + \sqrt{x} = x^2 + x^{\frac{1}{2}} \Rightarrow \frac{dy}{dx} = 2x + \frac{1}{2\sqrt{x}}$

$\frac{dy}{dx} > 0$ for all $x > 0$, so the function is increasing for all $x > 0$.

b) $y = 4x^2 + \frac{1}{x} = 4x^2 + x^{-1} \Rightarrow \frac{dy}{dx} = 8x - \frac{1}{x^2}$

The function is increasing when $\frac{dy}{dx} > 0$

$\Rightarrow 8x - \frac{1}{x^2} > 0 \Rightarrow x^3 > \frac{1}{8} \Rightarrow x > \frac{1}{2}$

Q3 a) $f(x) = \frac{1}{2}x^2 + 7x + 36x^{-1}$

$\Rightarrow f'(x) = x + 7 - 36x^{-2} = x + 7 - \frac{36}{x^2}$

$f'(x) = 0 \Rightarrow x + 7 - \frac{36}{x^2} = 0 \Rightarrow x^3 + 7x^2 - 36 = 0$

Factorise $x^3 + 7x^2 - 36$:
We know there's a turning point at $(-6, -30)$, so $f'(-6) = 0$, so $(x + 6)$ is a factor of $x^3 + 7x^2 - 36$.

Using the equating coefficients method:
$x^3 + 7x^2 - 36 = (x + 6)(px^2 + qx + r)$
$\Rightarrow x^3 + 7x^2 - 36 = px^3 + (6p + q)x^2 + (6q + r)x + 6r$

Equating coefficients of x^3 gives $p = 1$.
Equating constant terms gives $r = -6$.
Equating coefficients of x gives $q = 1$.

So $x^3 + 7x^2 - 36 = (x + 6)(x^2 + x - 6)$
$= (x + 6)(x + 3)(x - 2)$

So the other turning points are at $x = -3$ and $x = 2$.

$f(-3) = \frac{9}{2} - 21 - 12 = -28.5$
$f(2) = 2 + 14 + 18 = 34$

The other turning points are $(-3, -28.5)$ and $(2, 34)$.

b) $f''(x) = 1 + 72x^{-3} = 1 + \frac{72}{x^3}$

$f''(-6) = 1 - \frac{1}{3} = \frac{2}{3} \Rightarrow (-6, -30)$ is a minimum

$f''(-3) = 1 - \frac{8}{3} = -\frac{5}{3} \Rightarrow (-3, -28.5)$ is a maximum

$f''(2) = 1 + 9 = 10 \Rightarrow (2, 34)$ is a minimum

c) The function $f(x)$ is increasing between the minimum at $(-6, -30)$ and the maximum at $(-3, -28.5)$, and also after it has passed the minimum at $(2, 34)$.
So $f(x)$ is increasing when $-6 < x < -3$ and when $x > 2$.

You could also have solved the inequality $f'(x) > 0$ to find when $f(x)$ is increasing, but the question starts 'Hence find the range...' — the 'hence' means you're supposed to use the answer from the previous part of the question here.

Review Exercise — Chapter 5

Q1 a) $\frac{dy}{dx} = 9x^2 - 5$ **b)** $\frac{dy}{dx} = 4x^3 + \frac{1}{2\sqrt{x}}$

c) $\frac{dy}{dx} = -\frac{14}{x^3} + \frac{3}{2\sqrt{x^3}} + 36x^2$

Q2 The tangent and normal must go through (16, 6).
Differentiate to find $\frac{dy}{dx} = \frac{3}{2}\sqrt{x} - 3$, so gradient at (16, 6) is 3.
Therefore tangent can be written $y = 3x + c_T$; putting $x = 16$ and $y = 6$ gives $6 = 3 \times 16 + c_T$, so $c_T = -42$, and the equation of the tangent is $y = 3x - 42$.

The gradient of the normal must be $-\frac{1}{3}$, so the equation of the normal is $y = -\frac{1}{3}x + c_N$
Substituting in the coordinates of the point (16, 6) gives $6 = -\frac{16}{3} + c_N \Rightarrow c_N = \frac{34}{3}$; so the normal is $y = -\frac{1}{3}x + \frac{34}{3} = \frac{1}{3}(34 - x) \Rightarrow x + 3y - 34 = 0$.

Q3 The tangent must go through (1, 7).
Differentiate to find $\frac{dy}{dx} = 3x^2 - \frac{4}{x^2} + \frac{1}{\sqrt{x}}$, so gradient at (1, 7) is 0.
Therefore tangent can be written $y = c$; putting $x = 1$ and $y = 7$ gives $7 = c$, so $c = 7$, and the equation of the tangent is $y = 7$.

Q4 On the first curve, when $x = 4$,

$y = \frac{(4)^3}{3} - 2(4)^2 - 4(4) + \frac{86}{3}$

$= \frac{64}{3} - 32 - 16 + \frac{86}{3} = \frac{150}{3} - 48 = 2$

On the second curve, when $x = 4$, $y = \sqrt{4} = 2$.
For both curves, when $x = 4$, $y = 2$, so they meet at (4, 2).

Differentiating the first curve gives $\frac{dy}{dx} = x^2 - 4x - 4$, which at $x = 4$ is equal to -4.

Differentiating the other curve gives $\frac{dy}{dx} = \frac{1}{2\sqrt{x}}$, and so the gradient at (4, 2) is $\frac{1}{4}$. If you multiply these two gradients together you get –1, so the two curves are perpendicular at (4, 2).

Q5 a) C and L intersect when
$-\frac{10}{x} - 9 = 2x - 21 \Rightarrow 2x - 12 + \frac{10}{x} = 0$
$\Rightarrow 2x^2 - 12x + 10 = 0 \Rightarrow x^2 - 6x + 5 = 0$
$\Rightarrow (x-1)(x-5) = 0 \Rightarrow x = 1$ or $x = 5$
$x = 1 \Rightarrow y = 2 - 21 = -19$
$x = 5 \Rightarrow y = 10 - 21 = -11$
So the points are $A(1, -19)$ and $B(5, -11)$.

b) $y = -10x^{-1} - 9 \Rightarrow \frac{dy}{dx} = 10x^{-2} = \frac{10}{x^2}$
At point A, $\frac{dy}{dx} = 10$. At point B, $\frac{dy}{dx} = \frac{2}{5}$.

c) At A, the gradient of the normal is –0.1.
So the equation of the normal can be written $y = -0.1x + c_A$
Let $x = 1$ and $y = -19$:
$-19 = -0.1 + c_A$, so $c_A = -18.9$
So the normal at A is given by $y = -0.1x - 18.9$
$\Rightarrow x + 10y + 189 = 0$
At B, the gradient of the normal is –2.5.
So the equation of the normal can be written $y = -2.5x + c_B$
Let $x = 5$ and $y = -11$: $-11 = -12.5 + c_B$,
so $c_B = 1.5$
So the normal at A is given by $y = -2.5x + 1.5$
$\Rightarrow 5x + 2y - 3 = 0$

Q6 $\frac{dy}{dx} = \frac{3}{2}x^{\frac{1}{2}}$. At $x = 16$, $\frac{dy}{dx} = \frac{3}{2}\sqrt{16} = \frac{12}{2} = 6$.
For the tangent, the gradient is 6 and it has equation $y = 6x + c$.
At $x = 16$, $y = 65$, so $65 = 96 + c \Rightarrow c = -31$.
So the equation of the tangent is $y = 6x - 31$.
For the normal, the gradient is $-\frac{1}{6}$ and it has equation
$y = -\frac{1}{6}x + c$.
At $x = 16$, $y = 65$ so $65 = -\frac{16}{6} + c \Rightarrow c = \frac{203}{3}$.
So the equation of the normal is $y = -\frac{1}{6}x + \frac{203}{3}$
$\Rightarrow 6y = -x + 406 \Rightarrow x + 6y - 406 = 0$.

Q7 $f(x) = x^2 + 2x^{-1}$
$\Rightarrow f'(x) = 2x - 2x^{-2} = 2x - \frac{2}{x^2}$
$\Rightarrow f''(x) = 2 + 4x^{-3} = 2 + \frac{4}{x^3}$
So $f''(x) + 2f'(x) - 4f(x) = 2 + \frac{4}{x^3} + 2\left(2x - \frac{2}{x^2}\right) - 4\left(x^2 + \frac{2}{x}\right)$
$= -4x^2 + 4x + 2 - \frac{8}{x} - \frac{4}{x^2} + \frac{4}{x^3}$

Q8 a) $x = 3t^{\frac{1}{2}} + \frac{1}{2}t^2 \Rightarrow \frac{dx}{dt} = \frac{3}{2}t^{-\frac{1}{2}} + t = \frac{3}{2\sqrt{t}} + t$
$\Rightarrow \frac{d^2x}{dt^2} = -\frac{3}{4}t^{-\frac{3}{2}} + 1 = -\frac{3}{4\sqrt{t^3}} + 1$

b) $t = 9 \Rightarrow \frac{dx}{dt} = \frac{3}{6} + 9 = 9.5$ ms^{-1}

c) $t = 25 \Rightarrow \frac{d^2x}{dt^2} = -\frac{3}{500} + 1 = 0.994$ ms^{-2}

Don't forget to include the correct units when you calculate speed and acceleration.

Q9 $f(x) = \frac{1}{2}x - 3 - 16x^{-2} \Rightarrow f'(x) = \frac{1}{2} + 32x^{-3} = \frac{1}{2} + \frac{32}{x^3}$
$f'(x) = 0 \Rightarrow \frac{1}{2} + \frac{32}{x^3} = 0 \Rightarrow x^3 = -64 \Rightarrow x = -4$
$f(-4) = -2 - 3 - 1 = -6$
So the stationary point is at (–4, –6).

Q10 a) $y = x^3 + \frac{3}{x} = x^3 + 3x^{-1}$
$\frac{dy}{dx} = 3x^2 - 3x^{-2} = 3x^2 - \frac{3}{x^2}$.
When $\frac{dy}{dx} = 0$, $3x^2 - \frac{3}{x^2} = 0 \Rightarrow x^4 = 1 \Rightarrow x = \pm 1$.
When $x = 1$, $y = 1^3 + \frac{3}{1} = 4$.
When $x = -1$, $y = (-1)^3 + \frac{3}{-1} = -4$.
So the stationary points are (1, 4) and (–1, –4).

b) $\frac{d^2y}{dx^2} = 6x + 6x^{-3}$.
At (1, 4), $\frac{d^2y}{dx^2} = 6 + 6 = 12$, so it's a minimum.
At (–1, –4), $\frac{d^2y}{dx^2} = -6 + (-6) = -12$, so it's a maximum.

Q11 $y = 75x^{\frac{1}{3}} - \frac{1}{4}x + 20$
$\Rightarrow \frac{dy}{dx} = 25x^{-\frac{2}{3}} - \frac{1}{4} = \frac{25}{\sqrt[3]{x^2}} - \frac{1}{4}$
$\Rightarrow \frac{d^2y}{dx^2} = -\frac{50}{3}x^{-\frac{5}{3}} = -\frac{50}{3\sqrt[3]{x^5}}$
$\frac{dy}{dx} = 0 \Rightarrow \frac{1}{4} = \frac{25}{\sqrt[3]{x^2}} \Rightarrow \sqrt[3]{x^2} = 100$
$\Rightarrow x^2 = 1\,000\,000 \Rightarrow x = \pm 1000$
When $x = -1000$:
$y = -750 + 250 + 20 = -480$
$\frac{d^2y}{dx^2} = -\frac{50}{3(-10)^5} = \frac{50}{300\,000} = \frac{1}{6000}$
When $x = 1000$:
$y = 750 - 250 + 20 = 520$
$\frac{d^2y}{dx^2} = -\frac{50}{3(10)^5} = -\frac{50}{300\,000} = -\frac{1}{6000}$
So the stationary points are a minimum at (–1000, –480) and a maximum at (1000, 520).

Q12 a) $y = \frac{1}{x^2} = x^{-2}$, $\frac{dy}{dx} = -2x^{-3} = -\frac{2}{x^3}$
The function is increasing when $\frac{dy}{dx} > 0$
$\Rightarrow -\frac{2}{x^3} > 0 \Rightarrow x < 0$
The function is decreasing when $\frac{dy}{dx} < 0$
$\Rightarrow -\frac{2}{x^3} < 0 \Rightarrow x > 0$.

b) $y = 6\left(\frac{1}{x^2} - \frac{1}{x} - 6\right) = 6x^{-2} - 6x^{-1} - 36$

$\Rightarrow \frac{dy}{dx} = -12x^{-3} + 6x^{-2} = -\frac{12}{x^3} + \frac{6}{x^2}$

The function is increasing when $\frac{dy}{dx} > 0$

$\Rightarrow -\frac{12}{x^3} + \frac{6}{x^2} > 0 \Rightarrow \frac{6}{x^2} > \frac{12}{x^3} \Rightarrow 6x > 12$

$\Rightarrow x > 2$

The function is decreasing when $\frac{dy}{dx} < 0$

$\Rightarrow -\frac{12}{x^3} + \frac{6}{x^2} < 0 \Rightarrow 6x < 12 \Rightarrow 0 < x < 2$

$x > 0$ was given in the question — this needs to be included in the answer. And because $x > 0$, x^3 is always positive, so it's OK to multiply both sides of the inequality by x^3 without worrying about negative values flipping the inequality sign.

Q13 a) There are 6 rectangular sides of the box which make up 3 identical pairs of sides. The total surface area is $A = 2(xy + 2x^2 + 2xy) = 4x^2 + 6xy$. To get rid of y, rearrange the formula for the volume of the box: $2x^2y = 200 \Rightarrow y = \frac{100}{x^2}$

so $A = 4x^2 + 6x\left(\frac{100}{x^2}\right) = 4x^2 + \frac{600}{x}$.

b) $\frac{dA}{dx} = 8x - \frac{600}{x^2} = 0 \Rightarrow x^3 = 75$

$\Rightarrow x = 4.217... = 4.22$ cm (3 s.f.)

Check this is a minimum by differentiating again:

$\frac{d^2A}{dx^2} = 8 + \frac{1200}{x^3}$. When $x = 4.217...$, $\frac{d^2A}{dx^2} = 24$, so it's a minimum.

c) Surface area $= 4(4.217...)^2 + \frac{600}{4.21...}$

$= 213$ cm^2 (3 s.f.).

Exam-Style Questions — Chapter 5

Q1 a) $f(x) = 2\sqrt{x} + \frac{1}{x} = 2x^{\frac{1}{2}} + x^{-1}$

Differentiate to get :

$f'(x) = 2\left(\frac{1}{2}x^{-\frac{1}{2}}\right) - x^{-2} = \frac{1}{\sqrt{x}} - \frac{1}{x^2}$

[3 marks available — 1 mark for rewriting f(x) as powers of x and 1 mark for each correct term of f′(x).]

b) $g(x) = \frac{(x+2)(x+1)}{\sqrt{x}} = \frac{x^2 + 3x + 2}{x^{\frac{1}{2}}}$

$= x^{\frac{3}{2}} + 3x^{\frac{1}{2}} + 2x^{-\frac{1}{2}}$

Differentiate to get:

$g'(x) = \frac{3}{2}x^{\frac{1}{2}} + 3\left(\frac{1}{2}x^{-\frac{1}{2}}\right) + 2\left(-\frac{1}{2}x^{-\frac{3}{2}}\right)$

$= \frac{3}{2}\sqrt{x} + \frac{3}{2\sqrt{x}} - \frac{1}{(\sqrt{x})^3}$

[4 marks available — 1 mark for rewriting g(x) as powers of x and 1 mark for each correct term of g′(x).]

Q2 a) Rewrite all the terms as powers of x:

$y = x^7 + \frac{2}{x^3} = x^7 + 2x^{-3}$ ***[1 mark]***

and then differentiate each term:

$\frac{dy}{dx} = 7x^6 + (-3)2x^{-4}$

$= 7x^6 - \frac{6}{x^4}$ ***[1 mark]***

b) This is a second-order derivative — just differentiate the answer for part a):

$\frac{d^2y}{dx^2} = \frac{d}{dx}(7x^6 - 6x^{-4})$ ***[1 mark]***

$= 7(6x^5) - 6(-4x^{-5})$

$= 42x^5 + \frac{24}{x^5}$ ***[1 mark]***

Q3 Rewrite the expression in powers of x, so it becomes $x^{-\frac{1}{2}} + x^{-1}$ ***[1 mark]***. Then differentiate to get $\frac{dy}{dx} = -\frac{1}{2}x^{-\frac{3}{2}} - x^{-2}$ ***[1 mark for each correct term]***.

Putting $x = 4$ into the derivative gives:

$-\frac{1}{2}4^{-\frac{3}{2}} - 4^{-2} = -\frac{1}{2}(\sqrt{4})^{-3} - \frac{1}{4^2}$

$= -\frac{1}{2}\cdot\frac{1}{2^3} - \frac{1}{16} = -\frac{1}{2}\cdot\frac{1}{8} - \frac{1}{16}$

$= -\frac{1}{16} - \frac{1}{16} = -\frac{1}{8}$

[1 method mark, 1 answer mark]

Q4 a) Rewrite the expression in powers of x:

$\frac{x^2 + 3x^{\frac{3}{2}}}{x^{\frac{1}{2}}}$ ***[1 mark]***

Then divide the top of the fraction by the bottom:

$\frac{x^2}{x^{\frac{1}{2}}} + \frac{3x^{\frac{3}{2}}}{x^{\frac{1}{2}}} = x^{\frac{3}{2}} + 3x$

So $p = \frac{3}{2}$ ***[1 mark]*** and $q = 1$ ***[1 mark]***.

b) Use the answer to part a) to rewrite the equation:

$y = 3x^3 + 5 + x^{\frac{3}{2}} + 3x$ ***[1 mark]***.

Then differentiate each term to give:

$\frac{dy}{dx} = 9x^2 + \frac{3}{2}x^{\frac{1}{2}} + 3$

[1 mark for each correct term].

Q5 a) Rewrite all the terms as powers of x:

$f(x) = \frac{1}{4}x^4 + 7 + 3x^{-\frac{3}{2}}$ ***[1 mark]***

and then differentiate each term:

$f'(x) = \frac{1}{4}(4x^3) + 3\left(-\frac{3}{2}x^{-\frac{5}{2}}\right)$

$= x^3 - \frac{9}{2(\sqrt{x})^5}$ ***[1 mark for each term]***

b) This is a second-order derivative — just differentiate the answer for part a):

$\frac{d^2y}{dx^2} = \frac{d}{dx}\left(x^3 - \frac{9}{2(\sqrt{x})^5}\right)$ ***[1 mark]***

$= \frac{d}{dx}\left(x^3 - \frac{9}{2}x^{-\frac{5}{2}}\right)$

$= 3x^2 - \frac{9}{2}(-\frac{5}{2}x^{-\frac{7}{2}})$

$= 3x^2 + \frac{45}{4(\sqrt{x})^7}$ ***[1 mark for each term]***

Q6 a) Find the value of x that gives the minimum value of y — the stationary point of the curve $y = 2\sqrt{x} + \frac{27}{x}$.

Differentiate, and then solve $\frac{dy}{dx} = 0$:

$\frac{dy}{dx} = \frac{1}{\sqrt{x}} - \frac{27}{x^2}$ ***[1 mark for each term]***

$\frac{1}{\sqrt{x}} - \frac{27}{x^2} = 0$ ***[1 mark]*** $\Rightarrow \frac{1}{\sqrt{x}} = \frac{27}{x^2}$

$\frac{x^2}{x^{\frac{1}{2}}} = 27 \Rightarrow x^{\frac{3}{2}} = 27$ ***[1 mark]***

$x = \sqrt[3]{27^2} = 9$ ***[1 mark]***. So 9 miles an hour gives the minimum rate of coal consumption.

b) $\frac{d^2y}{dx^2} = \frac{54}{x^3} - \frac{1}{2\sqrt{x^3}}$ ***[1 mark]***

At the stationary point $x = 9$,

so $\frac{54}{9^3} - \frac{1}{2\sqrt{9^3}} = 0.05555...$ which is positive,

therefore $x = 9$ does give a minimum value for y ***[1 mark]***.

c) $y = 2\sqrt{9} + \frac{27}{9} = 9$ ***[1 mark]***.

So the minimum rate of coal consumption is 9 units of coal per hour.

Q7 a) Surface area of the tank = sum of the areas of all 5 sides = $x^2 + x^2 + xy + xy + xy = 2x^2 + 3xy$ ***[1 mark]***.

Volume of the tank = length × width × height $= x^2y = 40\,000$ cm³ ***[1 mark]*** $\Rightarrow y = \frac{40\,000}{x^2}$

Putting this into formula for the area,

$A = 2x^2 + 3xy = 2x^2 + 3x(\frac{40\,000}{x^2})$ ***[1 mark]***

$= 2x^2 + \frac{120\,000}{x}$ ***[1 mark]***

b) To find stationary points, first find $\frac{dA}{dx}$ ***[1 mark]***.

$\frac{dA}{dx} = 4x - \frac{120\,000}{x^2}$ ***[1 mark]***

Then find the value of x where $\frac{dA}{dx} = 0$

$\frac{dA}{dx} = 4x - \frac{120\,000}{x^2} = 0$ ***[1 mark]*** $\Rightarrow x^3 = 30\,000$

$\Rightarrow x = 31.07... = 31.1$ cm (3 s.f.) ***[1 mark]***

To check if it's a minimum, find $\frac{d^2A}{dx^2}$

$\frac{d^2A}{dx^2} = 4 + \frac{240\,000}{x^3} = 12$ ***[1 mark]***.

Second derivative is positive, so it's a minimum ***[1 mark]***

c) Put the value of x found in part b) into the formula for the area given in part a)

$A = 2(31.07...)^2 + \frac{120\,000}{31.07...}$ ***[1 mark]*** $= 5792.936...$

$= 5790$ cm² (3 s.f.) ***[1 mark]***

Q8 a) $y = 4x + 3 + x^{-1}$, so $\frac{dy}{dx} = 4 - x^{-2} = 4 - \frac{1}{x^2}$ ***[1 mark]***

At the stationary points, $\frac{dy}{dx} = 0 \Rightarrow 4 = \frac{1}{x^2}$

$\Rightarrow x^2 = \frac{1}{4} \Rightarrow x = \pm\frac{1}{2}$ ***[1 mark]***

$x = \frac{1}{2} \Rightarrow y = 2 + 3 + 2 = 7$

$x = -\frac{1}{2} \Rightarrow y = -2 + 3 - 2 = -1$

So the stationary points are $\left(-\frac{1}{2}, -1\right)$ ***[1 mark]*** and $\left(\frac{1}{2}, 7\right)$ ***[1 mark]***.

b) $\frac{d^2y}{dx^2} = \frac{2}{x^3}$ ***[1 mark]***

$x = \frac{1}{2} \Rightarrow \frac{d^2y}{dx^2} = 16 > 0$,

so $\left(\frac{1}{2}, 7\right)$ is a minimum ***[1 mark]***

$x = -\frac{1}{2} \Rightarrow \frac{d^2y}{dx^2} = -16 < 0$,

so $\left(-\frac{1}{2}, -1\right)$ is a maximum ***[1 mark]***.

Chapter 6: Integration

1. Integration

Exercise 1.1 — Integrating x^n

Q1 a) $y = \int x^{10}\,dx = \frac{x^{11}}{11} + C$

b) $y = \int 7x^2\,dx = 7\left(\frac{x^3}{3}\right) + C = \frac{7x^3}{3} + C$

c) $y = \int 11\,dx = 11x + C$

d) $y = \int x^{-2}\,dx = \frac{x^{-1}}{-1} + C = -\frac{1}{x} + C$

e) $y = \int 4x^{-4}\,dx = 4\left(\frac{x^{-3}}{-3}\right) + C = \frac{4x^{-3}}{-3} + C = -\frac{4}{3x^3} + C$

f) $y = \int -6x^{-5}\,dx = -6\left(\frac{x^{-4}}{-4}\right) + C$

$= \frac{3x^{-4}}{2} + C = \frac{3}{2x^4} + C$

g) $y = \int x^{\frac{1}{2}}\,dx = \frac{x^{\frac{3}{2}}}{\left(\frac{3}{2}\right)} + C = \frac{2x^{\frac{3}{2}}}{3} + C$

Don't forget that dividing by a fraction is the same as multiplying by the flipped fraction.

h) $y = \int x^{\frac{1}{3}}\,dx = \frac{x^{\frac{4}{3}}}{\left(\frac{4}{3}\right)} + C = \frac{3x^{\frac{4}{3}}}{4} + C$

Q2 a) $\int x^{\frac{2}{3}}\,dx = \frac{x^{\frac{5}{3}}}{\left(\frac{5}{3}\right)} + C = \frac{3x^{\frac{5}{3}}}{5} + C$

b) $\int 7x^{\frac{4}{3}}\,dx = 7\left(\frac{x^{\frac{7}{3}}}{\left(\frac{7}{3}\right)}\right) + C = 3x^{\frac{7}{3}} + C$

c) $\int x^{-\frac{1}{2}}\,dx = \frac{x^{\frac{1}{2}}}{\left(\frac{1}{2}\right)} + C = 2x^{\frac{1}{2}} + C$

d) $\int 2x^{-\frac{1}{3}}\,dx = 2\frac{x^{\frac{2}{3}}}{\left(\frac{2}{3}\right)} + C = 3x^{\frac{2}{3}} + C$

e) $\int 14x^{0.4}\,dx = 14\left(\frac{x^{1.4}}{1.4}\right) + C = 10x^{1.4} + C$

f) $\int -1.2x^{-0.6}\,dx = -1.2\left(\frac{x^{0.4}}{0.4}\right) + C = -3x^{0.4} + C$

g) $\int -2x^{-\frac{5}{4}}\,dx = -2\frac{x^{-\frac{1}{4}}}{\left(-\frac{1}{4}\right)} + C = 8x^{-\frac{1}{4}} + C$

h) $\int -\frac{3}{2}x^{-\frac{1}{2}}\,dx = -\frac{3}{2}\left(\frac{x^{\frac{1}{2}}}{\left(\frac{1}{2}\right)}\right) + C = -3x^{\frac{1}{2}} + C$

i) $\int -\frac{4}{3}x^{-\frac{4}{3}}\,dx = -\frac{4}{3}\left(\frac{x^{-\frac{1}{3}}}{\left(-\frac{1}{3}\right)}\right) + C = 4x^{-\frac{1}{3}} + C$

Exercise 1.2 — Integrating functions

Q1 a) $f(x) = \int (5x + 3x^{-4})\,dx$

$= 5\left(\frac{x^2}{2}\right) + 3\left(\frac{x^{-3}}{-3}\right) + C$

$= \frac{5x^2}{2} - x^{-3} + C$

b) $f(x) = \int 3x(3 - x)\,dx$

$= \int (9x - 3x^2)\,dx$

$= 9\left(\frac{x^2}{2}\right) - 3\left(\frac{x^3}{3}\right) + C = \frac{9x^2}{2} - x^3 + C$

c) $f(x) = \int (x + 4)^2\,dx$

$= \int (x^2 + 8x + 16)\,dx$

$= \frac{x^3}{3} + 8\left(\frac{x^2}{2}\right) + 16x + C$

$= \frac{x^3}{3} + 4x^2 + 16x + C$

d) $f(x) = \int x\left(6x + \frac{4}{x^4}\right)dx$

$= \int \left(6x^2 + \frac{4}{x^3}\right)dx$

$= \int (6x^2 + 4x^{-3})\,dx$

$= 6\left(\frac{x^3}{3}\right) + 4\left(\frac{x^{-2}}{-2}\right) + C$

$= 2x^3 - 2x^{-2} + C = 2x^3 - \frac{2}{x^2} + C$

e) $f(x) = \int \left(x + \frac{2}{x}\right)^2 dx$

$= \int \left(x^2 + 4 + \frac{4}{x^2}\right)dx$

$= \int (x^2 + 4 + 4x^{-2})\,dx$

$= \frac{x^3}{3} + 4\left(\frac{x^1}{1}\right) + 4\left(\frac{x^{-1}}{-1}\right) + C$

$= \frac{x^3}{3} + 4x - \frac{4}{x} + C$

f) $f(x) = \int x\left(3x^{\frac{1}{2}} - \frac{2}{x^{\frac{4}{3}}}\right)dx$

$= \int \left(3x^{\frac{3}{2}} - \frac{2}{x^{\frac{1}{3}}}\right)dx$

$= \int (3x^{\frac{3}{2}} - 2x^{-\frac{1}{3}})\,dx$

$= 3\left(\frac{x^{\frac{5}{2}}}{\left(\frac{5}{2}\right)}\right) - 2\frac{x^{\frac{2}{3}}}{\left(\frac{2}{3}\right)} + C$

$= \frac{6}{5}x^{\frac{5}{2}} - 3x^{\frac{2}{3}} + C$

g) $f(x) = \int \left(6\sqrt{x} - \frac{1}{x^2}\right)dx$

$= \int (6x^{\frac{1}{2}} - x^{-2})\,dx$

$= 6\left(\frac{x^{\frac{3}{2}}}{\left(\frac{3}{2}\right)}\right) - \frac{x^{-1}}{-1} + C$

$= \frac{12}{3}x^{\frac{3}{2}} + \frac{1}{x} + C = 4x^{\frac{3}{2}} + \frac{1}{x} + C$

h) $f(x) = \int \left(\frac{2}{\sqrt{x}} - 7x^2\sqrt{x}\right) dx$
$= \int (2x^{-\frac{1}{2}} - 7x^2x^{\frac{1}{2}})\, dx$
$= \int (2x^{-\frac{1}{2}} - 7x^{\frac{5}{2}})\, dx$
$= 2\left(\frac{x^{\frac{1}{2}}}{(\frac{1}{2})}\right) - 7\frac{x^{\frac{7}{2}}}{(\frac{7}{2})} + C$
$= 4x^{\frac{1}{2}} - 2x^{\frac{7}{2}} + C = 4\sqrt{x} - 2(\sqrt{x})^7 + C$

i) $f(x) = \int \left(5(\sqrt{x})^3 - \frac{3x}{\sqrt{x}}\right) dx$
$= \int (5(x^{\frac{1}{2}})^3 - 3xx^{-\frac{1}{2}})\, dx$
$= \int 5x^{\frac{3}{2}} - 3x^{\frac{1}{2}}\, dx$
$= 5\left(\frac{x^{\frac{5}{2}}}{(\frac{5}{2})}\right) - 3\left(\frac{x^{\frac{3}{2}}}{(\frac{3}{2})}\right) + C$
$= 2x^{\frac{5}{2}} - 2x^{\frac{3}{2}} + C = 2(\sqrt{x})^5 - 2(\sqrt{x})^3 + C$

Q2 a) $\int (0.55x^{0.1} - 3x^{-1.5}x)\, dx$
$= \int (0.55x^{0.1} - 3x^{-0.5})\, dx$
$= 0.55\left(\frac{x^{1.1}}{1.1}\right) - 3\left(\frac{x^{0.5}}{0.5}\right) + C$
$= 0.5x^{1.1} - 6x^{0.5} + C$

b) $\int \left(8x^3 - \frac{2}{\sqrt{x}} + \frac{5}{x^2}\right) dx = \int \left(8x^3 - 2x^{-\frac{1}{2}} + 5x^{-2}\right) dx$
$= 8\left(\frac{x^4}{4}\right) - 2\left(\frac{x^{\frac{1}{2}}}{(\frac{1}{2})}\right) + 5\left(\frac{x^{-1}}{-1}\right) + C$
$= 2x^4 - 4x^{\frac{1}{2}} - 5x^{-1} + C$
$= 2x^4 - 4\sqrt{x} - \frac{5}{x} + C$

c) $\int \left((\sqrt{x})^5 + \frac{1}{2\sqrt{x}}\right) dx = \int \left((x^{\frac{1}{2}})^5 + \frac{1}{2}x^{-\frac{1}{2}}\right) dx$
$= \int x^{\frac{5}{2}} + \frac{1}{2}x^{-\frac{1}{2}}\, dx$
$= \left(\frac{x^{\frac{7}{2}}}{(\frac{7}{2})}\right) + \frac{1}{2}\left(\frac{x^{\frac{1}{2}}}{(\frac{1}{2})}\right) + C$
$= \frac{2x^{\frac{7}{2}}}{7} + x^{\frac{1}{2}} + C$
$= \frac{2}{7}(\sqrt{x})^7 + \sqrt{x} + C$

d) $\int \left(\sqrt{x}\left(7x^2 - 1 - \frac{2}{x}\right)\right) dx$
$= \int \left(x^{\frac{1}{2}}(7x^2 - 1 - 2x^{-1})\right) dx$
$= \int (7x^{\frac{5}{2}} - x^{\frac{1}{2}} - 2x^{-\frac{1}{2}})\, dx$
$= 7\left(\frac{x^{\frac{7}{2}}}{(\frac{7}{2})}\right) - \left(\frac{x^{\frac{3}{2}}}{(\frac{3}{2})}\right) - 2\left(\frac{x^{\frac{1}{2}}}{(\frac{1}{2})}\right) + C$
$= 2x^{\frac{7}{2}} - \frac{2}{3}x^{\frac{3}{2}} - 4x^{\frac{1}{2}} + C$
$= 2(\sqrt{x})^7 - \frac{2}{3}(\sqrt{x})^3 - 4\sqrt{x} + C$

e) $\int (3x - 5\sqrt{x})^2\, dx = \int (9x^2 - 30x\sqrt{x} + 25x)\, dx$
$= \int \left(9x^2 - 30x^{\frac{3}{2}} + 25x\right) dx$
$= 9\left(\frac{x^3}{3}\right) - 30\left(\frac{2}{5}x^{\frac{5}{2}}\right) + 25\left(\frac{1}{2}x^2\right) + C$
$= 3x^3 - 12(\sqrt{x})^5 + \frac{25}{2}x^2 + C$

f) $\int \left(\frac{2x^3 - \sqrt{x}}{x}\right) dx = \int \left(\frac{2x^3}{x} - \frac{\sqrt{x}}{x}\right) dx$
$= \int (2x^2 - x^{-\frac{1}{2}})\, dx$
$= 2\left(\frac{x^3}{3}\right) - \left(\frac{x^{\frac{1}{2}}}{(\frac{1}{2})}\right) + C$
$= \frac{2}{3}x^3 - 2\sqrt{x} + C$

g) $\int \left(\frac{10x^2 + 3x + 4}{\sqrt{x}}\right) dx = \int \left(\frac{10x^2}{\sqrt{x}} + \frac{3x}{\sqrt{x}} + \frac{4}{\sqrt{x}}\right) dx$
$= \int \left(\frac{10x^2}{x^{\frac{1}{2}}} + \frac{3x}{x^{\frac{1}{2}}} + \frac{4}{x^{\frac{1}{2}}}\right) dx$
$= \int \left(10x^{\frac{3}{2}} + 3x^{\frac{1}{2}} + 4x^{-\frac{1}{2}}\right) dx$
$= 10\left(\frac{x^{\frac{5}{2}}}{(\frac{5}{2})}\right) + 3\left(\frac{x^{\frac{3}{2}}}{(\frac{3}{2})}\right) + 4\left(\frac{x^{\frac{1}{2}}}{(\frac{1}{2})}\right) + C$
$= 4x^{\frac{5}{2}} + 2x^{\frac{3}{2}} + 8x^{\frac{1}{2}} + C$
$= 4(\sqrt{x})^5 + 2(\sqrt{x})^3 + 8\sqrt{x} + C$

h) $\int \left(\frac{(5x - 3)^2}{\sqrt{x}}\right) dx = \int \left(\frac{(25x^2 - 30x + 9)}{\sqrt{x}}\right) dx$
$= \int \left(\frac{25x^2}{\sqrt{x}} - \frac{30x}{\sqrt{x}} + \frac{9}{\sqrt{x}}\right) dx$
$= \int \left(25x^{\frac{3}{2}} - 30x^{\frac{1}{2}} + 9x^{-\frac{1}{2}}\right) dx$
$= 25\left(\frac{x^{\frac{5}{2}}}{(\frac{5}{2})}\right) - 30\left(\frac{x^{\frac{3}{2}}}{(\frac{3}{2})}\right) + 9\left(\frac{x^{\frac{1}{2}}}{(\frac{1}{2})}\right) + C$
$= 10x^{\frac{5}{2}} - 20x^{\frac{3}{2}} + 18x^{\frac{1}{2}} + C$
$= 10(\sqrt{x})^5 - 20(\sqrt{x})^3 + 18\sqrt{x} + C$

i) $\int (\sqrt{x}(3 - \sqrt{x})^2)\, dx = \int (\sqrt{x}(9 - 6\sqrt{x} + x))\, dx$
$= \int (9\sqrt{x} - 6\sqrt{x}\sqrt{x} + x\sqrt{x})\, dx$
$= \int \left(9x^{\frac{1}{2}} - 6x + x^{\frac{3}{2}}\right) dx$
$= 9\left(\frac{x^{\frac{3}{2}}}{(\frac{3}{2})}\right) - 6\left(\frac{x^2}{2}\right) + \left(\frac{x^{\frac{5}{2}}}{(\frac{5}{2})}\right) + C$
$= 6x^{\frac{3}{2}} - 3x^2 + \frac{2}{5}x^{\frac{5}{2}} + C$
$= 6(\sqrt{x})^3 - 3x^2 + \frac{2}{5}(\sqrt{x})^5 + C$

j) $\int (x^{\frac{1}{2}} + 1)(x^{-\frac{1}{2}} - 3)\, dx = \int (1 - 3x^{\frac{1}{2}} + x^{-\frac{1}{2}} - 3)\, dx$
$= \int (x^{-\frac{1}{2}} - 3x^{\frac{1}{2}} - 2)\, dx$
$= \left(\frac{x^{\frac{1}{2}}}{(\frac{1}{2})}\right) - 3\left(\frac{x^{\frac{3}{2}}}{(\frac{3}{2})}\right) - 2\left(\frac{x^1}{1}\right) + C$
$= 2x^{\frac{1}{2}} - 2x^{\frac{3}{2}} - 2x + C$

Q3 $y = \int\left(1.5x^2 - \frac{4}{x^3}\right)dx$

$= \int(1.5x^2 - 4x^{-3})\,dx$

$= 1.5\left(\frac{x^3}{3}\right) - 4\left(\frac{x^{-2}}{-2}\right) + C$

$= \frac{x^3}{2} + \frac{2}{x^2} + C$

Q4 $f(x) = \int\left(\frac{4}{3(x^{\frac{1}{3}})^4} + 5x^{\frac{3}{2}}\right)dx$

$= \int\left(\frac{4}{3x^{\frac{4}{3}}} + 5x^{\frac{3}{2}}\right)dx$

$= \int\left(\frac{4}{3}x^{-\frac{4}{3}} + 5x^{\frac{3}{2}}\right)dx$

$= \frac{4}{3}\left(\frac{x^{-\frac{1}{3}}}{(-\frac{1}{3})}\right) + 5\frac{x^{\frac{5}{2}}}{(\frac{5}{2})} + C$

$= -4x^{-\frac{1}{3}} + 2x^{\frac{5}{2}} + C$

$= -\frac{4}{\sqrt[3]{x}} + 2(\sqrt{x})^5 + C$

Q5 $\int\left(\sqrt{x}\left(\frac{3x^3}{2} - \frac{1}{x^2}\right)\right)dx = \int\left(\frac{3x^3\sqrt{x}}{2} - \frac{\sqrt{x}}{x^2}\right)dx$

$= \int\left(\frac{3}{2}x^{\frac{7}{2}} - x^{-\frac{3}{2}}\right)dx$

$= \frac{3}{2}\left(\frac{x^{\frac{9}{2}}}{(\frac{9}{2})}\right) - \left(\frac{x^{-\frac{1}{2}}}{(-\frac{1}{2})}\right) + C$

$= \frac{x^{\frac{9}{2}}}{3} + 2x^{-\frac{1}{2}} + C$

$= \frac{(\sqrt{x})^9}{3} + \frac{2}{\sqrt{x}} + C$

Q6 $\int\left(\frac{(\sqrt{x}+3)(\sqrt{x}-1)}{\sqrt{x}}\right)dx = \int\left(\frac{x + 2\sqrt{x} - 3}{\sqrt{x}}\right)dx$

$= \int\left(\frac{x}{\sqrt{x}} + \frac{2\sqrt{x}}{\sqrt{x}} - \frac{3}{\sqrt{x}}\right)dx$

$= \int\left(x^{\frac{1}{2}} + 2 - 3x^{-\frac{1}{2}}\right)dx$

$= \left(\frac{x^{\frac{3}{2}}}{(\frac{3}{2})}\right) + 2\left(\frac{x^1}{1}\right) - 3\left(\frac{x^{\frac{1}{2}}}{(\frac{1}{2})}\right) + C$

$= \frac{2}{3}x^{\frac{3}{2}} + 2x - 6x^{\frac{1}{2}} + C$

$= \frac{2}{3}(\sqrt{x})^3 + 2x - 6\sqrt{x} + C$

Q7 $\int\left(\sqrt{x}\left(\sqrt{x} - \frac{1}{\sqrt{x}}\right)^2\right)dx = \int\left(\sqrt{x}\left(x - 2 + \frac{1}{x}\right)\right)dx$

$= \int\left(x\sqrt{x} - 2\sqrt{x} + \frac{\sqrt{x}}{x}\right)dx$

$= \int\left(x^{\frac{3}{2}} - 2x^{\frac{1}{2}} + x^{-\frac{1}{2}}\right)dx$

$= \left(\frac{x^{\frac{5}{2}}}{(\frac{5}{2})}\right) - 2\left(\frac{x^{\frac{3}{2}}}{(\frac{3}{2})}\right) + \left(\frac{x^{\frac{1}{2}}}{(\frac{1}{2})}\right) + C$

$= \frac{2}{5}x^{\frac{5}{2}} - \frac{4}{3}x^{\frac{3}{2}} + 2x^{\frac{1}{2}} + C$

$= \frac{2}{5}(\sqrt{x})^5 - \frac{4}{3}(\sqrt{x})^3 + 2\sqrt{x} + C$

Exercise 1.3 — Integrating to find equations of curves

Q1 a) $f(x) = \int 12x^2\,dx$

$= 12\left(\frac{x^3}{3}\right) + C = 4x^3 + C$

At the point (–1, –1), $x = -1$ and $f(x) = -1$,
so $-1 = 4(-1)^3 + C = -4 + C \Rightarrow C = 3$
$\Rightarrow f(x) = 4x^3 + 3$

b) $f(x) = \int(9x^2 + 5x - 2)\,dx$

$= 9\left(\frac{x^3}{3}\right) + 5\left(\frac{x^2}{2}\right) - 2x + C$

$= 3x^3 + \frac{5}{2}x^2 - 2x + C$

At the point (2, 25), $x = 2$ and $f(x) = 25$,
so $25 = 3(2)^3 + \frac{5}{2}(2)^2 - 2(2) + C$
$\Rightarrow 25 = 24 + 10 - 4 + C = 30 + C \Rightarrow C = -5$
$\Rightarrow f(x) = 3x^3 + \frac{5}{2}x^2 - 2x - 5$

c) $f(x) = \int\left(\frac{5}{x^2} + 2x\right)dx$

$= \int(5x^{-2} + 2x)\,dx$

$= 5\left(\frac{x^{-1}}{-1}\right) + 2\left(\frac{x^2}{2}\right) + C$

$= -\frac{5}{x} + x^2 + C$

At the point (5, 4), $x = 5$ and $f(x) = 4$,
so $4 = -\frac{5}{5} + 5^2 + C = 24 + C \Rightarrow C = -20$
$\Rightarrow f(x) = -\frac{5}{x} + x^2 - 20$

d) $f(x) = \int 2x(1 - x)\,dx$

$= \int(-2x + 2x^2)\,dx$

$= -2\left(\frac{x^2}{2}\right) + 2\left(\frac{x^3}{3}\right) + C$

$= \frac{2}{3}x^3 - x^2 + C$

At the point (6, 104), $x = 6$ and $f(x) = 104$,
so $104 = \frac{2}{3}(6)^3 - (6)^2 + C = 144 - 36 + C = 108 + C$
$\Rightarrow C = -4 \Rightarrow f(x) = \frac{2}{3}x^3 - x^2 - 4$

e) $f(x) = \int x\left(x + \frac{3}{x^3}\right)dx$

$= \int\left(x^2 + \frac{3}{x^2}\right)dx$

$= \frac{x^3}{3} + 3\left(\frac{x^{-1}}{-1}\right) + C = \frac{x^3}{3} - \frac{3}{x} + C$

At the point (–3, 5), $x = -3$ and $f(x) = 5$,
so $5 = \frac{(-3)^3}{3} - \frac{3}{-3} + C = -8 + C \Rightarrow C = 13$
$\Rightarrow f(x) = \frac{x^3}{3} - \frac{3}{x} + 13$

f) $f(x) = \int \frac{9x^3 + 2x^{-2}}{x} dx$

$= \int \left(\frac{9x^3}{x} + \frac{2x^{-2}}{x}\right) dx = \int (9x^2 + 2x^{-3}) dx$

$= 9\left(\frac{x^3}{3}\right) + 2\left(\frac{x^{-2}}{-2}\right) + C$

$= 3x^3 - \frac{1}{x^2} + C$

At the point (–1, 2), $x = -1$ and $f(x) = 2$,

so $2 = 3(-1)^3 - \frac{1}{(-1)^2} + C = -4 + C \Rightarrow C = 6$

$\Rightarrow f(x) = 3x^3 - \frac{1}{x^2} + 6$

Q2 $y = f(x) = \int \left(\frac{3}{\sqrt{x}} + 2x\right) dx$

$= \int \left(3x^{-\frac{1}{2}} + 2x\right) dx$

$= 3\left(\frac{x^{\frac{1}{2}}}{(\frac{1}{2})}\right) + 2\left(\frac{x^2}{2}\right) + C = 6x^{\frac{1}{2}} + x^2 + C$

$= 6\sqrt{x} + x^2 + C$

At the point (4, 9) $x = 4$ and $y = 9$, so

$9 = 6\sqrt{4} + 4^2 + C = 28 + C$

So C = –19 and $y = 6\sqrt{x} + x^2 - 19$

Q3 $y = \int \left(3\sqrt{x} + \frac{1}{x^2}\right) dx$

$= \int \left(3x^{\frac{1}{2}} + x^{-2}\right) dx$

$= 3\left(\frac{x^{\frac{3}{2}}}{(\frac{3}{2})}\right) + \left(\frac{x^{-1}}{-1}\right) + C$

$= 2x^{\frac{3}{2}} - \frac{1}{x} + C = 2(\sqrt{x})^3 - \frac{1}{x} + C$

At the point (1, 7), $x = 1$ and $y = 7$, so

$7 = 2((\sqrt{1})^3) - \frac{1}{1} + C = 1 + C$

So C = 6 and $y = 2(\sqrt{x})^3 - \frac{1}{x} + 6$

Q4 $y = \int (\sqrt{t} - 3)^2 dt$

$= \int (t - 6\sqrt{t} + 9) dt$

$= \int \left(t - 6t^{\frac{1}{2}} + 9\right) dt$

$= \frac{t^2}{2} - 6\left(\frac{t^{\frac{3}{2}}}{(\frac{3}{2})}\right) + 9\left(\frac{t^1}{1}\right) + C$

$= \frac{t^2}{2} - 4t^{\frac{3}{2}} + 9t + C = \frac{t^2}{2} - 4(\sqrt{t})^3 + 9t + C$

When $t = 4$, $y = 9$ so

$9 = \frac{4^2}{2} - 4(\sqrt{4})^3 + 9(4) + C = 12 + C$

So C = –3 and $y = \frac{t^2}{2} - 4(\sqrt{t})^3 + 9t - 3$

Q5 $f(x) = \int (\sqrt{x}(5x - 1)) dx = \int (5x\sqrt{x} - \sqrt{x}) dx$

$= \int (5x^{\frac{3}{2}} - x^{\frac{1}{2}}) dx$

$= 5\left(\frac{x^{\frac{5}{2}}}{(\frac{5}{2})}\right) - \left(\frac{x^{\frac{3}{2}}}{(\frac{3}{2})}\right)$

$= 2x^{\frac{5}{2}} - \frac{2}{3}x^{\frac{3}{2}} + C = 2(\sqrt{x})^5 - \frac{2}{3}(\sqrt{x})^3 + C$

When $x = 1$, $f(x) = \frac{1}{3}$ so

$\frac{1}{3} = 2(\sqrt{1})^5 - \frac{2}{3}(\sqrt{1})^3 + C = \frac{4}{3} + C$

So C = –1 and $f(x) = 2(\sqrt{x})^5 - \frac{2}{3}(\sqrt{x})^3 - 1$

Q6 $y = f(x) = \int \left(x^2 + \frac{2}{x^{\frac{3}{2}}}\right) dx$

$= \int \left(x^2 + 2x^{-\frac{3}{2}}\right) dx$

$= \frac{x^3}{3} + 2\left(\frac{x^{-\frac{1}{2}}}{(-\frac{1}{2})}\right) + C = \frac{x^3}{3} - \frac{4}{\sqrt{x}} + C$

When $x = 1$, $y = -\frac{5}{3}$ so

$-\frac{5}{3} = \frac{1^3}{3} - \frac{4}{\sqrt{1}} + C = -\frac{11}{3} + C$

So C = 2 and $y = \frac{x^3}{3} - \frac{4}{\sqrt{x}} + 2$

Exercise 1.4 — Definite integrals

Q1 a) $\int_2^5 24x^3 dx = [6x^4]_2^5 = 6(5^4) - 6(2^4)$

$= 3750 - 96 = 3654$

b) $\int_{-2}^{-1} (2x^2 + 3x - 1) dx = \left[\frac{2}{3}x^3 + \frac{3}{2}x^2 - x\right]_{-2}^{-1}$

$= \left(\frac{2}{3}(-1) + \frac{3}{2}(1) - (-1)\right) - \left(\frac{2}{3}(-8) + \frac{3}{2}(4) - (-2)\right)$

$= \left(-\frac{2}{3} + \frac{3}{2} + 1\right) - \left(-\frac{16}{3} + 6 + 2\right)$

$= \frac{11}{6} - \frac{8}{3} = -\frac{5}{6}$

Remember, if you have to find the ***area*** *represented by an integral, you have to make sure it's positive, but the* ***value*** *of an integral (which is what was asked for here) can be positive or negative.*

c) $\int_1^4 x^{-2} dx = \left[\frac{x^{-1}}{-1}\right]_1^4 = \left[-\frac{1}{x}\right]_1^4$

$= \left(-\frac{1}{4}\right) - \left(-\frac{1}{1}\right) = \frac{3}{4}$

d) $\int_2^7 (x^{-3} + x) dx = \left[\frac{x^{-2}}{-2} + \frac{x^2}{2}\right]_2^7 = \left[-\frac{1}{2x^2} + \frac{x^2}{2}\right]_2^7$

$= \left(-\frac{1}{2(7^2)} + \frac{7^2}{2}\right) - \left(-\frac{1}{2(2^2)} + \frac{2^2}{2}\right)$

$= \left(-\frac{1}{98} + \frac{49}{2}\right) - \left(-\frac{1}{8} + \frac{4}{2}\right) = \frac{8865}{392}$

e) $\int_3^4 (6x^{-4} + x^{-2}) dx = \left[\frac{6x^{-3}}{-3} + \frac{x^{-1}}{-1}\right]_3^4$

$= \left[-\frac{2}{x^3} - \frac{1}{x}\right]_3^4 = \left(-\frac{2}{4^3} - \frac{1}{4}\right) - \left(-\frac{2}{3^3} - \frac{1}{3}\right)$

$= -\frac{2}{64} - \frac{1}{4} + \frac{2}{27} + \frac{1}{3} = \frac{109}{864}$

f) $\int_1^2 \left(x^2 + \frac{1}{x^2}\right) dx = \int_1^2 (x^2 + x^{-2}) dx = \left[\frac{x^3}{3} + \frac{x^{-1}}{-1}\right]_1^2$

$= \left[\frac{x^3}{3} - \frac{1}{x}\right]_1^2 = \left(\frac{2^3}{3} - \frac{1}{2}\right) - \left(\frac{1^3}{3} - \frac{1}{1}\right)$

$= \frac{8}{3} - \frac{1}{2} - \frac{1}{3} + 1 = \frac{17}{6}$

Q2 $\int_1^a x^{-2}\,dx = \left[\frac{x^{-1}}{-1}\right]_1^a = \left[-\frac{1}{x}\right]_1^a = -\frac{1}{a} + 1$

So $1 - \frac{1}{a} = \frac{1}{4} \Rightarrow \frac{1}{a} = \frac{3}{4} \Rightarrow a = \frac{4}{3}$

Q3 a) $\int_0^1 \sqrt{x}\,dx = \int_0^1 x^{\frac{1}{2}}\,dx = \left[\frac{x^{\frac{3}{2}}}{\left(\frac{3}{2}\right)}\right]_0^1 = \left[\frac{2}{3}(\sqrt{x})^3\right]_0^1$

$= \left(\frac{2}{3}(\sqrt{1})^3\right) - \left(\frac{2}{3}(\sqrt{0})^3\right) = \frac{2}{3} - 0 = \frac{2}{3}$

b) $\int_8^{27} \sqrt[3]{x}\,dx = \int_8^{27} x^{\frac{1}{3}}\,dx = \left[\frac{x^{\frac{4}{3}}}{\left(\frac{4}{3}\right)}\right]_8^{27} = \left[\frac{3}{4}(\sqrt[3]{x})^4\right]_8^{27}$

$= \left(\frac{3}{4}(\sqrt[3]{27})^4\right) - \left(\frac{3}{4}(\sqrt[3]{8})^4\right) = \left(\frac{3}{4} \times 3^4\right) - \left(\frac{3}{4} \times 2^4\right)$

$= \frac{195}{4}$

You can take the constants outside the square brackets if you find it easier to work with.

c) $\int_0^9 (x^2 + \sqrt{x})\,dx = \int_0^9 (x^2 + x^{\frac{1}{2}})\,dx = \left[\frac{x^3}{3} + \frac{x^{\frac{3}{2}}}{\left(\frac{3}{2}\right)}\right]_0^9$

$= \left[\frac{x^3}{3} + \frac{2}{3}(\sqrt{x})^3\right]_0^9$

$= \left(\frac{9^3}{3} + \frac{2}{3}(\sqrt{9})^3\right) - \left(\frac{0^3}{3} + \frac{2}{3}(\sqrt{0})^3\right)$

$= \left(\frac{729}{3} + \left(\frac{2}{3} \times 3^3\right)\right) - 0 = 261$

d) $\int_1^4 (3x^{-4} + \sqrt{x})\,dx = \int_1^4 (3x^{-4} + x^{\frac{1}{2}})\,dx$

$= \left[\frac{3x^{-3}}{-3} + \frac{x^{\frac{3}{2}}}{\left(\frac{3}{2}\right)}\right]_1^4 = \left[-\frac{1}{x^3} + \frac{2}{3}(\sqrt{x})^3\right]_1^4$

$= \left(-\frac{1}{4^3} + \frac{2}{3}(\sqrt{4})^3\right) - \left(-\frac{1}{1^3} + \frac{2}{3}(\sqrt{1})^3\right)$

$= \left(-\frac{1}{64} + \frac{2}{3} \times 2^3\right) - \left(-1 + \frac{2}{3}\right)$

$= \frac{1085}{192}$

e) $\int_0^1 (2x + 3)(x + 2)\,dx = \int_0^1 (2x^2 + 7x + 6)\,dx$

$= \left[\frac{2x^3}{3} + \frac{7x^2}{2} + 6x\right]_0^1$

$= \left(\frac{2 \times 1^3}{3} + \frac{7 \times 1^2}{2} + (6 \times 1)\right)$

$- \left(\frac{2 \times 0^3}{3} + \frac{7 \times 0^2}{2} + (6 \times 0)\right)$

$= \left(\frac{2}{3} + \frac{7}{2} + 6\right) - 0 = \frac{61}{6}$

f) $\int_1^4 \frac{1}{\sqrt{x}}\,dx = \int_1^4 x^{-\frac{1}{2}}\,dx = \left[\frac{x^{\frac{1}{2}}}{\left(\frac{1}{2}\right)}\right]_1^4 = [2\sqrt{x}]_1^4$

$= (2\sqrt{4}) - (2\sqrt{1}) = 4 - 2 = 2$

Q4 a) $\int_1^4 \frac{x^2 + 2}{\sqrt{x}}\,dx = \int_1^4 (x^{\frac{3}{2}} + 2x^{-\frac{1}{2}})\,dx$

$= \left[\frac{x^{\frac{5}{2}}}{\left(\frac{5}{2}\right)} + 2\frac{x^{\frac{1}{2}}}{\left(\frac{1}{2}\right)}\right]_1^4 = \left[\frac{2}{5}(\sqrt{x})^5 + 4\sqrt{x}\right]_1^4$

$= \left(\frac{2}{5}(\sqrt{4})^5 + 4\sqrt{4}\right) - \left(\frac{2}{5}(\sqrt{1})^5 + 4\sqrt{1}\right)$

$= \left(\frac{2}{5} \times 2^5 + 8\right) - \left(\frac{2}{5} + 4\right)$

$= \frac{64}{5} + 8 - \frac{2}{5} - 4 = \frac{82}{5}$

b) $\int_0^1 (\sqrt{x} + 1)^2\,dx = \int_0^1 (x + 2\sqrt{x} + 1)\,dx$

$= \int_0^1 (x + 2x^{\frac{1}{2}} + 1)\,dx = \left[\frac{x^2}{2} + \frac{2x^{\frac{3}{2}}}{\left(\frac{3}{2}\right)} + x\right]_0^1$

$= \left[\frac{x^2}{2} + \frac{4}{3}(\sqrt{x})^3 + x\right]_0^1$

$= \left(\frac{1^2}{2} + \frac{4}{3}(\sqrt{1})^3 + 1\right) - \left(\frac{0^2}{2} + \frac{4}{3}(\sqrt{0})^3 + 0\right)$

$= \left(\frac{1}{2} + \frac{4}{3} + 1\right) - 0 = \frac{17}{6}$

c) $\int_4^9 \left(\frac{1}{x} + \sqrt{x}\right)^2 dx = \int_4^9 \left(\frac{1}{x^2} + 2\frac{\sqrt{x}}{x} + x\right) dx$

$= \int_4^9 (x^{-2} + 2x^{-\frac{1}{2}} + x)\,dx$

$= \left[\frac{x^{-1}}{-1} + \frac{2x^{\frac{1}{2}}}{\left(\frac{1}{2}\right)} + \frac{x^2}{2}\right]_4^9$

$= \left[-\frac{1}{x} + 4\sqrt{x} + \frac{x^2}{2}\right]_4^9$

$= \left(-\frac{1}{9} + 4\sqrt{9} + \frac{9^2}{2}\right) - \left(-\frac{1}{4} + 4\sqrt{4} + \frac{4^2}{2}\right)$

$= -\frac{1}{9} + 12 + \frac{81}{2} + \frac{1}{4} - 8 - 8 = \frac{1319}{36}$

Q5 a) $\int_0^4 (x + \sqrt{x})\,dx = \int_0^4 (x + x^{\frac{1}{2}})\,dx$

$= \left[\frac{x^2}{2} + \frac{x^{\frac{3}{2}}}{\left(\frac{3}{2}\right)}\right]_0^4 = \left[\frac{1}{2}x^2 + \frac{2}{3}(\sqrt{x})^3\right]_0^4$

$= \left(\frac{1}{2}4^2 + \frac{2}{3}(\sqrt{4})^3\right) - \left(\frac{1}{2}0^2 + \frac{2}{3}(\sqrt{0})^3\right)$

$= \left(\frac{16}{2} + \frac{2}{3} \times 2^3\right) - 0$

$= \frac{40}{3}$

b) $\int_1^5 (6x - 31 + 25x^{-2})\,dx = [3x^2 - 31x - 25x^{-1}]_1^5$

$= \left(3(25) - 31(5) - \frac{25}{5}\right) - (3 - 31 - 25)$

$= (75 - 155 - 5) - (-53) = -32$

The value of the integral is negative because the area is below the x-axis. The shaded area is 32.

Q6 $y = \frac{3}{\sqrt{x}} + 2x$ is positive for all positive values of x, so the area required is the value of the integral between $x = 3$ and $x = 12$.

$\int_3^{12} (3x^{-\frac{1}{2}} + 2x)\,dx = [6x^{\frac{1}{2}} + x^2]_3^{12}$

$= (6\sqrt{12} + 12^2) - (6\sqrt{3} + 3^2)$

$= 12\sqrt{3} + 144 - 6\sqrt{3} - 9$

$= 135 + 6\sqrt{3}$

Q7 $y = \frac{20}{x^5}$ is always positive between $x = 1$ and $x = 2$ so just integrate:

$\int_1^2 \frac{20}{x^5}\,dx = \int_1^2 20x^{-5}\,dx = \left[\frac{20x^{-4}}{-4}\right]_1^2 = \left[-\frac{5}{x^4}\right]_1^2$

$= \left(-\frac{5}{2^4}\right) - \left(-\frac{5}{1^4}\right) = -\frac{5}{16} + 5 = \frac{75}{16}$

So the area is $\frac{75}{16} = 4.6875$

Exercise 1.5 — Finding the area between a curve and a line

Q1 a) Solve to find the point of intersection of $y = 4$ and $y = \frac{1}{x^2}$: $4 = \frac{1}{x^2} \Rightarrow 4x^2 = 1 \Rightarrow x^2 = \frac{1}{4}$

$\Rightarrow x = \pm\frac{1}{2}$ so the intersection in the diagram is $x = \frac{1}{2}$:

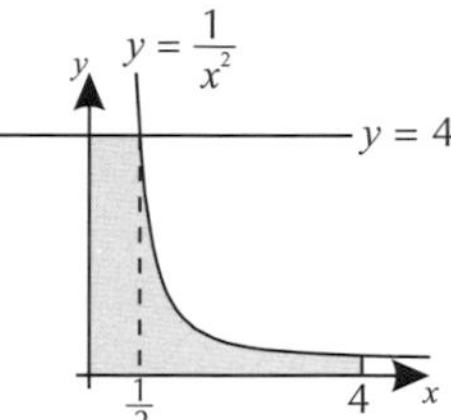

So required area is the area under the line $y = 4$ between $x = 0$ and $x = \frac{1}{2}$ added to the area under the curve $y = \frac{1}{x^2}$ from $x = \frac{1}{2}$ and $x = 4$.

The first area is just a rectangle which is $\frac{1}{2}$ by 4 so the area is $\frac{1}{2} \times 4 = 2$.

Area under curve $= \int_{\frac{1}{2}}^{4} \frac{1}{x^2}\,dx = \int_{\frac{1}{2}}^{4} x^{-2}\,dx$

$= \left[\frac{x^{-1}}{-1}\right]_{\frac{1}{2}}^{4} = \left[-\frac{1}{x}\right]_{\frac{1}{2}}^{4}$

$= \left(-\frac{1}{4}\right) - \left(-\frac{1}{\left(\frac{1}{2}\right)}\right)$

$= -\frac{1}{4} + 2 = \frac{7}{4}$

So the area is $2 + \frac{7}{4} = \frac{15}{4}$.

b) The area is the integral of $y = -2x + 23 - 36x^{-2}$ between 2 and 6, minus the integral of $y = x^2 - 8x + 22$ between 2 and 6.

These can be combined into a single integral:

A =

$\int_2^6 (-2x + 23 - 36x^{-2})\,dx - \int_2^6 (x^2 - 8x + 22)\,dx$

$= \int_2^6 (-2x + 23 - 36x^{-2} - x^2 + 8x - 22)\,dx$

$= \int_2^6 (-x^2 + 6x + 1 - 36x^{-2})\,dx$

$= \left[-\frac{1}{3}x^3 + 3x^2 + x + \frac{36}{x}\right]_2^6$

=

$\left(-\frac{216}{3} + 3(36) + 6 + \frac{36}{6}\right) - \left(-\frac{8}{3} + 3(4) + 2 + \frac{36}{2}\right)$

$= (-72 + 108 + 6 + 6) - \left(-\frac{8}{3} + 12 + 2 + 18\right)$

$= 48 - \frac{88}{3} = \frac{56}{3}$

You might have done this as two separate integrals and subtracted one from the other at the end.

c) Start by finding where the curve crosses the x-axis. Solve $-8\sqrt{x} + x^2 = 0$:

$-8\sqrt{x} + x^2 = 0 \Rightarrow \sqrt{x}(-8 + x\sqrt{x}) = 0$

$\Rightarrow \sqrt{x} = 0$ or $8 - x\sqrt{x} = 0$

$8 - x\sqrt{x} = 0 \Rightarrow 8 = x\sqrt{x} = (\sqrt{x})^3$

$\Rightarrow \sqrt{x} = 2 \Rightarrow x = 4$

So the line and the curve meet at (4, 0).

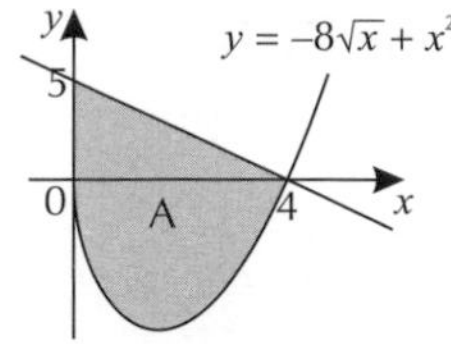

So the shaded area, A, is found by adding the area of a triangle of base 4 and height 5 to the negative integral (because the area's below the x-axis) of $-8\sqrt{x} + x^2$ between 0 and 4.

$A = -\int_0^4 (-8x^{\frac{1}{2}} + x^2)\,dx + \frac{1}{2}(5 \times 4)$

$= -\left[-\frac{16}{3}x^{\frac{3}{2}} + \frac{x^3}{3}\right]_0^4 + 10$

$= -\left[\left(-\frac{16}{3}(2^3) + \frac{4^3}{3}\right) - 0\right] + 10$

$= -\left(-\frac{128}{3} + \frac{64}{3}\right) + 10$

$= \frac{64}{3} + 10 = \frac{94}{3}$

d) Find where the line and curve intersect. Start by rewriting the equation of the line as $y = \frac{3}{2}x$.

So they intersect when $5\sqrt{x} - x = \frac{3}{2}x$

$\Rightarrow 5\sqrt{x} = \frac{5}{2}x \Rightarrow 2\sqrt{x} = x \Rightarrow 2\sqrt{x} - x = 0$

$\Rightarrow \sqrt{x}(2 - \sqrt{x}) = 0 \Rightarrow \sqrt{x} = 0$ or $\sqrt{x} = 2$

$\Rightarrow x = 0$ or $x = 4$

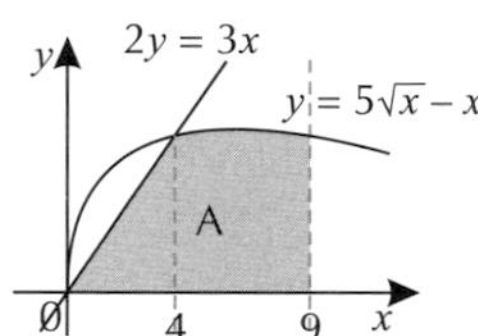

So the shaded area, A, is the area under the line between $x = 0$ and $x = 4$, plus the integral of the curve between $x = 4$ and $x = 9$.

The area under the line is a triangle of base 4 and height $\frac{3}{2}(4) = 6$.

So $A = \frac{1}{2}(4 \times 6) + \int_4^9 (5x^{\frac{1}{2}} - x)\,dx$

$= 12 + \left[\frac{10}{3}x^{\frac{3}{2}} - \frac{x^2}{2}\right]_4^9$

$= 12 + \left(\frac{10}{3}(3^3) - \frac{81}{2}\right) - \left(\frac{10}{3}(2^3) - \frac{16}{2}\right)$

$= 12 + \left(90 - \frac{81}{2}\right) - \left(\frac{80}{3} - 8\right)$

$= 12 + \frac{99}{2} - \frac{56}{3} = \frac{257}{6}$

2. The Trapezium Rule

Exercise 2.1 — The trapezium rule

Q1 a) You need to use 4 strips, so $n = 4$.

$h = \frac{(b-a)}{n} = \frac{(3-1)}{4} = \frac{2}{4} = 0.5$

So set up a table of x- and y-values:

x	$y = \frac{1}{x}$ (4 d.p.)
$x_0 = 1$	$y_0 = \frac{1}{1} = 1$
$x_1 = 1.5$	$y_1 = \frac{1}{1.5} = 0.6667$
$x_2 = 2$	$y_2 = \frac{1}{2} = 0.5$
$x_3 = 2.5$	$y_3 = \frac{1}{2.5} = 0.4$
$x_4 = 3$	$y_4 = \frac{1}{3} = 0.3333$

$$\int_1^3 \frac{1}{x}\,dx \approx \frac{0.5}{2}[1 + 2(0.6667 + 0.5 + 0.4) + 0.3333]$$
$$= 1.116675 = 1.12 \text{ (2 d.p.)}$$

b) You need to use 4 strips, so $n = 4$.

$h = \frac{(b-a)}{n} = \frac{(2-0)}{4} = \frac{2}{4} = 0.5$

So set up a table of x- and y-values:

x	$y = \sqrt{1+3^x}$ (4 d.p.)
$x_0 = 0$	$y_0 = \sqrt{1+3^0} = \sqrt{2} = 1.4142$
$x_1 = 0.5$	$y_1 = \sqrt{1+3^{0.5}} = 1.6529$
$x_2 = 1$	$y_2 = \sqrt{1+3^1} = \sqrt{4} = 2$
$x_3 = 1.5$	$y_3 = \sqrt{1+3^{1.5}} = 2.4892$
$x_4 = 2$	$y_4 = \sqrt{1+3^2} = 3.1623$

$$\int_0^2 \sqrt{1+3^x}\,dx \approx \frac{0.5}{2}[1.4142 + 2(1.6529 + 2 + 2.4892) + 3.1623]$$
$$= 4.215175 = 4.22 \text{ (2 d.p.)}$$

c) You need to use 4 strips, so $n = 4$.

$h = \frac{(b-a)}{n} = \frac{(6-1)}{4} = \frac{5}{4} = 1.25$

So set up a table of x- and y-values:

x	$y = \frac{10}{8-x}$ (4 d.p.)
$x_0 = 1$	$y_0 = \frac{10}{7} = 1.4286$
$x_1 = 2.25$	$y_1 = \frac{10}{5.75} = 1.7391$
$x_2 = 3.5$	$y_2 = \frac{10}{4.5} = 2.2222$
$x_3 = 4.75$	$y_3 = \frac{10}{3.25} = 3.0769$
$x_4 = 6$	$y_4 = \frac{10}{2} = 5$

$$\int_1^6 \frac{10}{8-x}\,dx \approx \frac{1.25}{2}[1.4286 + 2(1.7391 + 2.2222 + 3.0769) + 5]$$
$$= 12.815625 = 12.82 \text{ (2 d.p.)}$$

d) You need to use 4 strips, so $n = 4$.

$h = \frac{(b-a)}{n} = \frac{(3-0)}{4} = \frac{3}{4} = 0.75$

So set up a table of x- and y-values:

x	$y = 2^x$ (4 d.p.)
$x_0 = 0$	$y_0 = 2^0 = 1$
$x_1 = 0.75$	$y_1 = 2^{0.75} = 1.6818$
$x_2 = 1.5$	$y_2 = 2^{1.5} = 2.8284$
$x_3 = 2.25$	$y_3 = 2^{2.25} = 4.7568$
$x_4 = 3$	$y_4 = 2^3 = 8$

$$\int_0^3 2^x\,dx \approx \frac{0.75}{2}[1 + 2(1.6818 + 2.8284 + 4.7568) + 8]$$
$$= 10.32525$$
$$= 10.33 \text{ (2 d.p.)}$$

Q2 a)

x	0	$\frac{\pi}{6}$	$\frac{\pi}{3}$	$\frac{\pi}{2}$
$y = \sin x$	0	$\frac{1}{2}$	$\frac{\sqrt{3}}{2}$	1

b) You just need to find the value of h.

The x-values increase by $\frac{\pi}{6}$ each time so $h = \frac{\pi}{6}$.

$$\int_0^{\frac{\pi}{2}} \sin x\,dx \approx \frac{\left(\frac{\pi}{6}\right)}{2}\left[0 + 2\left(\frac{1}{2} + \frac{\sqrt{3}}{2}\right) + 1\right]$$
$$= 0.977048...$$
$$= 0.98 \text{ (2 d.p.)}$$

Q3 a) $\int_{-4}^{0} (x^2 + 2x + 3)\,dx = \left[\frac{x^3}{3} + x^2 + 3x\right]_{-4}^{0}$

$$= \left(\frac{0^3}{3} + 0^2 + 3 \times 0\right) - \left(\frac{(-4)^3}{3} + (-4)^2 + 3(-4)\right)$$
$$= 0 - \left(\frac{-64}{3} + 16 - 12\right)$$
$$= \frac{52}{3} = 17.33 \text{ (2 d.p.)}$$

b) 5 ordinates means 4 strips, so $n = 4$.

So $h = \frac{(b-a)}{n} = \frac{(0-(-4))}{4} = \frac{4}{4} = 1$

So set up a table of x- and y-values:

x	$y = x^2 + 2x + 3$
$x_0 = -4$	$y_0 = 11$
$x_1 = -3$	$y_1 = 6$
$x_2 = -2$	$y_2 = 3$
$x_3 = -1$	$y_3 = 2$
$x_4 = 0$	$y_4 = 3$

$$\int_{-4}^{0} x^2 + 2x + 3\,dx \approx \frac{1}{2}[11 + 2(6 + 3 + 2) + 3]$$
$$= 18$$

c) The answer to part a), $\frac{52}{3} = 17.333...$ is the exact solution to the integral.
The answer to part b) is an estimate of the integral and is within 1 unit of the exact solution.

Q4 The only value you need to find now to use the trapezium rule is h. It is just the difference between the x-values, so $h = 1$.

$$\int_{-2}^{2} f(x)\,dx \approx \tfrac{1}{2}[10 + 2(8 + 7 + 6.5) + 3] = 28$$

Q5 a) You need 4 strips so $n = 4$.

$$h = \frac{(b-a)}{n} = \frac{(5-0)}{4} = \frac{5}{4} = 1.25$$

So set up a table:

x	$y = 2^{-x}$ (4 d.p.)
$x_0 = 0$	$y_0 = 1$
$x_1 = 1.25$	$y_1 = 0.4204$
$x_2 = 2.5$	$y_2 = 0.1768$
$x_3 = 3.75$	$y_3 = 0.0743$
$x_4 = 5$	$y_4 = 0.0313$

$$\int_0^5 2^{-x}\,dx \approx \frac{1.25}{2}[1 + 2(0.4204 + 0.1768 + 0.0743) + 0.0313]$$
$$= 1.4839375$$
$$= 1.484 \text{ (3 d.p.)}$$

b) You need 5 strips so $n = 5$.

$$h = \frac{(b-a)}{n} = \frac{(5-0)}{5} = \frac{5}{5} = 1$$

So set up a table:

x	$y = 2^{-x}$
$x_0 = 0$	$y_0 = 1$
$x_1 = 1$	$y_1 = 0.5$
$x_2 = 2$	$y_2 = 0.25$
$x_3 = 3$	$y_3 = 0.125$
$x_4 = 4$	$y_4 = 0.0625$
$x_5 = 5$	$y_5 = 0.03125$

$$\int_0^5 2^{-x}\,dx \approx \tfrac{1}{2}[1 + 2(0.5 + 0.25 + 0.125 + 0.0625) + 0.03125]$$
$$= 1.453125$$
$$= 1.453 \text{ (3 d.p.)}$$

c) The estimate in part b) should be more accurate because the area is split into more trapeziums, so they will be closer to the actual area under the curve.

Q6 a) 9 ordinates means 8 strips so $n = 8$.

$$h = \frac{(b-a)}{n} = \frac{(3-1)}{8} = \frac{2}{8} = \frac{1}{4} = 0.25$$

So set up a table:

x	$y = 3 - (2 - x)^2$
$x_0 = 1$	$y_0 = 2$
$x_1 = 1.25$	$y_1 = 2.4375$
$x_2 = 1.5$	$y_2 = 2.75$
$x_3 = 1.75$	$y_3 = 2.9375$
$x_4 = 2$	$y_4 = 3$
$x_5 = 2.25$	$y_5 = 2.9375$
$x_6 = 2.5$	$y_6 = 2.75$
$x_7 = 2.75$	$y_7 = 2.4375$
$x_8 = 3$	$y_8 = 2$

$$\int_1^3 (3-(2-x)^2)\,dx \approx \frac{0.25}{2}[2 + 2(2.4375 + 2.75 + 2.9375 + 3 + 2.9375 + 2.75 + 2.4375) + 2]$$
$$= 5.3125$$

b) The function $y = 3 - (2 - x)^2 = -x^2 + 4x - 1$ is a quadratic with a negative x^2 coefficient, so it is n-shaped. When $x = 0$, $y = -1$ so it intersects the y-axis at -1. Find the x-intercepts by letting $y = 0$, so $3 - (2 - x)^2 = 0 \Rightarrow 3 = (2 - x)^2$
$\Rightarrow \pm\sqrt{3} = 2 - x \Rightarrow x = 2 \pm \sqrt{3}$
$\frac{dy}{dx} = -2x + 4$, so $\frac{dy}{dx} = 0 \Rightarrow x = 2$
So there is a maximum at $x = 2$.

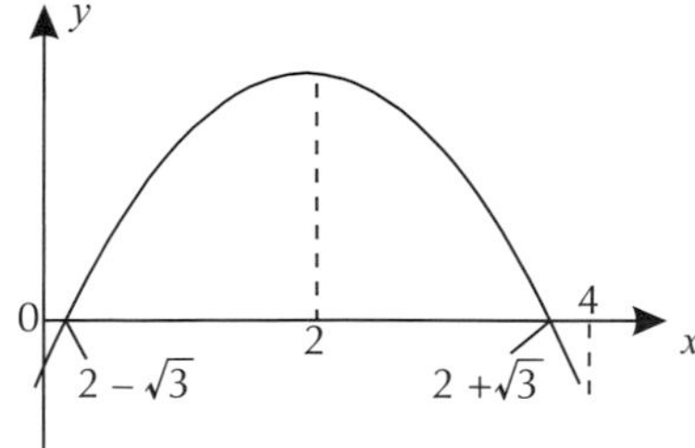

c) The approximation will be an underestimate because the graph curves in such a way that the trapeziums will lie underneath the curve.

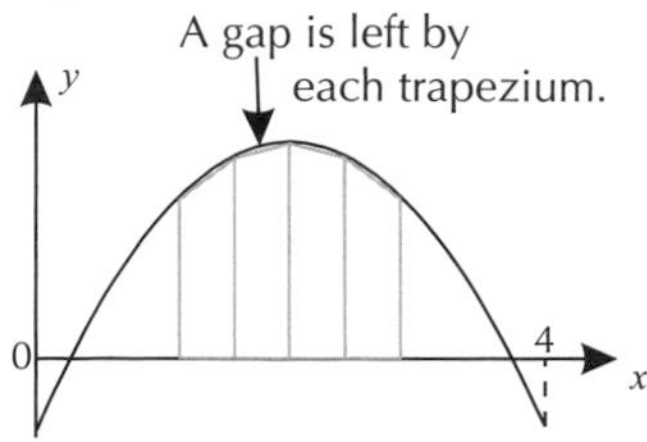

Q7 a)

x	$-\frac{\pi}{2}$	$-\frac{\pi}{3}$	$-\frac{\pi}{6}$	0	$\frac{\pi}{6}$	$\frac{\pi}{3}$	$\frac{\pi}{2}$
y	0	0.5	$\frac{\sqrt{3}}{2}$	1	$\frac{\sqrt{3}}{2}$	0.5	0

b) Use the trapezium rule. You just need to find h, the difference between the x values.

So $h = \frac{\pi}{6}$

$$\int_{-\frac{\pi}{2}}^{\frac{\pi}{2}} \cos x \, dx \approx \frac{\left(\frac{\pi}{6}\right)}{2}[0 + 2(0.5 + \frac{\sqrt{3}}{2} + 1 + \frac{\sqrt{3}}{2} + 0.5) + 0]$$

$$= \frac{\pi}{12}[0 + 2(2 + \sqrt{3}) + 0]$$

$$= \pi\left(\frac{2(2 + \sqrt{3})}{12}\right)$$

$$= \frac{\pi(2 + \sqrt{3})}{6}$$

c) The graph of $y = \cos x$ looks like this between the two limits:

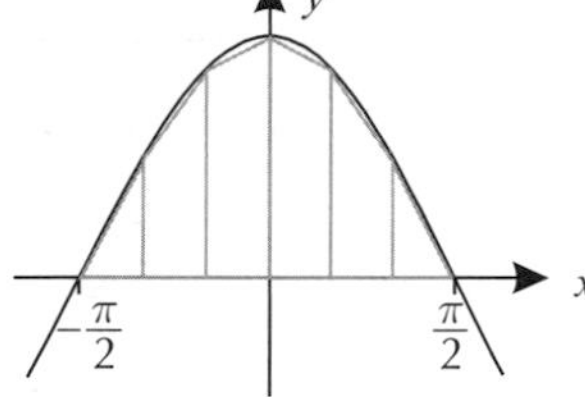

So the trapeziums will lie underneath the curve and so the approximation will be an underestimate.

Review Exercise — Chapter 6

Q1 a) $f(x) = \frac{x^{\frac{1}{2}}}{\left(\frac{1}{2}\right)} + 4x - \frac{5x^4}{4} + C$

and then simplify each term further if possible...

$= 2x^{\frac{1}{2}} + 4x - \frac{5x^4}{4} + C$

b) First rewrite everything in terms of powers of x: $f'(x) = 3x^2 - 2x^{-2}$

Now integrate each term (don't forget to add C): $f(x) = \frac{3x^3}{3} - \frac{2x^{-1}}{-1} + C$

Then simplify each term: $f(x) = x^3 + \frac{2}{x} + C$

c) Following the same process as in part b):

$f'(x) = 6x^2 - \frac{1}{3}x^{-\frac{1}{2}}$

$f(x) = \frac{6x^3}{3} + \frac{1}{3}\frac{x^{\frac{1}{2}}}{\left(\frac{1}{2}\right)} + C$

$f(x) = 2x^3 + \frac{2}{3}\sqrt{x} + C$

Q2 $\int\left(4x^2 + \frac{3}{\sqrt{x}} - 2\right)dx = \int\left(4x^2 + 3x^{-\frac{1}{2}} - 2\right)dx$

$= 4\left(\frac{x^3}{3}\right) + 3\left(\frac{x^{\frac{1}{2}}}{\left(\frac{1}{2}\right)}\right) - 2\left(\frac{x^1}{1}\right) + C$

$= \frac{4}{3}x^3 + 6x^{\frac{1}{2}} - 2x + C$

$= \frac{4}{3}x^3 + 6\sqrt{x} - 2x + C$

Q3 $\int(3\sqrt{x} + 3)^2 \, dx = \int(9x + 18\sqrt{x} + 9)\,dx$

$= \int\left(9x + 18x^{\frac{1}{2}} + 9\right)dx$

$= 9\left(\frac{x^2}{2}\right) + 18\left(\frac{x^{\frac{3}{2}}}{\left(\frac{3}{2}\right)}\right) + 9\left(\frac{x^1}{1}\right) + C$

$= \frac{9}{2}x^2 + 12x^{\frac{3}{2}} + 9x + C$

$= \frac{9}{2}x^2 + 12(\sqrt{x})^3 + 9x + C$

Q4 To find y in terms of x, just integrate $\frac{dy}{dx}$ with respect to x.

a) $y = \int\frac{dy}{dx}dx = \int\left(\frac{1}{\sqrt{x}} + \sqrt{x}\right)dx$

$= \int\left(x^{-\frac{1}{2}} + x^{\frac{1}{2}}\right)dx = \frac{x^{\frac{1}{2}}}{\left(\frac{1}{2}\right)} + \frac{x^{\frac{3}{2}}}{\left(\frac{3}{2}\right)} + C$

$= 2x^{\frac{1}{2}} + \frac{2x^{\frac{3}{2}}}{3} + C = 2\sqrt{x} + \frac{2(\sqrt{x})^3}{3} + C$

b) $y = \int\frac{dy}{dx}dx = \int\left(\frac{3}{x^2} + \frac{3}{\sqrt[3]{x}}\right)dx$

$= \int\left(3x^{-2} + 3x^{-\frac{1}{3}}\right)dx = \frac{3x^{-1}}{-1} + \frac{3x^{\frac{2}{3}}}{\left(\frac{2}{3}\right)} + C$

$= -\frac{3}{x} + \frac{9}{2}(\sqrt[3]{x})^2 + C$

Q5 a) $\frac{dy}{dx} = \frac{(x + 2)(x - 2)}{\sqrt{x}} = \frac{x^2 + 2x - 2x - 4}{\sqrt{x}}$

$= \frac{x^2 - 4}{\sqrt{x}} = \frac{x^2}{\sqrt{x}} - \frac{4}{\sqrt{x}} = \frac{x^2}{x^{\frac{1}{2}}} - \frac{4}{x^{\frac{1}{2}}}$

$= x^2x^{-\frac{1}{2}} - 4x^{-\frac{1}{2}} = x^{\frac{3}{2}} - 4x^{-\frac{1}{2}}$

So $A = 1$ and $B = -4$.

b) $y = \int\frac{dy}{dx}dx = \int(x^{\frac{3}{2}} - 4x^{-\frac{1}{2}})\,dx$

$= \int x^{\frac{3}{2}}dx - 4\int x^{-\frac{1}{2}}dx$

$= \frac{x^{\frac{5}{2}}}{\left(\frac{5}{2}\right)} - 4\left(\frac{x^{\frac{1}{2}}}{\left(\frac{1}{2}\right)}\right) + C$

$= \frac{2}{5}x^{\frac{5}{2}} - 8x^{\frac{1}{2}} + C = \frac{2}{5}(\sqrt{x})^5 - 8\sqrt{x} + C$

When $x = 1$, $y = \frac{7}{5}$.

So $\frac{7}{5} = \frac{2}{5}(\sqrt{1})^5 - 8\sqrt{1} + C = -\frac{38}{5} + C \Rightarrow C = 9$

So the equation is $y = \frac{2}{5}(\sqrt{x})^5 - 8\sqrt{x} + 9$.

Q6 $f(x) = \int f'(x)\,dx = \int\left(6x^2 - 12 - \frac{8}{x^2}\right)dx$

$= \int(6x^2 - 12 - 8x^{-2})\,dx$

$= 6\left(\frac{x^3}{3}\right) - 12\left(\frac{x^1}{1}\right) - 8\left(\frac{x^{-1}}{-1}\right) + C$

$= 2x^3 - 12x + \frac{8}{x} + C$

When $x = -2$, $y = 5$ and $y = f(x)$ so $f(x) = 5$.

So $5 = 2(-2)^3 - 12(-2) + \frac{8}{(-2)} + C = 4 + C$

$\Rightarrow C = 1$

So the equation is $y = 2x^3 - 12x + \frac{8}{x} + 1$.

Q7 $f(x) = \int f'(x)\,dx = \int \left(\frac{5x^2+1}{x^{\frac{1}{2}}} - 10\right)dx$

$= \int \left(\frac{5x^2}{x^{\frac{1}{2}}} + \frac{1}{x^{\frac{1}{2}}} - 10\right)dx$

$= \int \left(5x^{\frac{3}{2}} + x^{-\frac{1}{2}} - 10\right)dx$

$= 5\left(\frac{x^{\frac{5}{2}}}{\left(\frac{5}{2}\right)}\right) + \left(\frac{x^{\frac{1}{2}}}{\left(\frac{1}{2}\right)}\right) - 10\left(\frac{x^1}{1}\right) + C$

$= 2x^{\frac{5}{2}} + 2x^{\frac{1}{2}} - 10x + C$

$= 2(\sqrt{x})^5 + 2\sqrt{x} - 10x + C$

When $x = 1$, $y = -9$ and $y = f(x)$ so $f(x) = -9$.

So $-9 = 2(\sqrt{1})^5 + 2\sqrt{1} - 10(1) + C = -6 + C$

$\Rightarrow C = -3$

So the equation is $y = 2(\sqrt{x})^5 + 2\sqrt{x} - 10x - 3$.

Q8 a) $\int_1^2 \left(\frac{8}{x^5} + \frac{3}{\sqrt{x}}\right)dx = \int_1^2 (8x^{-5} + 3x^{-\frac{1}{2}})dx$

$= \left[-\frac{2}{x^4} + 6\sqrt{x}\right]_1^2 = \left(-\frac{2}{16} + 6\sqrt{2}\right) - (-2 + 6)$

$= -\frac{33}{8} + 6\sqrt{2}$

b) $\int_1^6 \frac{3}{x^2}\,dx = \int_1^6 3x^{-2}\,dx = \left[\frac{-3}{x}\right]_1^6 = -\frac{1}{2} - (-3) = \frac{5}{2}$

Q9 $\int_1^8 y\,dx = \int_1^8 x^{-\frac{1}{3}}\,dx = \left[\frac{3}{2}x^{\frac{2}{3}}\right]_1^8$

$= \left(\frac{3}{2} \times 8^{\frac{2}{3}}\right) - \left(\frac{3}{2} \times 1^{\frac{2}{3}}\right)$

$= \left(\frac{3}{2} \times 4\right) - \left(\frac{3}{2} \times 1\right) = \frac{9}{2}$

Q10 a) $A = \int_1^5 (x^{-2} + 3)\,dx$

$= \left[-\frac{1}{x} + 3x\right]_1^5$

$= \left(-\frac{1}{5} + 15\right) - (-1 + 3)$

$= \frac{74}{5} - 2 = \frac{64}{5}$

b) $A = \int_1^4 2\sqrt{x}\,dx = \int_1^4 2x^{\frac{1}{2}}dx = \left[\frac{4}{3}x^{\frac{3}{2}}\right]_1^4$

$= \frac{4}{3}(8) - \frac{4}{3}(1) = \frac{28}{3}$

c) A is the area below the line (a rectangle of width 3 and height 9), minus the area under the curve:

$A = 9 \times 3 - \int_{-4}^{-1}\left(-5x - 12 + \frac{16}{x^2}\right)dx$

$= 27 - \left[-\frac{5}{2}x^2 - 12x - \frac{16}{x}\right]_{-4}^{-1}$

$= 27 - \left(\left(-\frac{5}{2} + 12 + 16\right) - (-40 + 48 + 4)\right)$

$= 27 - \left(\frac{51}{2} - 12\right)$

$= 27 - \frac{27}{2} = \frac{27}{2}$

d) $A = \int_0^1 (x^{\frac{1}{3}} - x + 3)\,dx - \int_0^1 (x^3 + 2x^2 - 3x + 3)\,dx$

$= \int_0^1 (x^{\frac{1}{3}} - x^3 - 2x^2 + 2x)\,dx$

$= \left[\frac{3}{4}x^{\frac{4}{3}} - \frac{x^4}{4} - \frac{2}{3}x^3 + x^2\right]_0^1$

$= \left(\frac{3}{4} - \frac{1}{4} - \frac{2}{3} + 1\right) - 0 = \frac{5}{6}$

Q11 a) $y_0 = \sqrt{1+0} = 1$, $y_1 = \sqrt{1+0.5} = 1.2247$,
$y_2 = \sqrt{1+1} = 1.4142$, $y_3 = \sqrt{1+1.5} = 1.5811$,
$y_4 = \sqrt{1+2} = 1.7321$

b) The value of h is 0.5.

$\int_0^2 \sqrt{1+x}\,dx \approx \frac{0.5}{2}[1 + 2(1.2247 + 1.4142 + 1.5811) + 1.7321]$

$= 2.793025$

$= 2.79$ (2 d.p.)

Q12 a) $h = \frac{(3-0)}{3} = 1$

x	$y = \sqrt{9 - x^2}$
$x_0 = 0$	$y_0 = \sqrt{9} = 3$
$x_1 = 1$	$y_1 = \sqrt{8} = 2.82843$
$x_2 = 2$	$y_2 = \sqrt{5} = 2.23607$
$x_3 = 3$	$y_3 = \sqrt{0} = 0$

$\int_a^b y\,dx \approx \frac{1}{2}[3 + 2(2.82843 + 2.23607) + 0]$

$= 6.5645 = 6.56$ (3 s.f.)

b) $h = \frac{(1.2 - 0.2)}{5} = 0.2$

x	$y = x^{x^2}$
$x_0 = 0.2$	$y_0 = 0.2^{0.04} = 0.93765$
$x_1 = 0.4$	$y_1 = 0.4^{0.16} = 0.86363$
$x_2 = 0.6$	$y_2 = 0.6^{0.36} = 0.83202$
$x_3 = 0.8$	$y_3 = 0.8^{0.64} = 0.86692$
$x_4 = 1$	$y_4 = 1^1 = 1$
$x_5 = 1.2$	$y_5 = 1.2^{1.44} = 1.30023$

$\int_a^b y\,dx \approx \frac{0.2}{2}[0.93765 + 2(0.86363 + 0.83202 + 0.86692 + 1) + 1.30023]$

$= 0.1 \times 9.36302 = 0.936$ (3 s.f.)

c) $h = \frac{(3-1)}{4} = \frac{2}{4} = 0.5$

x	$y = 2^{x^2}$
$x_0 = 1$	$y_0 = 2^1 = 2$
$x_1 = 1.5$	$y_1 = 2^{2.25} = 4.75683$
$x_2 = 2$	$y_2 = 2^4 = 16$
$x_3 = 2.5$	$y_3 = 2^{6.25} = 76.10926$
$x_4 = 3$	$y_4 = 2^9 = 512$

$\int_a^b y\,dx \approx \frac{0.5}{2}[2 + 2(4.75683 + 16 + 76.10926) + 512]$

$= 176.933045 = 177$ (3 s.f.)

d) $h = \frac{(3-1)}{5} = \frac{2}{5} = 0.4$

x	$y = 2^{x^2}$
$x_0 = 1$	$y_0 = 2^1 = 2$
$x_1 = 1.4$	$y_1 = 2^{1.96} = 3.89062$
$x_2 = 1.8$	$y_2 = 2^{3.24} = 9.44794$
$x_3 = 2.2$	$y_3 = 2^{4.84} = 28.64080$
$x_4 = 2.6$	$y_4 = 2^{6.76} = 108.3834$
$x_5 = 3$	$y_5 = 2^9 = 512$

$$\int_a^b y\,dx \approx \frac{0.4}{2}[2 + 2(3.89062 + 9.44794 + 28.64080 + 108.3834) + 512]$$
$$= 162.945104 = 163 \text{ (3 s.f.)}$$

Exam-Style Questions — Chapter 6

Q1 To find $f(x)$ you integrate $f'(x)$, but it helps to write all terms in powers of x, so $5\sqrt{x} = 5x^{\frac{1}{2}}$ and $\frac{6}{x^2} = 6x^{-2}$ ***[1 mark]***

Now integrate each term:

$$f(x) = \int\left(2x + 5x^{\frac{1}{2}} + 6x^{-2}\right)dx$$
$$= \frac{2x^2}{2} + 5\left(\frac{x^{\frac{3}{2}}}{\left(\frac{3}{2}\right)}\right) + \left(\frac{6x^{-1}}{-1}\right) + C$$
$$f(x) = x^2 + \frac{10\sqrt{x^3}}{3} - \frac{6}{x} + C$$

[2 marks for correct terms, 1 mark for +C]

You've been given a point on the curve so you can calculate the value of C:

If $y = 7$ when $x = 3$, then

$3^2 - \frac{6}{3} + \frac{10\sqrt{3^3}}{3} + C = 7$ ***[1 mark]***

$9 - 2 + 10\sqrt{3} + C = 7$

$7 + 10\sqrt{3} + C = 7$

$C = -10\sqrt{3}$

$f(x) = x^2 + \frac{10\sqrt{x^3}}{3} - \frac{6}{x} - 10\sqrt{3}$ ***[1 mark]***

Q2 First find the x-values at A and B — by solving for x when $y = 0$.

$-\frac{1}{x^2}(x+2)(x-3)(x-6) = 0$

$\Rightarrow x = -2, x = 3$ or $x = 6$

The diagram shows that A and B are positive and $B > A$,

so $A = (3, 0)$ and $B = (6, 0)$. ***[1 mark]***

So to find the shaded area, integrate $-\frac{1}{x^2}(x+2)(x-3)(x-6)$ between $x = 3$ and $x = 6$.

$$\int_3^6 -\frac{1}{x^2}(x+2)(x-3)(x-6)\,dx$$
$$= \int_3^6 -\frac{1}{x^2}(x^3 - 7x^2 + 36)\,dx$$
$$= \int_3^6 (-x + 7 - 36x^{-2})\,dx \quad \textbf{\textit{[1 mark]}}$$
$$= \left[-\frac{x^2}{2} + 7x + \frac{36}{x}\right]_3^6 \quad \textbf{\textit{[1 mark]}}$$
$$= \left(-\frac{6^2}{2} + 7(6) + \frac{36}{6}\right) - \left(-\frac{3^2}{2} + 7(3) + \frac{36}{3}\right) \quad \textbf{\textit{[1 mark]}}$$
$$= (-18 + 42 + 6) - \left(-\frac{9}{2} + 21 + 12\right)$$
$$= 30 - \frac{57}{2}$$
$$= \frac{3}{2} \quad \textbf{\textit{[1 mark]}}$$

Q3 a) The tangent at (1, 2) has the same gradient as the curve at that point, so use $f'(x)$ to calculate the gradient:

$f'(1) = 1^3 - 2$ ***[1 mark]***

$= -1$ ***[1 mark]***

Put this into the straight-line equation $y - y_1 = m(x - x_1)$:

$y - 2 = -1(x - 1)$ ***[1 mark]***

$y = -x + 1 + 2$

$y = -x + 3$ ***[1 mark]***

b) $f(x) = \int\left(x^3 - \frac{2}{x^2}\right)dx$

$= \int(x^3 - 2x^{-2})\,dx$ ***[1 mark]***

$= \frac{x^4}{4} - 2\left(\frac{x^{-1}}{-1}\right) + C$

$= \frac{x^4}{4} + 2x^{-1} + C$ ***[1 mark]***

$= \frac{x^4}{4} + \frac{2}{x} + C$

Now use the coordinates (1, 2) to find the value of C:

$2 = \frac{1^4}{4} + \frac{2}{1} + C$ ***[1 mark]***

$2 - \frac{1}{4} - 2 = C$

$C = -\frac{1}{4}$ ***[1 mark]***

So $f(x) = \frac{x^4}{4} + \frac{2}{x} - \frac{1}{4}$ ***[1 mark]***

Q4 a) (i) $h = \frac{8-2}{3} = 2$ ***[1 mark]***

$x_0 = 2 \quad y_0 = \sqrt{(3 \times 2^3)} + \frac{2}{\sqrt{2}} = 6.31319$

$x_1 = 4 \quad y_1 = \sqrt{(3 \times 4^3)} + \frac{2}{\sqrt{4}} = 14.85641$

$x_2 = 6 \quad y_2 = \sqrt{(3 \times 6^3)} + \frac{2}{\sqrt{6}} = 26.27234$

$x_3 = 8 \quad y_3 = \sqrt{(3 \times 8^3)} + \frac{2}{\sqrt{8}} = 39.89894$

[1 mark]

$\int_2^8 y\,dx \approx \frac{2}{2}[6.31319 + 2(14.85641 + 26.27234) + 39.89894]$

[1 mark]

$= 128.46963 = 128.47$ to 2 d.p. ***[1 mark]***

(ii) $h = \frac{5-1}{4} = 1$ ***[1 mark]***

$x_0 = 1 \quad y_0 = \frac{1^3 - 2}{4} = -0.25$

$x_1 = 2 \quad y_1 = \frac{2^3 - 2}{4} = 1.5$

$x_2 = 3 \quad y_2 = \frac{3^3 - 2}{4} = 6.25$

$x_3 = 4 \quad y_3 = \frac{4^3 - 2}{4} = 15.5$

$x_4 = 5 \quad y_4 = \frac{5^3 - 2}{4} = 30.75$ ***[1 mark]***

$\int_1^5 y\,dx \approx \frac{1}{2}[-0.25 + 2(1.5 + 6.25 + 15.5) + 30.75]$ ***[1 mark]***

$= 38.5$ ***[1 mark]***

b) Increase the number of intervals. ***[1 mark]***

Q5 $\int_2^7 (2x - 6x^2 + \sqrt{x})\,dx = \left[x^2 - 2x^3 + \frac{2\sqrt{x^3}}{3}\right]_2^7$

[1 mark for each correct term]

$= \left(7^2 - (2 \times 7^3) + \frac{2\sqrt{7^3}}{3}\right)$

$- \left(2^2 - (2 \times 2^3) + \frac{2\sqrt{2^3}}{3}\right)$ ***[1 mark]***

$= -624.6531605 - (-10.11438192)$

$= -614.5387786 = -614.5388$ (4 d.p.) ***[1 mark]***

Q6 $n = 5$, $h = \frac{4 - 1.5}{5} = 0.5$ ***[1 mark]***

$x_1 = 2.0, x_2 = 2.5, x_3 = 3.0$ ***[1 mark]***

$y_0 = 2.8182, y_3 = 6.1716, y_4 = 7.1364$ ***[1 mark]***

$\int_{1.5}^4 y\,dx \approx \frac{0.5}{2}[2.8182 + 2(4 + 5.1216 + 6.1716 + 7.1364) + 8]$ ***[1 mark]***

$= 13.91935 = 13.9$ to 3 s.f. ***[1 mark]***

Q7 a) $\frac{dy}{dx} = 3\sqrt{x} - \frac{5}{\sqrt{x}} = 3x^{\frac{1}{2}} - 5x^{-\frac{1}{2}}$ ***[1 mark]***

Now integrate each term to find y:

$y = \int \frac{dy}{dx}\,dx = \int (3x^{\frac{1}{2}} - 5x^{-\frac{1}{2}})\,dx$

$= 3\left(\frac{x^{\frac{3}{2}}}{(\frac{3}{2})}\right) - 5\left(\frac{x^{\frac{1}{2}}}{(\frac{1}{2})}\right) + C$ ***[1 mark]***

$= 2(\sqrt{x})^3 - 10\sqrt{x} + C$ ***[1 mark]***

Use the coordinates to find the value of C:

$-6 = 2(\sqrt{4})^3 - 10\sqrt{4} + C$

$= 16 - 20 + C$

$= -4 + C$

So $C = -2$ ***[1 mark]***

So the equation of the curve is
$y = 2(\sqrt{x})^3 - 10\sqrt{x} - 2.$ ***[1 mark]***

b) First calculate the gradient of f(x) when $x = 4$:

$\frac{dy}{dx} = 3\sqrt{4} - \frac{5}{\sqrt{4}} = (3 \times 2) - \frac{5}{2} = \frac{7}{2}$ ***[1 mark]***

Use the fact that the tangent gradient multiplied by the normal gradient must equal –1 to find the gradient of the normal (n):

$\frac{7}{2} \times n = -1$ therefore $n = -\frac{2}{7}$ ***[1 mark]***.

Put n and $P(4, -6)$ into the formula for the equation of a line and rearrange until it's in the form $ax + by + c = 0$:

$y + 6 = -\frac{2}{7}(x - 4)$ ***[1 mark]***

$7y + 42 = -2x + 8$

$7y = -2x - 34$

$2x + 7y + 34 = 0$ ***[1 mark]***

Q8 a) Rearrange the equation for L into $y = mx + c$ form:

$4y = x - 9 \Rightarrow y = \frac{x}{4} - \frac{9}{4}$

So C and L intersect when

$x - 3\sqrt{x} = \frac{x}{4} - \frac{9}{4}$ ***[1 mark]***

$\Rightarrow 4x - 12\sqrt{x} = x - 9$

$\Rightarrow 3x - 12\sqrt{x} + 9 = 0$

$\Rightarrow x - 4\sqrt{x} + 3 = 0$ ***[1 mark]***

$\Rightarrow (\sqrt{x} - 1)(\sqrt{x} - 3) = 0$ ***[1 mark]***

$\Rightarrow \sqrt{x} = 1$ or $\sqrt{x} = 3$

$\Rightarrow x = 1$ or $x = 9$ ***[1 mark]***

From the graph, the points of intersection are P and (9, 0), so at P, $x = 1$

$\Rightarrow y = \frac{1}{4} - \frac{9}{4} = -2$ (or $y = 1 - 3\sqrt{1} = -2$),

so $P = (1, -2)$ ***[1 mark]***

The tricky step here was the factorisation halfway through. The equation is a 'disguised quadratic' — try using a substitution like $\sqrt{x} = t$ if you didn't follow that bit.

It helps that the question tells you that the x-values of the points of intersection are x = 1 and x = 9, so you know what values you're aiming for.

b) $\int_1^9 (x - 3\sqrt{x})\,dx = \int_1^9 (x - 3x^{\frac{1}{2}})\,dx$

$= \left[\frac{x^2}{2} - 2x^{\frac{3}{2}}\right]_1^9$ ***[1 mark]***

$= \left(\frac{9^2}{2} - 2(\sqrt{9})^3\right) - \left(\frac{(1)^2}{2} - 2(\sqrt{1})^3\right)$ ***[1 mark]***

$= \left(\frac{81}{2} - 54\right) - \left(\frac{1}{2} - 2\right)$

$= -\frac{27}{2} + \frac{3}{2} = -12$ ***[1 mark]***

c) Subtract the area between the line and the x-axis from the area above the curve between $x = 1$ and $x = 9$ to give the shaded area.

The area above the line is a triangle of base 8 and height 2. The area above the curve is minus the integral found in part b). So the shaded area is:

$A = -\int_1^9 (x - 3\sqrt{x})\,dx - \frac{1}{2}(8 \times 2)$ ***[1 mark]***

$= 12 - 8 = 4$ ***[1 mark]***

You could also have found the area of the triangle by integrating the equation of the line — you'd have got the same answer.

Glossary

Arc
The curved edge of a **sector** of a circle.

Arithmetic sequence / series
A **sequence** or **series** where successive terms have a **common difference**.

Asymptote
A line which a curve gets infinitely close to, but never touches.

Binomial
A polynomial with only two terms e.g. $a + bx$.

Binomial expansion
The result of expanding a **binomial** raised to a **power** — e.g. $(a + bx)^n$.

Binomial formula
A formula which describes the general terms of a **binomial expansion**.

Coefficient
The constant multiplying the variable(s) in an algebraic term e.g. 4 in the term $4x^2y$.

Common difference
The difference between two successive terms in an **arithmetic sequence** or **series**.

Common ratio
The constant that you multiply by to get from one term to the next in a **geometric sequence** or **series**.

Constant of integration
A constant term coming from an **indefinite integration** representing any number.

Convergent sequence/series
A **sequence/series** that tends towards a **limit**.

Cosine rule
A rule for finding the missing sides or angles in a triangle when you know all of the sides, or two sides and the angle between them.

Decreasing function
A function for which the **gradient** is always less than zero.

Definite integral
An **integral** which is evaluated over an interval given by two **limits**, representing the area under the curve between those limits.

Derivative
The result after **differentiating** a function.

Differentiation
A method of finding the rate of change of a function with respect to a variable.

Divergent sequence / series
A **sequence/series** that does not have a **limit**.

Exponential decay
Exponential decay happens when the rate of decay gets slower and slower as the amount gets smaller (negative **exponential growth**).

Exponential function
A function of the form $y = a^x$.

Exponential growth
Exponential growth happens when the rate of growth gets faster and faster as the amount gets bigger.

Factorial
n factorial, written $n!$, is the product of all the **integers** from 1 to n. So $n! = 1 \times 2 \times ... \times n$.

Finite sequence
A **sequence** with a finite number of terms (i.e. it doesn't go on forever).

Function notation f(x)
Standard way of referring to functions. E.g. function f defined by $f(x) = x^2 + 5$.

f′(x)
The **derivative** of f(x) with respect to x.

f″(x)
The **second order derivative** of f(x) with respect to x.

Geometric sequence/series
A **sequence/series** in which you multiply by a **common ratio** to get from one term to the next.

Gradient
The gradient of a curve at a given point is how steep the curve is at that point.

Gradient function
A function that can be used to find the **gradient** at any point on a curve.

Identity
An equation that is true for all values of a variable, usually denoted by the '≡' sign.

Increasing function
A function for which the **gradient** is always greater than zero.

Indefinite integral
An **integral** which includes a **constant of integration** that comes from integrating without **limits**.

Index
For a^n, n is the index and is often referred to as a power.

Infinite sequence
A **sequence** that goes on forever (it doesn't have a finite number of terms).

Integer
A positive or negative whole number (including 0).

Integral
The result you get when you **integrate** something.

Integration
Process for finding a function, given its **derivative** — the opposite of **differentiation**.

Intercept
The coordinates at which the graph of a function crosses one of the axes.

L

Limit (sequences and series)
The value that the individual terms in a **sequence**, or the sum of the terms in a **series**, tends towards.

Limits (integration)
The numbers between which you **integrate** to find a **definite integral**.

Logarithm
The logarithm to the base a of a number x (written $\log_a x$) is the **power** to which a must be raised to give that number.

M

Maximum
The highest point on a graph, or on a section of a graph (this is a local maximum). A type of **stationary point**.

Minimum
The lowest point on a graph or on a section of a graph (this is a local minimum). A type of **stationary point**.

Modulus
The modulus of a number is its positive numerical value.

$^n\mathbf{C}_r$
The binomial coefficient of x^r in the **binomial expansion** of $(1 + x)^n$.
Also written $\binom{n}{r}$.

Normal
A straight line passing through a curve that is perpendicular (at right angles) to the curve at the point where it crosses the curve.

***n*th term**
A formula that gives any term in a **sequence** or **series** from its position n.

Pascal's triangle
A triangle of numbers showing the binomial coefficients. Each term is the sum of the two above it.

Period
The period of a trigonometric graph is the interval over which the graph repeats itself.

Periodic sequence
A **sequence** that repeats the same set of values over and over again.
E.g. 2, 5, 2, 5, ...

Point of inflection
A point on a graph where the curve briefly flattens out without changing direction. A type of **stationary point**.

Power
Another word for **index**.

Progression
Another word for **sequence**.

Radian
A unit of measurement for angles.
1 radian is the angle in a **sector** of a circle with radius r that has an **arc** of length r.

Recurrence relation
A formula or rule for a **sequence** that shows how each term can be found from the previous one.

Root
The roots of a function f(x) are the values of x where f(x) = 0.

S

Second order derivative
The result of **differentiating** a function twice.

Sector
A section of a circle formed by two radii and part of the circumference.

Sequence
An ordered list of numbers (referred to as terms) that follow a set pattern.
E.g. 2, 6, 10, ... or –4, 1, –4, 1, ...

Series
An ordered list of numbers, just like a **sequence**, but where the terms are added together (to find their sum).

Sigma notation
Used for the sum of a **series**.
E.g. $\sum_{n=1}^{15} 3^n$ is the sum of all the values of 3^n for every **integer** n from 1 to 15.

Sine rule
A rule for finding missing sides or angles in a triangle. It can be used if you know any two angles and a side, and in some cases, if you know two sides and an angle that isn't between them.

Stationary point
A point on a curve where the **gradient** is zero.

Sum to infinity
The sum to infinity of a **series** is the value the sum tends towards as more and more terms are added.
Also known as the **limit** of a series.

Tangent
A straight line which just touches a curve at a point, without going through it and that has the same **gradient** as the curve at that point.

Trapezium rule
A way of estimating the area under a curve by dividing it into trapezium-shaped strips.

Turning point
A **stationary point** that is a (local) **maximum** or **minimum** point of a curve.

Index

A

arcs 16, 18, 19
area of a triangle 22-25
arithmetic sequences 71, 72, 89
  common difference 71, 72
arithmetic series 74-79, 89

B

base 50-59
binomial expansions 92-101

C

CAST diagram 37-44
common difference 71, 72
cosine rule 22-25

D

decreasing functions 118, 119
differentiation 106-119
  second order derivatives 113-114, 116
  stationary points 115-119
  tangents and normals 111, 112

E

exponentials 55-59
  growth and decay 58, 59

F

factorials 94

G

geometric sequences 80, 81
  common ratio 80, 81
geometric series 83-90
  convergent series 85-88
    sum to infinity 87, 88
  divergent series 88
  sum of the first n terms 83, 84
graphs
  exponential functions 55
  transformations 5-12, 31-33
  trig functions 30-33

I

identities 28, 29, 43-45
increasing functions 118, 119
indices 1-3
integration 124-133
  area between a curve and a line 132-133
  area under a curve 130, 131
  constant of integration 124
  definite integrals 129-133
  indefinite integrals 124-127

L

laws of indices 1-3
logs 50-59
  changing the base 54
  laws of logs 52, 53

M

maximum / minimum points 30, 31, 115-119

N

^nC_r notation 95
normals 111, 112

P

Pascal's triangle 92
points of inflection 115
powers 1-3

R

radians 16-19
recurrence relations 64-67

S

second order derivatives 113, 114, 116
sectors 16, 18, 19
sequences 63-72, 80, 81, 85, 89
  arithmetic sequences 71, 72, 89
  convergent sequences 69, 85
  divergent sequences 69, 85
  finite sequences 67
  geometric sequences 80, 81
  infinite sequences 67
  limits 69, 85-88
  n^{th} terms 63
  periodic sequences 67
  recurrence relations 64-67
series 74-79, 83-90
  arithmetic series 74-79
  geometric series 83-90
  sigma notation 77, 84
  sum of the first n natural numbers 78, 79
  sum of the first n terms 74, 75
sine rule 22-25
SOHCAHTOA 21
stationary points 115-119

T

tangents 111, 112
transformations 5-12, 31-33
  reflections 9-12, 32, 33
  stretches 9-12, 32, 33
  translations 5-7, 33
  trig transformations 31-33
trapezium rule 134-137
trigonometry 16-45
  area of a triangle 22-25
  CAST diagram 37-44
  changing the interval 39-42
  cosine rule 22-25
  graphs 30-33
  sine rule 22-25
  solving trig equations 35-45
  transformations 31-33
  trig identities 28, 29, 43-45
  trig values from triangles 21

C2 Formula Sheet

The formulas below will be included in the formula book for your exams — make sure you know exactly **when you need them** and **how to use them**. These are the formulas relating specifically to the C2 module, but remember you might also need any formulas relevant to C1 in C2.

Cosine Rule

$$a^2 = b^2 + c^2 - 2bc\cos A$$

Summations

$$\sum_{r=1}^{n} r = \frac{1}{2}n(n+1)$$

Arithmetic Series

$$u_n = a + (n-1)d$$

$$S_n = \frac{1}{2}n(a+l) = \frac{1}{2}n[2a + (n-1)d]$$

Geometric Series

$$u_n = ar^{n-1}$$

$$S_n = \frac{a(1-r^n)}{1-r}$$

$$S_\infty = \frac{a}{1-r} \text{ for } |r| < 1$$

Binomial Series

$$(a+b)^n = a^n + \binom{n}{1}a^{n-1}b + \binom{n}{2}a^{n-2}b^2 + \ldots + \binom{n}{r}a^{n-r}b^r + \ldots + b^n \quad (n \in \mathbb{N})$$

$$\text{where } \binom{n}{r} = {}^nC_r = \frac{n!}{r!(n-r)!}$$

$$(1+x)^n = 1 + nx + \frac{n(n-1)}{1 \times 2}x^2 + \ldots + \frac{n(n-1)\ldots(n-r+1)}{1 \times 2 \times \ldots \times r}x^r + \ldots \quad (|x| < 1,\ n \in \mathbb{R})$$

Numerical Integration

The trapezium rule:

$$\int_a^b y\,dx \approx \frac{1}{2}h\{(y_0 + y_n) + 2(y_1 + y_2 + \ldots + y_{n-1})\}, \text{ where } h = \frac{b-a}{n}$$

MAC2T51